PENN

COLLECTION
VOLUME 2

CONTENTS:

Fire With Fire

Capable of Feeling

Substitute Lover

FIRE WITH FIRE

BY
PENNY JORDAN

WORLDWIDE BOOKS
LONDON • SYDNEY • TORONTO

First published in Great Britain in 1985
Reprinted in Great Britain in 1993
by Worldwide Books, Eton House,
18-24 Paradise Road, Richmond, Surrey TW9 1SR

© Penny Jordan 1985

ISBN 0 373 58952 2

99-9305

Made and printed in Great Britain

CHAPTER ONE

WHEN the central heating boiler had refused to reignite despite all her efforts Emma sat back on her heels and scowled ferociously at it. They really ought to have a new one, but her father's income as vicar of a small country parish did not run to such self-indulgences.

Sighing, she pushed her hair back out of her eyes. Thick and curly, its dark chestnut colour was a striking foil for her creamy skin and widely spaced cool grey eyes, their coolness masking an intelligence and humour only perceived by the most discerning observer.

'Emma. Oh thank God you're here. You must help me, I'm in the most awful mess.'

It was far from being the first time Emma had heard those words on her younger sister's lips, and she didn't pay too much attention at first, her brain still trying to resolve the problem of the central heating boiler, but when Camilla burst into tears and gulped hysterically about 'going to prison' and 'losing David', she realised that whatever the 'mess' that she was in, it was something more serious than her usual small traumas.

Petite and blonde, Camilla had a way of attracting trouble that was completely at odds with her delicate appearance. The trouble was that her fairy prettiness had meant that her sister had been petted and spoiled almost from the moment of her birth, Emma reflected, brushing the dust off her hands and getting to her feet.

'Come on Cammy,' she began bracingly, 'whatever it is it can't be as bad as all that . . . David adores you . . .'

'Don't call me "Cammy",' came the tearful response. 'You know David doesn't like it . . . and it *is* bad Emma, just as bad as it could be . . .'

More tears flowed.

'Well then you'd better tell me all about it.' Calmly pulling out two chairs from the wooden kitchen table, Emma sat down in one and waited for Camilla to settle herself in the other. The trouble was that as their mother had died when Emma was ten and Camilla barely six, she had somehow taken over the role of mothering and protecting her younger sister and Camilla had grown used to expecting Emma to resolve all her life's crises for her. What on earth could it be this time? Probably a quarrel with David's mother over arrangements for the wedding, Emma thought wryly. Since she had become engaged to David Turner, the highly-strung Camilla had seemed to mature a little, but with the wedding approaching fast her tearful outbursts had become more and more common. A frown creased Emma's forehead. There were times when she wondered if her younger sister actually wanted to marry David. They had known him for most of their lives and while she liked him, Emma couldn't blind herself to the fact that he was very much under his mother's thumb, and that if Camilla wanted a happy and smooth married life she would have to learn to get on better with her prospective mother-in-law than she did at the moment.

The main problem was that at heart Mrs Turner was an arrant snob. Her husband had been extremely wealthy and they had moved to the village when David was four and Emma the same age. Emma suspected that the only reason they had been admitted to David's group of friends was because of their father's family connections—his uncle had been a colonel in one of the better regiments and had married the daughter of a baronet.

It didn't seem to matter to Mrs Turner that the vicar and his wife had very little contact with these minor relations; their existence was sufficient to make his children acceptable playmates for her son. But that had been twenty years ago. She was not as keen to welcome one of the vicar's daughters as her daughter-in-law as she had been as 'friends' of her son. The Turners were comparatively wealthy. They owned the largest house in the district and Mrs Turner rather liked to play 'Lady Bountiful'. The village fête was always held in the grounds of the Manor and Mrs Turner liked it to be known that she was heavily involved in several prestigious charities. Emma didn't much like her, but Camilla was marrying her son, and the fact that David was dominated by his mother was something she was going to have to accept.

Mrs Turner never lost an opportunity of pointing out that David could have done much better for himself. In Camilla's place Emma doubted that she could have stomached it, but Camilla claimed that she loved David and that he loved her, and that together they would be strong enough to withstand Mrs Turner's acid barbs.

Privately Emma doubted it. Beautiful though
Camilla was, like David she was inclined always to
look for the easiest route through life. If David had
not been an extremely wealthy young man Emma
doubted if Camilla would have looked twice at him.
Camilla had always deplored the poverty that went
with their father's vocation; as a teenager she had
never ceased bemoaning the lack of material assets
when compared to those of her friends; the problem
was that because of her blonde prettiness she had
been petted and spoiled—friends' parents had
included her on various holiday treats; their father
had always been coaxed to find from somewhere the
extra pennies needed for new clothes . . . Not that
Emma begrudged her any of it—no, in character as
well as looks they were completely dissimilar. From
being a young teenager Emma had known what she
wanted from life and it hadn't been marriage to a
man like David.

Now, she was poised on the brink of taking the
all important step forward in her new career. After
leaving college she had been lucky enough to get a
job with their local radio station; from there she
had progressed to regional television and now her
current boss had advised her of a plum job coming
up with one of the National networks, which he
thought she stood a good chance of getting.

At present she was a co-presenter on an early
news local programme, but she had been doing the
job for several years and was ready for something
else. Her goal was a top newsreading or anchorwoman job; perhaps if she was very, very lucky,
even something on breakfast television, but she
had a long way to go before reaching that
objective she reminded herself.

However, the interview her boss had lined up for this new National job sounded extremely promising. She wouldn't be the only one going after it, but Robert Evans considered that she had a more than fair chance.

'You've got the looks,' he had told her only this morning, 'and the brains. And let's not disillusion ourselves, you need both, unfair though that sounds.'

Emma hadn't disputed it. It was an unfair fact of life that while male presenters were chosen on ability and personality alone, female ones needed to have an acceptably attractive face and figure. Although nowhere near as pretty as her younger sister, Emma knew she was reasonably attractive. Her bone structure was good, her figure elegantly slender. Her air of cool self-containment put a lot of men off, she knew, David in particular ... she frowned a little remembering Mrs Turner's latest broadside. She had called round the day after the local newspaper had carried a small article mentioning the fact that Emma was being considered for a top London job.

Being in television was all very well in its way, she had begun when Emma asked her in, 'but it wasn't really the sort of thing David wanted to be connected with. Reading the news was all very well ... but it could lead to other things. . .'

Anyone would have thought she was proposing to pose nude for a Page 3 photograph, Emma thought sardonically. She knew that Mrs Turner was being ridiculous and so she suspected did the older woman, but David took his mother's every word seriously and she had boiled with angry indignation at the suggestion that her job somehow made Camilla unfit to become David's wife.

Camilla was twenty-two years old and should be able to cope with her own problems, she knew, but she didn't have the heart to tell her so, saying instead, 'Come on then, what's it all about.'

'Do you remember last month when I went to stay with Fiona?'

Emma nodded. Fiona Blake was one of Camilla's old schoolfriends. At the moment she was flat-sharing in London with two other girls while she tried her hand at modelling. Fiona's parents were wealthy enough for it not to matter whether Fiona made a success of her 'career' or not, and privately Emma did not think she would.

'Well while I was there Fiona took me to this party. I didn't want to go, but she insisted.'

Listening to the aggrieved note in her sister's voice Emma sighed. Nothing that went wrong in her life was ever Camilla's fault; she had always been victimised by someone else.

'Fiona wanted to go because the party was being held by Drake Harwood . . .'

Drake Harwood? The name was familiar, as well it might be Emma thought, recollecting how the first time she had heard it it had conjured up visions of a tough, buccaneering individual. He was an up and coming entrepreneur who had recently bought out Scanda Enterprises and he was reputed to be extremely wealthy.

'Fiona wanted to go because he's taken over *Macho* magazine, and she thought she might be able to persuade him to use her as one of his models.'

'*Macho*? Fiona wants to appear in that?' Emma

grimaced distastefully. 'Honestly Camilla that girl has more hair than wit. What on earth would her parents say? It's a girlie mag isn't it?'

'Fiona says it's the only way for unknowns to break into modelling these days.' Camilla defended her friend. 'She says. . .'

'Never mind what she says,' Emma broke in, 'Just tell me what's got you in such a state. He didn't ask you to pose for him did he?' she guessed, darting a frowning look at her sister. Despite her plans to marry David Camilla had always had a yen for the glamour of a 'Hollywood' type existence. It was just as well she lacked the ambition to do anything other than daydream about it, Emma decided, hiding her relief at Camilla's vigorous shake of her head. Camilla simply did not have the determination to succeed in such a dangerous world.

'No . . . no . . . nothing like that.' She bit her lip. 'Promise you won't be cross, and that you won't breathe a word to David. He'll never marry me if he finds out.'

'Good heavens, what on earth have you done?' She asked it light-heartedly not wanting Camilla to see her concern. Snippets of gossip she had heard and read about Drake Harwood were coming back to her. He had made it the hard way, grafting for every penny of the first few thousand pounds he made; working on a building site until he had enough to start up his own contracting firm. From then on he had gradually built up his empire until now at thirty-four he was considered one of the shrewdest and most dangerous businessmen around.

Macho magazine was just a small part of that

empire, she recollected, something he had acquired
when he took over Scanda Enterprises. She
recollected reading somewhere that it had a pretty
poor circulation and that he had been challenged
by a rival magazine owner to beat their figures.

No doubt the whole thing was simply a publicity
ploy she reflected cynically, certainly the supposed
'rivalry' had gained them both a good deal of
newspaper space, but how much of an interest he
intended to take in what was only a small part of
his empire she didn't really know. Certainly if he
intended to use girls like Fiona as his models he
wouldn't do much to improve circulation.

'So, you went to this party with Fiona,' Emma
pressed, 'and. . .'

'And I don't remember anything else until the
next morning,' Camilla gulped tearfully, 'when I
woke up in a strange bedroom and . . .'

'An even stranger man in bed beside you?'
Emma supplemented drily. 'Mrs Turner's going to
love that.'

'No . . . no I was in bed on my own . . . in a
room of my own,' Camilla protested. 'I must have
had too much to drink . . . either that or there was
something in them, but Emma, I was so frightened
. . . I just had to get out of that house . . . I kept
thinking what if David could see me now, so . . .'

'So . . .' Emma prompted.

'Well, I was still fully dressed, so I just got up
and went downstairs. There was no one about, but
there was a car outside—a red Ferrari, and the
keys were in it . . . so I . . . I took it. . .'

'You did what?' Emma stared at her. 'But
Camilla you don't drive. You've always hated it
. . . you don't have a licence . . .'

'I know, but I was so terrified of being found there . . . I daren't ring for a taxi . . . I had to leave . . . and I do know how to drive . . . but the car was so big . . .'

Closing her eyes Emma forced herself not to interrupt.

'Don't tell me,' she said at last. 'You hit something?'

'A stone bollard,' Camilla admitted. 'You see it was very early in the morning—there wasn't any traffic, but I saw this milk cart coming and I panicked. I hit the kerb and then this bollard . . .'

'And . . .?'

'I just got out and ran. Eventually I found a taxi, and I went back to the flat . . . Fiona wasn't there, but when she came in I told her what had happened, and she told Drake Harwood, and he's threatening to sue me for stealing his car and smashing it up . . .'

Fresh tears started to fall. 'It will be in all the papers and everyone will know I spent the night there. David will find out and he'll never marry me . . . His mother wouldn't let him.'

Emma suspected that she was right. She gnawed thoughtfully on her lower lip, silently condemning both her sister and Fiona as a pair of stupid fools.

'Haven't you been to see Drake Harwood, and tried to explain? I'm sure if you told him the full story . . .'

Camilla shuddered. 'You haven't met him. He's dreadful . . . So uncouth. Fiona thinks he's exciting . . . but I didn't like him. I couldn't go and see him Emma, I just couldn't . . . but his solicitor has already written to me. He wants me to pay for the damage to his car, otherwise he's going to sue . . . and I can't afford it.'

'So what do you want me to do about it,' Emma asked, already mentally bowing to the inevitable.

Tears were transformed into a radiant smile as Camilla turned towards her. 'Oh Emma, I was hoping you would help me. Couldn't you go and see him . . . Explain . . .'

'Explain what?' Emma asked drily. 'That you don't want your mother-in-law to know that you spent the night in one of his beds and then stole his car. . . . And what about paying for the damage Camilla?'

'He doesn't need the money, he's filthy rich,' Camilla said sulkily, 'he's just doing this because I wouldn't pay any attention to him . . .'

'Ah . . . You mean he fancied you and you gave him the cold shoulder? Umm, I can see that in those circumstances he might not be prepared to let you off the hook so lightly.'

'But you will try and do something . . . you will go and see him?' Camilla pleaded. 'There's still a month to go to the wedding and this letter says if I don't pay for the damage within seven days, legal action will be taken.'

The man could always simply be trying it on, Emma thought, but then given his reputation and his tough upbringing it might not be wise to assume so. 'Camilla are you sure this marriage to David is what you really want,' she asked slowly. 'You know you ought to be able to tell him about this, to . . .'

'To ask him for several thousand pounds, a month before we get married?' Camilla asked bitterly. 'Yes I could tell David, Emma, but he would tell his mother and I could just imagine her reaction. You know she doesn't want him to marry me, and yes, I do want to marry him. Can't you see, I'm not like you, I don't want a career or to be independent. I just want to live quietly and comfortably. . .'

The accent probably being on the latter, Emma thought drily, but refrained from saying so. 'Let me look at the letter,' she requested.

She read it quickly, sifting through the legal verbiage to the nitty-gritty, and when she had done so, she could see why Camilla was in such a panic. Drake Harwood wanted and intended to have his pound of flesh. Well she would just have to try and find some means of persuading him otherwise.

'You won't tell him the truth will you?' Camilla begged. 'I wouldn't put it past him to tell one of his newspaper friends and then it will be all over the papers.'

'I hardly think the fact of your crashing his car merits such coverage Camilla,' Emma told her mildly. 'You're getting things a little out of perspective.'

'You don't know how furious he was about his car.' She shuddered. 'Fiona says he had only just bought it . . . *You* haven't met him Emma. You don't know what he's like. He isn't like us. He's. . .'

'The proverbial rough diamond?' Emma asked, her mouth twisting. 'Oh grow up Camilla and don't be so silly, otherwise you'll end up like Mrs T.—a dyed-in-the wool snob. I'll go and see him for you, and I'll do what I can to calm him down. How do you intend to pay him back though? Could you manage monthly instalments from the allowance David is giving you?'

'I suppose so . . . I don't suppose you could persuade him to forget the money completely . . . I mean,' she wheedled, when Emma's mouth compressed, 'it isn't as though he needs it.'

'Maybe he doesn't *need* it, but you do *owe* it to him Camilla,' Emma told her bitingly, 'and in your shoes I should be only too anxious to pay it back and get it off my mind . . .'

'Oh you always were too "goody two shoes" to be true,' Camilla snapped crossly. 'David says you're a real school-marm type and that that's why you've opted for a career instead of marriage . . .'

'Oh does he?' Emma was thoroughly incensed, both by her sister's stupidity and by her smug assumption that once Emma had done her dirty work for her she could forget all about her responsibility for the accident.

'Well, let me tell you that I'd choose a career over marriage to David any day of the week . . : he's about as exciting as . . . as cold rice pudding . . .'

She regretted the words when Camilla got up and ran out of the kitchen, telling herself that she should not have taken her irritation out on her sister. Camilla was so absurdly sensitive to criticism, so much so that she occasionally wondered if the younger girl didn't use her 'sensitivity' as a weapon to get her own way. She glanced down at the solicitor's letter again, and frowned. She might as well get the ordeal over as quickly as possible. She picked it up and went through to her father's shabby study, quickly typing out a letter on his ancient machine, requesting an interview with Drake Harwood.

She had to go to London next week for her interview anyway, and with a bit of luck she might be able to combine the two appointments. She

only hoped for Camilla's sake she was able to
come to some arrangement with him. He couldn't
be expected to forego the cost of the repairs
altogether, and Camilla was selfish and blind to
think he should, but if she could persuade him to
accept payment by instalments ... if she could
perhaps explain the reasons behind Camilla's rash
behaviour. She sighed, remembering that her
younger sister had bound her to silence. She would
just have to play it by ear, she decided, sticking a
stamp on the envelope and sealing it.

'Now remember, don't try any clever stuff, just be
your natural self.'

Emma grimaced as she listened to her boss
Robert Evans, giving her instructions concerning
her forthcoming interview. 'And remember we'll
all be rooting for you here. You've got more than
a fair chance Emma... You're goodlooking,
poised, intelligent, and you've got a personality of
your own that comes across on the screen.'

Emma knew that everything he said was true,
but even so she felt tensely anxious. She wanted to
succeed at this interview, as much for Robert's
sake as her own. He had been the one to give her
first 'on screen' chance when she came to
Television South. He had helped and encouraged
her giving her the self-confidence to project herself
well. He was forty-five and a burly, dark-haired
man with a pleasant sense of humour and a keenly
ambitious drive. Emma liked and admired him,
and knew that if she had not been the person she
was, or if her liking and respect had been less
strong she could quite easily have been persuaded
into an affair with him.

She admired him for his faithfulness to his wife—a quiet, serene woman she had met on several occasions. The temptations in a job like his must be never-ending and yet from somewhere he found the strength to resist them. Emma liked that in him. Her own strong moral code was due more to her own inner beliefs than being a vicar's daughter—their father had never tried to impose his faith on either her or Camilla; perhaps because she had had to grow up without a mother and be responsible for Camilla, Emma had formed her own moral code, based on her observations of life around her.

Her own self-respect was all important—without it she believed it was impossible for any human being to function properly. After all one had to live with oneself and her keenly honed ability to be self-critical was far sharper than any outside criticism she might have to face. An affair with a married man would be both messy and ultimately painful, but apart from that she could never feel completely comfortable in a relationship with someone else's husband, and then there was always the nagging doubt that having been unfaithful to her, how could he be expected to stay faithful to a mere mistress . . . No . . . such a role was not for her. She was acutely distrustful of sexual attraction; people so often mistook it for 'love' with disastrous results. She herself had never met a man she wanted so intensely that the need to make love with him over-rode everything else. Camilla thought her cold, even frigid, Emma knew differently but she respected her body sufficiently to listen to what it told her; and it told her it would never be happy with anything less than the best.

She had had menfriends; often dating people who worked for the television company, but always terminating the relationship when it threatened to get too intense. She had the reputation of an ambitious career woman, but it didn't worry her. Her career was important to her because it was a way of proving to herself her own ability but if she ever met a man who could fire both her emotions and her body; someone to whom she could give love and respect and who felt the same way about her, she suspected that all the energy she poured into her career would then go into her relationship with him. Sometimes the inner knowledge of her own intensity worried her; everyone thought she was so cool and controlled, but she didn't have chestnut hair for nothing. Her emotions were there all right, it was just that she had learned young the wisdom of leashing them under her own control.

She gave her boss a brilliant smile. 'I think everything's under control . . . right down to a new outfit for the big occasion.'

She had chosen her interview outfit with care. It was a beautifully cut fine wool suit in a sludgy nondescript olive that was a perfect foil for her hair and skin. The jacket was tailored and workmanlike, the skirt slim with a provocative slit at the front and back, just long enough to give a glimpse of her long legs—the suit combined both provocation and discretion, and it had amused her to buy it, knowing as she did that it was a contradiction of itself. If nothing else it should keep them guessing she thought drily, trying to concentrate on everything that Robert was telling her.

When she got home that night there was a letter from Drake Harwood's solicitors waiting for her. Mr Harwood was agreeable to seeing her, it told her. An appointment had been made on the day and at the time she had requested and that was a relief.

When she told Camilla, her sister pouted sulkily and complained that Emma was trying to make her feel guilty. 'I'm trying to forget all about that . . .' she told her, shuddering, 'and now you're trying to make me remember.'

'I should have thought that was all too easy,' Emma said drily, 'especially when it involved a bill of several thousand pounds. Have you tried to talk to David about it.'

'I can't. He'd understand, but his mother wouldn't. Do you know what she said to me today. . .?'

Emma closed her ears while Camilla set off on a long diatribe against David's mother. The newly married couple were to make their home at the Manor with her. They were going to have their own wing, and Camilla was already planning how she would re-decorate and re-furnish it. If Mrs T. allowed her to have anything other than very traditional Colefax and Fowler plus assorted antiques, she would be very surprised, Emma thought, but kept her thoughts to herself. Camilla thought that by marrying David she was gaining the freedom to spend his money and buy herself all the things she had never had, but what she was really doing was entering a prison . . . However, it was her own choice.

She had decided to spend the night before her interview in London—that would save arriving there with her clothes all creased from the train journey. She had booked herself a room at a fairly inexpensive hotel. Her father was busy writing his sermon when she went to tell him she was going. He looked up and smiled at her. The Reverend Richard Court had a vague, appealing smile. There had been several female parishioners eager to step into her mother's shoes, but he had managed to evade them all. Her father rather liked his bachelordom, Emma suspected. He had several friends at Oxford, dons with whom he spent long weekends re-living the days of their youth. He was also an avid reader. Outwardly gentle and mild, he possessed a core of inner steel. Emma suspected she had inherited from him. No one would ever persuade her father to do something he didn't wish to do. In many ways he was extremely selfish, but he was so gentle and mild, that very few people realised it. He was kind though and extremely adept at distancing himself from arguments and trouble. He could always see both sides of an argument—something else she had inherited from him Emma thought.

'I should be back tomorrow evening.' Her interview with the TV people was in the morning and she was seeing Drake Harwood after lunch.

'Camilla seems very anxious. I suppose it's all this fuss over the wedding.'

'She'll make a lovely bride. . .'

'Yes. Her one redeeming feature in Mrs T's eyes, no doubt,' he agreed, surprising Emma as he so often did by seeing what one had not believed that he had seen. 'It's lucky for her that she's so malleable. Marriage to a man like David would never do for you Emma.'

'No,' she agreed with a smile, 'I'm more likely to turn into another Mrs T.'

'I don't think so. No one could ever accuse you of being narrow-minded. I hope you get the job.'

Emma knew that he meant it, which was generous of him, because if she did she would have to find somewhere to live in London, and by removing herself from the vicarage she would deprive him of a housekeeper/secretary/general dogsbody. Being her father though, no doubt he would find someone else to take her place, with the minimum of fuss and inconvenience to himself.

She drove herself down to the station. It was only tiny and Joe the stationmaster promised to keep an eye on her car for her. 'Hope you get the job,' he told her, as he sold her her ticket. Everyone in the village probably knew why she was going to London—or at least thought they did. None of them knew of her appointment with Drake Harwood. It was ridiculous but she almost felt more apprehensive about that than she did about her interview for her new job.

The train arrived ten minutes late but was relatively empty. It took just over an hour and a half to reach London. Emma was both bored and stiff when it did. She allowed herself the extravagance of a taxi to her hotel, although she noticed that the driver looked less than impressed by its address. It seemed strange to think that if she got this job her face would be so familiar that almost everyone would recognise her. She wasn't sure yet how she would handle that sort of exposure. She liked her privacy and working for the local station had been able to preserve it. Robert had warned her against stressing too much how she felt about that. Perhaps it was something that one just grew accustomed to.

CHAPTER TWO

CONGRATULATING herself on her good timing Emma sat down gracefully in the chair indicated by the hovering secretary. Exactly three minutes to spare before the time appointed for her interview.

Across the other side of the room she caught sight of her own reflection in a mirrored section of wall surrounding an almost tropical plant display. The cool, graceful woman staring back at her was almost a stranger. She had never quite grown accustomed to the image she had learned to project during her years in the media, Emma reflected, hiding a rueful smile. As a teenager she had been gangly and awkward, lacking Camilla's blonde prettiness. It had been during her first job that an older colleague had suggested a grooming course at a local modelling school might be a good idea. At first she had been dismissive, but the advice had taken root and now she considered the money the course had cost her to be one of her best investments. She wasn't pretty and never would be, but knowing that she had learned to make the best of herself gave her a calm confidence which was reflected in the way she held her body and moved. What she never saw when she looked at herself was the purity of her bone structure and the sensual lure of the contrast between the dark russet of her hair, and her pale Celtic skin.

One or two curious glances came her way from

people passing through the foyer but Emma ignored them. She knew she wasn't the only candidate for the job, but they must have decided to interview them all on separate days because she was the only person waiting.

Having been kept waiting for the obligatory ten minutes the discreet sound of a buzzer on the secretary's desk heralded the commencement of her ordeal.

The room she was shown into was large and furnished in a modern high tech style. Three people were already in the room. All of them men. Robert had warned her against adopting a sexual approach to the interview. 'I know you won't anyway,' he had added, 'but just remember it's brains they're looking for as well as looks.'

Emma hadn't needed the warning. She had scorned using her sex to get her own way all her life. In fact her father had once commented that she was almost too direct. 'Men, on the whole, enjoy having their egos massaged, my dear,' had been his mild comment, one afternoon when she had delivered a blisteringly disdainful look in the direction of one of his parishioners. She had tried to explain that she hadn't liked the way the man had looked at her, or appreciated his heavy-handed compliments, but her father had simply shaken his head. 'Emma I suspect you're always going to take the hard route through life. Something in you demands that you meet situations head on. Try to learn that sometimes it's useful to have the ability to side-step them.' She had now mastered the art, but it had been a hard-won mastery, and she often had to bite her tongue to stop herself from saying what she thought. 'Too direct' other people had called her, while Camilla made no bones of her verdict. 'You're always so aggressive Emma,' she had told her once, 'and men don't like it.'

The interview progressed smoothly; she was able to answer all the questions put to her and she was also given the chance to air some of her own views, which she did cautiously. It was difficult to appear natural, when she knew that every movement, every inflection of her voice and manner was being studied to assess how appealing or otherwise it would appear to a viewer. Because that was what it all came down to—viewers, audience ratings . . . popularity.

She had promised herself before she left that she would be herself and that was what she tried to do. She was rewarded when her three interviewers stood up, signalling the end of her ordeal, and the most senior of them smiled broadly at her.

'I think you'll do us very nicely Emma,' he told her. 'I take it there won't be any problems with contracts or commitments to your present post?'

Her eyes widened fractionally. Was he offering her the job? What about the other applicants?

'None at all,' she managed to assure him crisply, 'but surely you'll want to . . .'

'You were our final interviewee, Emma,' another member of the trio interrupted. 'John here always believes in saving the best for last. In this case, I think he was right. If you have the time I'd like to take you down to our legal department so that we can run through a contract with you. There'll be a brief training period before you actually go on camera; we already know that you come across well. We'll have to take some

publicity shots of you. There'll be a good deal of
media interest of course. And a final word of
warning . . . unfair though this sounds, the public
expect our women newsreaders to be, for the lack
of a better description, morally sound, I think you
know what I mean?'

Emma did. As Robert had told her she had
nothing to fear on that score. 'You're not involved
with a married man and you don't have any
dubious lovers lurking in your past, so you should
be okay there.'

She had remarked at the time on the unfairness
of the double standard, but Robert had merely
shaken his head and told her that that was the way
things were.

'You'll come under a lot of pressure from the
media, but anything you're dubious about, refer to
us.'

She spent a further hour going over her
contract; the salary she was being offered was
reasonable rather than generous, but it should be
enough to enable her to live in London, and there
was a good wardrobe allowance.

'Initially at least, we'd like you to consult our
wardrobe department about what you wear on
screen.'

Nodding her head, Emma reflected wryly that
even her taste had to be checked; nothing was
going to be left to chance, but then the slot she
was going to occupy on the new early evening
programme was an important one, and it would be
fighting for viewers against a long-established and
very popular show on another channel.

'Now we'll leave you in peace,' she was told
when they left the legal office. 'You'll need time to

mull over everything that's happened. We won't need you here for another fortnight. Can you be ready to start then?'

They were in a corridor now and Emma automatically stepped to one side as a door opened and a man stepped through it. Tall and broad, he exuded an air of power and vitality. He nodded to the man accompanying Emma and then switched his attention to her, studying her with almost brutally open sexual appreciation. Strong though her control was, it wasn't strong enough to prevent the seep of angry colour into her skin. Her eyes fiercely grey in the frame of her face glared her resentment at him. The amused smile curling his mouth softened his features momentarily before his glance dropped to her breasts and lingered there quite blatantly.

Emma couldn't remember the last time she had felt so angry. She could feel the tension of it curling her fingers into talons, her tension increasing as she was forced to swallow her resentment down and force a coolly indifferent expression into her eyes as they met the knowing mockery in his. She had never seen anyone with such darkly green eyes before, she thought, hypnotised by them. Weren't green eyes a sign of a changeable, untrustworthy personality? The thought brought her a brief measure of satisfaction, quickly banished in the rage that almost choked her as he moved down the corridor and past her, deliberately allowing his body to brush against hers. There had been room for him to squeeze past without touching her, but he had not done so.

'I'm sorry we can't offer you lunch,' her companion was saying, 'but we have a busy schedule this afternoon discussing a new series we're thinking of buying.'

'That's all right,' Emma smiled automatically. 'I have another appointment anyway.'

Outside the television building she debated whether or not to go and ring Robert, and then glancing at her watch decided not to. He would be involved in preparations for the evening news programme now, and besides her news would wait until she got home. She wanted to savour it, to relish the knowledge that she had succeeded, but for some reason she could not.

It must be because she was so tensed up about her interview with Drake Harwood, she decided, looking round for a taxi. Once that was behind her then she could relax and congratulate herself. As she found one and waited for it to stop she recalled the man in the corridor and her mouth compressed.

Who on earth was he? Someone quite important. She hadn't missed the vaguely subservient response of her companion to his greeting. She frowned as she stepped into her taxi. Why waste time thinking about a man she was hardly likely to see again; he wasn't the first man who had irritated her with his attitude to her sex and he wouldn't be the last.

Not the first, but certainly the most blatant. Her skin tingled with renewed impotent rage as she recalled the mockery in his jade eyes. He had known exactly how furious she was and he had enjoyed her fury. She couldn't remember the last time she had seen such an aggressively sexual male. Not her type at all, she thought disdainfully, giving the driver the address of the modest restaurant where she had decided to have lunch.

She was quite content to lunch alone. She had a lot to think about and a lot to plan. She would have to find somewhere to live; sharing at first perhaps, and then later, she could find her own place. She did some quick sums on the back of an old envelope. She would need new clothes, but hopefully not too many. She had quite a good wardrobe, preferring to buy classic rather than fashion clothes and suspected that these would be in keeping with the image she would be expected to project. Her full mouth compressed slightly as she remembered what she had been told. Why was it perfectly acceptable for a man to possess a murky past but not for a woman? Luckily there was nothing at all in her past or present that could be used by the press. Her thoughts flashed to the man in the corridor. Undoubtedly the same could not be said for him. Her mouth curved in a cynical smile. Stop thinking about him, she chided herself eating the seafood salad she had ordered.

She took her time over her lunch, forcing down the jittery nerves clamouring in her stomach. She was more tense over this coming interview than she had been over this morning's. Damn Camilla, she thought exasperatedly, not for the first time. What on earth had possessed her to take the man's car in the first place, never mind crashing it?

She grimaced faintly to herself. She could just imagine her younger sister's reaction on wakening to find herself in a strange bed. Mrs T. held very strong views on what she considered to be the lack of morals among the younger generation. In time David would be very like his mother; humourless and rigorously strait-laced. Cynically she wondered if Camilla was telling her the entire truth. Her sister had had a positive phalanx of boyfriends before she became engaged to David. She enjoyed flirting with and teasing the male sex and was nowhere near as innocent as her blonde delicacy implied. She had admitted that Drake Harwood had shown an interest in her. On the other hand it could be perfectly feasible that she had simply had too much to drink and that he had dumped her in a spare bedroom to sleep it off. It all depended. Whatever the case he certainly didn't appear to be inclined to treat Camilla with indulgence now. His solicitor's letter had been starkly uncompromising. Finishing her coffee and settling her bill Emma stood up, and glanced at her watch. She had half an hour before her appointment with him ... it was time to go.

The block of offices her taxi driver took her to was everything one would expect for a going-places entrepreneur. Brashly new, the impressive foyer was designed to intimidate and impress. The receptionist looked as though she had just stepped out of *Vogue*, and eyed Emma unresponsively as she walked towards her.

At the sound of Drake Harwood's name she perked up a little. No doubt *she* was a far cry from the women normally asking to see him Emma reflected dourly. He had been mentioned in the gossip columns quite a lot recently, and she had read that he was currently escorting one of the 'models' featured in his newly acquired magazine. Although she had no deep-rooted objection to members of her sex making a living from capitalising on whatever they considered their most saleable assets to be, she viewed the men who made their living selling the female form both in the flesh and on celluloid with considerable distaste. It was true that Drake Harwood had merely gained control of his girlie magazine as part of a larger package, but he had been quick to accept the challenge thrown down by the rival magazine and to boast that he would soon boost its ailing circulation.

Emma didn't doubt that most of the women who posed for such magazines did so with their eyes open—witness Fiona's determined attempts to catch Drake Harwood's attention—but for herself ... Only last summer Camilla had commented on what she called her 'prudishness' when she had refused to go topless during their holiday in France. 'Everyone does ...' had been her younger sister's critical comment. Maybe, but Emma had never been one to follow the general herd. Her own body was something she rarely thought about. Camilla had laughed when she insisted on wearing a swimsuit, but her skin was fair and burned easily.

'Mr Harwood will see you now. Go up in the far lift,' the receptionist directed in bored accents. Reminding herself that she was twenty-six years old and had just been offered the sort of job which ought to boost anyone's self-confidence, Emma stepped into the lift and pressed the single button, hoping that the fluttering in her stomach was as a result of the upward surge of the lift rather than her own nervousness.

A secretary as elegant as the girl in the foyer was waiting for her; blonde hair immaculately in place.

'This way please.' She knocked briefly on a door and then held it open.

The room Emma walked into was enormous,

with a panoramic view over the rooftops of
London. The decor was almost austere; the
rosewood desk huge; the Beber carpet underfoot a
masculine blend of russets and browns.

'Miss Court...' He took advantage of her
momentary consternation to ask mockingly, 'I
take it you did get the job? I shall look forward to
seeing you on screen when the new programme
goes out.'

She had recognised him instantly of course, but
it had taken her several seconds to assimilate the
fact that the man in the corridor of the television
building and Drake Harwood were one and the
same. Remembering his open sexual inspection of
her, she felt her face burning with a mixture of
tension and anger. He had obviously known *then*
who she was. Tension sharpened her instincts.
How had he known about the job though? She
recalled the muted deference in her companion's
manner towards him and anxiety feathered along
her nerves. If he wanted her to comment on the
coincidence; on the fact that he knew about her
new job, he was going to be disappointed.
Exciting Fiona had called him, according to
Camilla, and she could understand why. If ever a
man exuded sexuality it was this one, she thought
clinically. His hair was thick and dark, almost
unruly as it grew low into his nape. Even seated he
gave the impression of height and breadth. His suit
was expensively tailored, discreetly dark and
Saville Row, and yet it left an unmistakable
impression of solid muscle and bone; a legacy from
his early days working on building sites, she
decided. His skin was olive toned and tanned, the
bones shaping his face arrogantly masculine. Even

without those green eyes she would have been
wary of him. He was a man whose every
movement revealed a raw pleasure in his masculinity; a man who would never consider a
woman to be his equal, Emma thought drily.

'Like what you see?' His words left her in no
doubt that he was aware of her scrutiny. Emma
fought down the urge to snap back that she
disliked everything about him, and said instead,
'It's always interesting to come face to face with
the people one reads about in the press.'

'Really?' His eyebrows rose. 'Surely you aren't
admitting that you succumb to hero-worship Miss
Court. Somehow I can't see you in that role.'

She wasn't admitting anything of the sort and
he knew it damn him. Angrily Emma suppressed
an inclination to bite out that far from hero-
worshipping, she was more likely to find herself
criticising him, and reminded herself of the
purpose of her appointment.

'Quite a coincidence, our meeting twice in the
one day.'

Emma had the distinct feel that he was toying
with her in some way, playing a game which was
giving him huge amusement and not a little
masculine satisfaction.

'They do happen.' She was fighting to control
her responses. Instinct told her she would need all
her wits about her to match this man. 'As you
know from my letter, I wanted to discuss my sister
with you. You may remember, she had a slight
accident in your car.'

She had wanted to get him off the subject of *her*
and on to the subject of Camilla and she had
succeeded. His eyes sharpened, his eyebrows lifting

tauntingly. 'A *slight* accident? Is that how you describe theft and several thousand pounds worth of damage? Why hasn't she come to see me herself?'

Not for the first time it crossed Emma's mind that the whole thing might simply be a ploy to get to know Camilla better—on his own terms, with him calling the tune. He would demand that sort of relationship she guessed intuitively; he would derive satisfaction from knowing that he was the one in command. Well he might as well know from the start where he stood with Camilla.

'She asked me to come because she doesn't want her fiancé to know anything about what happened.'

If he was disappointed to learn that Camilla was engaged, he wasn't showing it.

'And what did happen?' he asked softly. 'I have wondered . . . The first I knew of anything was when the police rang me to say that my car had been involved in an accident. Quite a surprise, as you can imagine.'

'Camilla attended one of your parties. It seems that she had rather too much to drink.' She managed to say it quite calmly, but could not bring herself to look at him. 'When she woke up in the morning and found herself in a strange bed, she panicked a little I'm afraid . . .'

'She did? I wonder why,' he mused sardonically. 'I take it this strange bed contained no one other than herself?'

'Not as far as I know.' Let him make what he liked of that.

'And this er . . . panic . . . motivated her into stealing my car.'

Stealing wasn't the word Emma would have used, but she forced herself not to say so. 'It was very early in the morning. She didn't want to draw attention to herself by calling a taxi ... I'm afraid she was in too much of a panic to think things through properly.'

'Unlike her sister, who I'm sure never does anything without doing so.' The way he said it, it wasn't a compliment. 'I take it this panic was on account of her fiancé. She doesn't want him to know she spent the night at my house is that it? Seems an odd relationship to have with a prospective husband. Why is she marrying him?'

'Because she loves him.'

His eyebrows really did rise then. 'My, my, does she so ... But not obviously to the extent of being able to tell him the truth.'

'There are complications.' Emma knew she sounded brusque. 'They need not concern you. Camilla wanted me to ask you if you would be prepared to take instalment payments to cover the repairs to your car. She can't afford to repay you in a lump sum. She simply doesn't have that sort of money.'

'But her fiancé does, presumably, otherwise she wouldn't be marrying him.'

The cynicism in his voice prompted Emma to snap, 'Yes he does, but naturally she wouldn't want to ask him to lend her such a sum before they are married, if that's what you were going to suggest. The repayments will include an interest element, if that's what's worrying you.'

'No, it does not worry me Miss Court, since I'm not prepared to accept them.' He got up and came towards her, surprisingly deft in his movements for such a tall man. 'However, if your sister genuinely can't repay me in cash, I am prepared to take another form of payment . . .'

He was watching her closely, and Emma burst out rashly, 'If you think Camilla will agree to have sex with you in return for you dropping the charges, you're way, way off course . . .'

'And so are you,' he told her smoothly, 'the payment I was thinking of wasn't so much your sister's body in my bed, as yours . . . in my magazine.'

For a moment Emma genuinely thought she might faint. She looked at him, grey eyes dazed and disbelieving, hot colour running up under her skin as she realised he was perfectly serious.

'Me? But . . . but I'm not a model, I don't . . .' She shook her head trying to sort out her muddled thoughts.

'Don't what,' he mocked her, 'take your clothes off for financial gain? But of course you don't Miss Court, that's what will make the fact that you're featuring in the magazine such a sales booster. I've been looking for something to up our ratings, and you could be just the thing.'

He was prowling round her now, studying her, stripping the clothes from her body with a careless masculine arrogance that made her long to smack him.

'Yes, I can see the captions now. Cool newsreader Emma Court, as you've never seen her before . . . except perhaps in dreams. It should make an extremely good feature.'

'You must be mad!'

He laughed mirthlessly, 'How predictable of you, somehow I had expected better. No, I'm far from mad Emma Court.'

'You knew who I was this morning, didn't you?' she demanded furiously, remembering the way he had looked at her then, probably already anticipating this very moment.

He was coolly amused. 'My dear girl, I knew everything there was to know about you ten minutes after I'd read your letter.'

Emma thought furiously. 'Did you arrange for me to get that job. . .? Did you?'

He smiled infuriatingly, 'How quick you are Emma, I like that in a woman, it saves so much tedious time wasting. What does it matter? You've got it haven't you?'

'And now you plan to use me to . . .'

'I'm offering you what you came here for,' he told her curtly, 'if the terms of payment are unacceptable to you, you can always refuse . . .'

'And if I do, you'll sue Camilla?'

He shrugged. 'Do I look like a man who'd let someone rob me of several thousand pounds and do nothing about it? Half the secret of being successful Emma Court is comprised of luck—pure and simple. I consider myself to be more lucky than most. The very day your letter arrived, I was trying to think of ways to boost the magazine's circulation, bringing it a little more upmarket. I don't know if you are aware of it, but a rival of mine has challenged me to beat his circulation figures.'

'Yes, I am aware of it.' Her response was terse. 'But I can't see how nude photographs of me . . .'

'Of you, Emma Court, no,' he agreed, interrupting swiftly, 'but of you Emma Court, the new anchorwoman of *"Newsview"*, yes. On screen you project a very cool, remote image, Emma. I know,

I've made it my business to watch you. A lot of
men find that very . . . challenging. The fact that
we are able to show them a different Emma . . .'

'No!' The denial burst past her lips before she
could stop it, her eyes wide and haunted as she
faced him. 'I'd never agree to anything like that,'
she told him fiercely.

'No?' He picked up his telephone receiver. 'Very
well then, I'll instruct my solicitors to continue
with the charges against your sister and to ensure
that they get as much media coverage as
possible . . .'

She knew he wasn't bluffing. He had the power
to do exactly what he was threatening. She could
just imagine Mrs T's face when she read what
Camilla had done, and no doubt the press would
have a field day making it sound even worse than
it was. She was sorely tempted to go home and tell
Camilla that she had been unsuccessful, but the
thought of her sister's hysterics; the knowledge
that it could well mean the end of her
engagement—because Mrs T. would put unholy
pressure on David to break the engagement, she
knew—overwhelmed her.

Forcing herself to think calmly and quickly, and
to detach herself from what was happening she
viewed her options, and could only come up with
one solution. Damn Drake Harwood and damn
Camilla. She would have to agree, she decided
bitterly. She had no real choice. Let him take his
photographs, but he'd never be able to use them in
the way he'd planned.

Bitter anger tensed her muscles as she envisaged
having to explain to Robert why she could not take
the job . . . but he would understand. They

wouldn't want her on local television either . . . not once Drake Harwood had splashed her photograph all over his magazine. So what, she told herself hardily, she would be able to find another job in some other field where her public image wasn't so important and at least she would have the satisfaction of defeating Drake Harwood. As he had said himself, photographs of her, as herself would have little appeal. As Emma Court she was no one and even though her mind and body screamed objections to what she would have to do she must ignore them.

'Well?'

She faced him coolly, 'I agree. but first I must have a document signed by you, clearing Camilla from any charges you might make against her.'

'You shall have it. I do admire a woman of keen perception Emma Court. Somehow I thought you and I would be able to reach a mutually acceptable agreement.'

He was taunting her, Emma was sure of it, but she wasn't going to respond.

'How long will it take to get the document prepared and signed,' she asked him coolly. She must know how much time she had. She daredn't say that she wasn't taking the job until she had that paper in her hand.

He was watching her face. 'It will be given to you immediately after the photographic session.'

'Do I have your word on that?' Her eyes were hard, and she noted the dull flush colouring his cheek bones.

'You have it,' he told her crisply. 'Now let's get down to the arrangements shall we?'

*　　*　　*

He obviously didn't believe in wasting any time Emma thought hollowly half an hour later as she left his office. Tomorrow she had to present herself at a studio whose address he had given her, and he had promised that she would also receive the documents releasing Camilla while she was there.

She went back to her hotel and booked in for another night. Then she telephoned home and told her father she had been delayed. 'Camilla wants to speak to you,' he told her.

Camilla sounded tense. 'Did you see him?' she demanded.

'Yes, and he's agreed to drop all the charges.' There wasn't much point in telling her sister the price she was having to pay for her freedom. There was nothing martyred or self-sacrificing in her decision; it was simply the only one she could make. She had grown so used to protecting Camilla that it was almost second nature.

She put off telephoning Robert, her interview with him was best left until she got home. Thank goodness she hadn't actually signed a new contract. The television company would be more than pleased to let her go when they knew why she was leaving. Once her photograph had appeared in Drake Harwood's obnoxious publication no serious television station would want to touch her with a bargepole. Bitterness welled up inside her, but she fought it down; at least she would have the satisfaction of defeating his main purpose and that, she sensed, was something very few people ever did. He had been quite cold and callous about his reasons for what he was doing; *her* thoughts and feelings meant nothing to him and neither did the fact that he was destroying her career. She had sensed beneath the mockery a fine contempt of the female sex, and she shuddered inwardly, trying not to think about the ordeal to come.

That evening after she had had her bath she forced herself to study her nude reflection in the bedroom mirror. Her body was slender and well formed, unmistakably feminine; the thought of exposing it to the eyes of some jaded photographer made her shudder with distaste. If only she could blot the whole thing out of her mind somehow ... but that wasn't possible.

Neither was sleep; she lay awake for what felt like hours, prey to her thoughts and too-active imagination. It was difficult to visualise anything more degrading than what she was going to have to do, and her pride rebelled fiercely against it, but there was no escape.

CHAPTER THREE

MORNING came; she was heavy eyed and lethargic. The thought of breakfast held no appeal and having showered she dressed quickly in plain cream underwear. The moment her fingers touched the pale, silky fabric she started to shiver. Dear God, she could not go through with this; she could not subject herself to such sexual debasement. She ran to the bathroom and retched painfully, shuddering convulsively afterwards. If only she could simply walk out of this hotel and away from ... from everything, she thought tiredly, but she couldn't. She had spent too many years as Camilla's older sister to do that. She could not desert the younger girl now.

A blessed numb calm seemed to engulf her the moment she walked outside; it was like being encased in a soft plastic bubble; safe from all harm; from all contact with her own feelings.

The taxi drive to the address Drake Harwood had given her was over all too soon. The studio was housed in an elegant Regency terrace; testament to how much money could be made from their business, Emma reflected bitterly as she paid off the taxi driver and rang the bell.

It took several minutes for the door to open. A girl of about her own age stood there, dressed in tatty jeans and a bulky sweater. 'Hi, come on in,' she directed. 'Drake warned me to expect you.' She gave Emma a wide grin. 'Feeling nervous?

Drake said you might be. This way.'

Following her down a narrow corridor, Emma gritted her teeth against the biting retort she was longing to make. Her relief at discovering that the photographer was another woman had quickly been displaced by fury that Drake Harwood should discuss her with her.

'In here . . .'

'Here . . .' was an expensively equipped studio, dominated by the large bed on which several spotlights were focused. The bed itself was covered in a satin spread, the colour of rich cream.

'Drake's idea. I'm Pat Devlin,' the other girl introduced herself. 'I don't normally accept commissions of this type, but Drake made me an offer I couldn't refuse, as the saying goes. That was his idea,' she added gesturing towards the bed and grimacing faintly. 'He said the spread would be a perfect foil for your hair. Fancy a cup of coffee?'

Nodding numbly, Emma tried to come to grips with reality. It seemed impossible to believe this was actually happening but it was . . . and there was no escape.

'Oh and Drake left something for you, said I was to give it to you after we'd finished. It's over there.'

Emma looked at the thick envelope. So he had kept his promise to her. Somehow she had never doubted that he would. 'Hey are you feeling okay?' There was genuine anxiety in the question.

Emma nodded her head. 'First time nerves,' she grimaced.

'And second thoughts. Why not have third ones and forget the whole thing. It's none of my business of course, but if you're really hating the thought of it as much as you look as though you are, it will show in the photographs, and no matter how much Drake is paying you, it can't possibly compensate for what it's costing you . . .'

'I have to do it.'

Emma knew her voice was shaking. She couldn't look at Pat, just in case she broke down and gave in to her suggestion not to go through with it. The papers were there and she could take them, but pride would not let her. She had to go through with it . . . but if Drake Harwood chose to print the finished product it would not be of Emma Court, TV newsreader, but simply Emma Court, out of work. He had demanded a price and she was prepared to pay it, but she wasn't prepared to involve anyone else in that payment.

'Okay, then let's get it over with shall we?'

Pat Devlin might not be used to doing the sort of work Drake had engaged her for, but she was a professional to her finger-tips Emma realised in the two hours that followed. Small, and wiry with a shock of thick black hair, she possessed an energy that left Emma limp.

'Take your hair down,' she had instructed, helping Emma to uncoil her chignon, after she had taken some initial shots of Emma as she had arrived at the studio.

'Look,' she asked in a kind voice when she had asked her to undress, 'are you sure . . .'

'Sure.'

'Okay then.'

If it wasn't as bad as she had dreaded it was bad enough. Drake's magazine was apparently more up-market than many of its competitors and for that reason she had been instructed to make sure all the shots were in good taste, Pat told Emma with a grimace. 'Personally if I had my way the things would be banned, but a girl has to make a living. He was right about your hair,' she added when she had positioned Emma on the satin spread. 'I think you'd better close your eyes,' she added, 'they give away too much. You're supposed to look as though you're enjoying this, not on the rack. Try to think of something pleasant . . .'

All she could think of was that at some future date, Drake Harwood would be looking at her like this. The thought made her so tense that Pat had to stop work. What was one man among thousands, Emma jeered at herself, glad of the mug of coffee Pat brought her.

'Nearly over,' she encouraged her. 'God I remember the first nude shots I ever did . . . I was nearly sick with nerves . . . but after a while you get used to it . . .'

Emma shuddered again, thankful when at last her ordeal was over and she could discard the cream satin underwear Pat had asked her to wear. The satin was soft and of excellent quality, the underwear perfectly respectable, sexy, but in an understated way; the sort of thing she herself might even have worn, for a lover perhaps . . . but now the mere thought of it against her body revolted her. All she wanted to do was to immerse herself in a tub of hot water and scrub her skin until she felt clean again.

Unfortunately, it would not be as easy to erase the morning from her mind.

'Okay, here's your envelope, don't forget it,' Pat instructed handing it to her when Emma emerged from behind the changing screen.

'I'll just pack up my things and then I'll be on my way too. You know you meet all types in this game, but you ... you're someone I just can't pigeonhole. You went through agony there, and yet you kept on ... why?'

When Emma shook her head, Pat shrugged. 'Well I guess it's your own affair. I'd better get back to my flat and get these developed before Drake starts screaming for them. It's the first time I've done this sort of work for him. Industrial stuff's more his line. Still it makes a change from working for *Vogue*, and photographing building sites.'

'Well come on, I want to hear all about it.'

The first thing Emma had done when she got home was to ring Robert. Now they were sitting in the bar of a quiet local pub, nursing their drinks.

'I can't take the job.' She hadn't meant to say it so baldly, but somehow the words were out and Robert was staring at her as though she had lost her mind.

'Emma have you gone mad. Of course you can take it... They offered it to you, I know that, and it's the chance of a life-time, just what you've always wanted.'

'Just what I did always want,' Emma corrected unsteadily, 'I've ... I've changed my mind ...'

Robert glared at her as though he was seeing her for the first time. 'I see, and is one allowed to ask why? Don't tell me,' he continued furiously, 'it has to be a man. God Emma, I thought you were different, I thought you had more sense, but it seems I was wrong. I thought you wanted a career, not ...'

'Love?' she supplemented drily. 'All women want that, Robert . . .'

Although Robert had leapt to the wrong conclusion, it was easier to let him go on believing it than to try and find some alternative explanation for her decision. Inside she felt sick and shaky, one part of her longing to pour out to him her pain and misery, and another warning her against doing so; against crossing the careful barrier she had always maintained between them.

Emma wasn't blind; she was aware that Robert was attracted to her, it would be easy to push that attraction into something more because she needed someone to confide in and comfort her, but if she did they would both end up regretting it. Robert loved his wife, and she wanted no part of a man who was committed to someone else.

'Well I hope to God he knows what you're giving up,' Robert said harshly, draining his glass. 'What do you intend to do now? Stay on with us?'

Emma shook her head. 'No that's not possible I'm afraid . . .'

'Lover-boy wants a little stay at home wife, is that it?' Robert practically snarled the words. 'Very well Emma, if that's what you want . . .'

'I'll give you my notice tomorrow.' She had to bend her head to hide from him the tears starting up in her eyes.

'If that's what you want. . . .'

It isn't what I want, her heart cried out rebelliously, but it's what I have to do . . . I don't have any alternative. If she kept quiet and signed her new contract, they would have to abide by it; they would not be able to get rid of her, as they would want to do, once the magazine came out, and she had too much pride to subject herself or them to that.

Robert drove her home in a stiff silence. She had holidays owing to her which meant that she need not work her notice period. When she told her father and Camilla, neither seemed overly concerned.

'Oh good, you'll be able to help with the wedding arrangements,' was Camilla's selfish remark, while her father commented that it would be nice to have her at home.

'I still can't believe that tomorrow David and I will be married,' Camilla said for the umpteenth time. They were in her bedroom, Emma doing her packing for the Caribbean honeymoon David was taking her on. 'Thank God you were able to persuade that beast Drake Harwood to drop charges.'

It was the first time Camilla had referred to Drake Harwood in the month since Emma's return from London.

'It's a shame that you wouldn't be my bridesmaid, David says his best man is an old friend from school—he comes from a frightfully wealthy family.'

'Mrs T. wanted you to have young attendants, and I think she was right, David's twin cousins will look adorable.'

'I just hope that the weather keeps fine,' Camilla continued fretfully.

The reception was being held in a marquee in the Manor grounds, and several fine June days had dried out the lawns and warmed up the air. The Manor would make a perfect setting for the occasion Emma admitted; Mrs T. was over the moon because she had persuaded Lady Cornwald and her husband to attend. In fact, apart from herself everyone seemed perfectly happy.

Since her return from London she had heard nothing from Drake Harwood. She had held her breath for a couple of days after the announcement of the new newsgirl had been made, half expecting to suffer the effects of his pique, but when a week went past and she had heard nothing, her jangling nerves settled down again. Doubtless he realised that there was simply nothing he could do. A rather unusual feeling for him, she reflected with acid satisfaction. It would do him good to be on the receiving end of what he was so fond of giving to others.

That he could have made her ordeal worse for her, she was forced to admit; there had been nothing personal in his humiliation of her, Emma knew that . . . No, that quick entrepreneurial brain of his had simply seen her as another asset; another commodity he could capitalise on.

Press interest in the previously much vaunted contest between *Macho* and its rival had died, confirming Emma's opinion that at least a good seventy-five per cent of it had been carefully organised publicity.

Once Camilla was safely married, she would have to start looking round for another job. One of her father's university lecturer friends was looking for a research assistant to help him with a project he had taken on for the summer recess, and Emma was toying with the idea of offering her services. She had a good degree in political science and the project promised to be quite interesting.

She couldn't stay at home playing surrogate vicar's wife for ever, she acknowledged, admitting ruefully to herself that her father, with all his charming lazy selfishness, was already inclined to expect her to take on many of his duties. At the moment she was enjoying them, but she knew that eventually they would pall.

Her secretarial skills were good, although perhaps slightly dulled. She wasn't too sure how good her shorthand speed would be after several years' neglect for instance, but it had occurred to her that perhaps a secretarial job at Westminster might be appealing—always supposing she could get one—and might serve as a jumping block to other things.

Only one thing was sure, and that was that she could not go back into television. If she did, every job she managed to land in front of the camera would raise the spectre of Drake Harwood's photographs being re-published. Something like that was just the sort of material the gutter-press loved to get their hands on. No ... if she could find herself some congenial work for long enough for the publicity to die down, she could then start to re-think her future career. Of course she was bitterly disappointed about what had happened and about losing Robert's friendship; he had had every right to be angry with her after he had promoted her career so intensely, and she could have explained to him, but pride would not let her. Perhaps in her secret heart she had hoped that he might object; that he might dig deep enough for the truth to have to come out, but he had accepted her explanation at face value, and in many ways that hurt.

The day of the wedding dawned fine and clear; a perfect June morning complete with cuckoo calls, Emma reflected drowsily, hearing the bird song through her open bedroom window. Fortune had a way of shining benevolently on her younger sister, although Camilla was the last person to think so.

Getting up and donning jeans and a T-shirt Emma hurried downstairs. Camilla had requested the traditional bridal breakfast in bed—the fact that Emma was supposed to go up to the house and give Mrs T. a hand with the caterers had somehow seemed to escape the younger woman's memory.

Sighing Emma opened the kitchen door to let Puss in Boots, the cat, out. The sunshine was still faintly hazy, promising the heat to come. On a morning like this there was nowhere to beat the English countryside, she reflected, enjoying the solitude and breathing in the clean air. Although she loved the frantic bustle and pace of city life, there was no doubt that it was good to get back to nature at times, to slow one's pace down and live in harmony with one's surroundings.

Her father was awake when she went upstairs with his breakfast. He was to conduct the service in the small local church and a very distant second cousin of the family had been coerced into giving Camilla away in his stead. That this distant relative was from the upper echelons of the family tree had greatly pleased Mrs T., although Emma wondered wryly if she would be quite as pleased when she discovered how eccentric Uncle Ted could be. To the best of her knowledge she had never seen him wearing anything other than a

particularly hairy and ancient looking brown
tweed suit which looked as though he had
inherited it from one of his ancestors.

Morning suits for the men was the order of
the day; Uncle Ted had been apprised of this,
but just to be on the safe side, Emma had taken
the precaution of hiring one for him, and was
hoping that she had managed to gauge his size
correctly.

Camilla was still asleep when she went in, her
peaches and cream skin glowing, her blonde hair
curling wildly over the pillow. She woke up when
Emma called her. David was at least getting value
for money as far as physical attractiveness went,
Emma reflected, as Camilla slid out of bed.

Dainty and femininely curved, Camilla took
great care to ensure that her figure remained
perfect. Watching her pout anxiously as she
studied a non-existent spot Emma prayed that the
marriage would be successful and that Camilla
would not grow bored and spoilt. David would pet
and indulge her, which was what she wanted, and
if she had the good sense to appreciate him for
what he was her life should be a very happy one.

She doubted that Camilla loved David in the
way that she would want to love any man with
whom she shared her life, but then for all her
prettiness and sex appeal, Emma had always
considered that Camilla lacked her own intensity
and depth of emotional need. Perhaps it was just
as well, she reflected. The shallows of life were
always much safer than the depths.

'Be an angel and lay my underwear out for me
will you,' Camilla called on her way to the
bathroom. 'The hairdresser's due at ten, and he's

bringing a girl with him to do my make-up . . . so
I'd better have my shower now.'

The underwear was new and delicately white.
She and Camilla had bought it from an expensive
shop just off Bond Street. It had been Emma's
trousseau present to her sister, but now, extracting
it from its tissue wrappings, Emma could not
repress a shudder of distaste, remembering the
cream satin that had clung so lovingly to her skin.

'I've got to go up to the house and help Mrs T.,'
she called as she passed the bathroom. 'I'll be back
just as soon as I can . . .'

'Emma don't stay there too long . . . Uncle Ted
should be arriving soon and you know he bores
me to tears . . . and then there's the flowers
and. . .'

Closing her ears to Camilla's petulant voice
Emma let herself out of the house. It was only a
ten minute drive to the Manor and at this time of
the morning she had the road to herself apart from
the milkman who called out a cheery greeting to
her. 'Nice day for the wedding,' he commented.
'I've just been up at the Manor. Chaos it is . . .'

Emma could well believe it. Despite her love of
organising Mrs T. had a knack of turning order
into chaos. The middle-aged cousin whom she
employed as companion/social secretary was the
person on whom the burden for most of the
arrangements had fallen. Emma liked Laura Petts.
Although quiet and self-effacing she was an
intelligent, and, on occasions, witty person. How
on earth she endured Mrs T.'s domineering
manner, Emma had no idea.

It was Laura who greeted her when she walked
into the Manor, giving her a quiet smile.

'All under control?' Emma asked.

'More or less. They put the marquee up last night and the caterers arrived on time. They've practically taken over the kitchen, and it looks as though the weather is going to be kind to us. How's Camilla?'

'Looking very bridal,' Emma told her. 'What can I do to help?'

'You might go downstairs for me and check on how Mrs Berry's getting on with breakfast. We've got nearly a dozen people staying here and what with the caterers and all the unaccustomed activity . . .'

'I'll go down now.'

Mrs Berry looked flustered and cross when Emma walked into the kitchen. 'Having all these folks to stay . . . as if I hadn't got enough to do . . .'

Having managed to soothe her down, Emma went back upstairs. The two small girls who were to be Camilla's attendants were up and dressed. Both pretty blondes they would look delightful in the spotted voile dresses Camilla had chosen for them. Her own dress was a lavish *Gone with the Wind* confection trimmed with antique lace and matching ribbons. It had cost a fortune, but she looked like a dream in it.

Having ascertained that there was nothing more she could do, and feeling that she had fulfilled any obligation she might have towards Mrs T., Emma was just on the point of leaving when the latter came hurrying downstairs. Tall and well built, there were times when she reminded Emma of a battleship under full steam.

'Emma . . . you weren't going were you?'

'Everything seems to be under admirable control,' Emma responded with a smile. 'Laura is doing a sterling job isn't she? I thought I'd better get back to check on Uncle Ted and father. You know what men can be like.'

'Yes ... yes of course ...' She frowned. 'I really had hoped you could stay to check on the flowers for me ... I told the florists exactly what was needed, but one can never rely entirely on these people.'

'I'm sure everything will be fine,' Emma soothed.

'I do hope so. My poor head is aching already. There is just so much to do ... Oh by the way my dear, your friend telephoned, and asked if it was all right if he came... I must say I was a little surprised, but of course, I agreed. He sounds quite charming ...'

Her friend? Who on earth was she talking about Emma wondered curiously. The only person she could think of was Robert. Her heart lifted. Had he perhaps had second thoughts; realised that there must be more to her leaving than he had first thought. It cheered her considerably that he had wanted to see her enough to ring Mrs T. and invite himself to the wedding. It was a curiously unRobert-like manoeuvre, and even though she knew it would be impossible for her to change her mind, she was still glad that he had apparently seen through her deception.

The service was being conducted at one o'clock and by twelve Emma was beginning to wonder if she was ever going to be ready on time. The yellow silk suit she was wearing was hanging upstairs in her room, but she was still no nearer getting into it than she had been at ten. Uncle Ted, as she had suspected, had arrived in his brown suit, and it had taken a considerable degree of cajoling to get him into the morning suit she had hired. Once in it, he presented a surprisingly dapper figure, his silver hair gleaming.

A step on the stairs warned her that the hairdresser and his assistant were on the point of departing. A large bouquet of red roses had arrived from David and Emma took them up to her sister, finding her sitting in front of her mirror pouting dangerously.

'My hair looks awful,' she cried out when Emma walked in. 'And just look at the mess that frightful girl's made of my make-up.'

'You look stunning,' Emma told her, studying her immaculate hairstyle and make-up, 'and look David's sent you these . . .'

The red roses got little more than a cursory glare. 'What about Uncle Ted, did you manage . . .'

'He looks every inch the elegant gentleman,' Emma assured her. 'How would you like a glass of champagne?'

Without waiting for Camilla's response she went downstairs to open the bottle she had bought purposely for the occasion. Knowing Camilla as she did, she had decided that a couple of glasses would do wonders to relax her highly-strung nerves, and although Camilla pulled a face, by the time she was ready to get into her dress, she was considerably more at ease.

Emma was now dressed herself. Her yellow silk suit with its straight skirt and blouson jacket was a perfect foil for her chestnut hair, which unlike

Camilla's had had to be content with its normal shampoo and blow dry. But then who was going to be looking at her? Emma mocked herself.

Camilla looked like a fairy princess in her dress, there was no doubt about that.

It was a view that was reinforced by the soft sounds of appreciation filling the church when Camilla walked down the aisle on her cousin's arm. Emma was sitting at the front, taking the place that would have been their mother's. Because she had had to be at the church early she had not been able to spot Robert—for all she knew he might only be intending to attend the reception. What was she getting so excited about she chided herself; nothing could change her decision. When, she wondered, would Drake Harwood publish her photographs? She shuddered deeply, suddenly cold.

At last the service was over and everyone was getting into cars for the journey to the Manor. Emma was driving her father and Uncle Ted. As she drove out into the road her eye was caught by a wickedly scarlet Ferrari parked just outside the church, and her heart thudded.

Oh stop being ridiculous, she chided herself. Of course it wouldn't be Drake Harwood's . . . what on earth would *he* be doing at Camilla's wedding? They barely knew one another. No it probably belonged to one of David's jet-setting ex-school friends.

They were among the first to arrive and having assured herself that Uncle Ted would be on hand to participate in the formal receiving line Emma wandered into the house, glancing appreciatively at the wedding presents which were set out in the

drawing room. It was cool and quiet inside away
from the mêlée of guests arriving but she could not
stay here for ever.

Sighing Emma went back outside, dazzled
momentarily by the strong sunlight.

'Emma my dear, where have you been
hiding. . .?'

There was no escape from Mrs T. Emma
reflected, walking across the lawn in obedience to
the commanding tone. 'My dear your friend here
has been waiting for you for the last ten minutes.'

Robert? Emma screwed her eyes up against the
harsh dazzle of the sun, all the colour leaving her
face as she found herself meeting the implaccable
gaze of Drake Harwood.

'Emma, darling . . .'

Quite how she came to be in his arms, Emma
wasn't sure, but what she did know was that his
arms constricted her body like a steel vice, making
sure there was no escape. His breath, clean and
fresh, brought goosebumps up under her skin, her
lips parting in instant protest as she tensed her
body furiously against him.

'Sweetheart, you look entrancing.' He said the
words loud enough for the half dozen or so people
standing close by to hear, and they numbered
among them the photographer from the local
newspaper who was covering the event for them,
Emma noticed tensely as she tried to fight off an
overwhelming feeling of disbelief. This could not
be happening. She could not be here in Drake
Harwood's arms, her palms pressed flat against his
chest, feeling the steady beat of his heart.

'Kiss me . . .' He made the command against her
lips, the words soundless.

Rage and rejection mingled hotly in Emma's eyes as she tried to force him away, but the moment she opened her mouth to demand that he release her it was captured by his.

His lips were warm and firm, skilled in the way they moved over hers, leaving tiny tremors of pleasure feathering over her skin. Hardly able to believe her response to him, Emma shivered in reaction. Of course she had not responded to him ... but her mouth tingled from his kiss as he released her, and his eyes mocked her as she cringed away.

'Emma my dear, what a dark horse you are ...' Mrs T. sounded both chagrined and excited. 'Why on earth didn't you tell us.'

Tell them what Emma thought numbly? What on earth had Drake Harwood said to her? Certainly he couldn't have revealed the fact that she had posed naked for his magazine ... there was far too much awe in Mrs T's voice for that.

'Emma didn't want to steal her sister's limelight ... did you my pet?'

The hard grip on her arm warned her against rebellion, the smooth voice coating an intent resolve revealed to her by the cold gleam in dark green eyes.

'Emma?' That was Camilla's voice sharp with anxiety and anger. 'What's going on?'

'I ...'

'Emma was just about to tell me off for letting the cat out of the bag about our engagement,' Drake Harwood intervened smoothly. 'Weren't you darling?'

She simply did not know what to say. She felt as though she had strayed into a make-believe world where nothing made sense. What on earth was Drake Harwood talking about? What was the purpose of his ridiculous announcement? She couldn't understand any of it. She opened her mouth to contradict his statement and then fell silent as he said softly to the hovering photographer. 'I hope you've taken some of Emma . . . she's most photogenic. I have some quite spectacular shots of her, haven't I darling?'

He was threatening her damn him, reminding her of the hold he had over her. She could just imagine Mrs T's face if he were to reveal now just what those photographs were and how he intended to use them.

She could see Camilla looking anxiously from Drake to herself. She came towards them, a fixed smile on her face, David at her side. Before Emma could intervene Drake was speaking, smiling pleasantly as he greeted her sister. 'Hello Camilla. What a beautiful bride you make, and this of course, must be . . .'

'David.' Camilla supplied in a tight, bitter voice. The glance she darted at Emma spoke volumes, and Emma was tempted to tell her that Drake's presence was none of her doing.

Emma could see that David was frowning slightly as he looked at Camilla. David possessed a deeply jealous streak which rarely surfaced, but when it did . . .

Camilla too had seen the look. 'I met Drake the last time I was in London, darling.' She was babbling tensely, and Emma had the uneasy sensation that David was none too pleased by this disclosure.

'Yes, it is thanks to your wife that I got to know

Emma,' Drake intervened. If she hadn't known him better she might almost have thought he was deliberately trying to reassure David, Emma thought cynically, but Drake Harwood had not struck her as a man who would put himself out for another human being unless he stood to gain something from doing so.

'Come on darling, I want to thank Uncle Ted for standing in for Daddy.' Camilla tugged tensely at David's arm, and he allowed himself to be led away.

Before she could take Drake to task Mrs T. bore down on them, beaming fulsomely, and Emma groaned inwardly, knowing it would be quite some time before they could escape.

CHAPTER FOUR

As Emma had suspected it was a good fifteen minutes before Mrs T. left, but the moment she could, she steered Drake out of earshot of the other guests and rounded on him, her eyes blazing as she demanded fiercely, 'And just what was all that about?'

'All what?'

He was laughing at her, damn him. Mentally grinding her teeth and trying to hold on to her temper, Emma said quietly, 'You know exactly what I mean, so don't pretend you don't ... I'm talking about the way you are giving the impression that you and I are ...' she struggled for words.

While she hesitated, Drake cut in smoothly, 'Are more than just good friends?' He smiled sardonically. 'We can't have the discussion you're obviously itching to have here; we'll discuss the whole thing over dinner tonight. I've booked us a table at the George ... I'm staying there for the whole weekend.'

His high-handedness robbed her of the breath to expostulate, and by the time she had regained it it was too late; her father was almost level with them, Uncle Ted in tow.

'Ah Emma, there you are ...' he smiled his usual vague smile at her, 'and this must be the young man Mrs T. has been telling me about.'

As Drake shook the vicar's extended hand,

Emma was struck anew by the leashed virility of him; the sensation of male power, so intensely heightened by her father's frailer more aesthetic appearance.

'I believe you're something of a name in financial circles,' he added conversationally.

The three men chatted for several minutes, and Emma was surprised to learn that Drake too had been up at Oxford, although not at her father's college. When Uncle Ted started describing at length the bad luck he had had with his shares, Emma judged it was time for them to move away. She could sense her father's quizzical speculation, and knew that he was wondering why Drake had never been brought into any of their conversations.

The vicar was a liberal, if somewhat vague, father, always inclined to take a distant and global view of any given situation and there was no earthly reason why, if Emma had genuinely been as involved with Drake as he was pretending, she would not have mentioned him to her parent.

The afternoon seemed to drag on interminably; Emma could scarcely touch her food, delicious though she was sure it was. The several glasses of champagne she consumed helped to steady her over-wrought nerves but they couldn't stop her from fuming inwardly every time she thought of Drake's high-handed behaviour. How dare he come down here and interfere with her life. What did he want from her anyway?

After the reception she had to go back to the house with Camilla to help her change. The moment the bedroom door closed behind them her sister turned on her, her pretty face flushed and angry as she demanded. 'What is he doing here? Emma how could you invite him. You know. . .'

'Just a minute, I didn't invite him, Mrs T. did. Somehow he managed to convince her that he and I are . . . "good friends".' Emma gritted her teeth over the last two words. 'I had no idea that he was going to turn up here, and I still don't know why he did . . .'

She didn't know, but she suspected it must have something to do with the fact that she had not accepted the television job. Initially she had expected a reaction from him but when weeks had gone by without one, she had decided that he had accepted that there was nothing he could do.

'David wanted to know where I'd met him. I'm sure he suspects something,' Camilla told her fretfully. 'Why did he have to come down here?'

'If you told David the truth it would save us both a lot of problems,' Emma responded astringently. 'Honestly Camilla, you're storing up a lot of trouble for yourself by not doing so. If I were you . . .'

'But you're not are you,' Camilla snapped. 'I suppose you couldn't resist encouraging him. After all it's not every day you get to meet a man like Drake Harwood. Well I'm warning you Em . . . he changes his girls like most men change their underwear, and you'll have some pretty stiff competition. I can't think what he sees in you,' she added tactlessly, 'he normally goes for the glamorous type; model girls, actresses. . .' Her expression changed as she stared into the mirror, a preening, self-satisfied look that Emma was familiar with, chasing the petulance out of her face. 'Of course . . . why didn't I think of it before

... I expect he's just using you as an excuse to see me.'

'On your wedding day?' Emma asked drily, suddenly and for no reason that she could think of, so angry with her sister that she wanted to slap her. 'Come on Camilla ...'

'You're just jealous.' Camilla whirled round to face her, two angry spots of colour burning in her cheeks. 'You've always been jealous of me ... that's why you want me to tell David, so that it will make trouble between us. Well I'm telling you now Emma, that a man like Drake Harwood wouldn't look twice at you, if you weren't my sister. He wants *me* all right. I'm sure of it, and he's come down here today to let me know it. He doesn't want to get married, everyone knows that, and I expect he thinks that now that I'm married ...'

'The two of you can indulge in an affair without anyone being the wiser... You might have a pretty face Camilla,' she told her sister shortly, 'but you've got an empty brain and a cold heart. I don't envy you ... I feel sorry for you.'

She walked out before she said anything more she might regret. Let Camilla finish changing by herself. If she had to stay with her sister a moment longer, she could not be responsible for her actions. She passed David on the stairs, already changed into casual slacks shirt and jacket. He caught her arm as she passed him, frowning slightly.

'Em about this Drake Harwood chap ... Just how well does Camilla know him?'

She was tired of shielding Camilla, she thought bitterly, tired of always having to put her first.

'Why don't you ask her that yourself David?' she suggested curtly. 'I . . .'

'So there you are darling . . . I was just coming to see if I could find you.'

Hard fingers circled her wrist, cool green eyes studying her flushed cheeks and angry eyes. 'I've barely been gone half an hour,' she said tersely, caught completely off her guard when Drake transferred his grip from her wrist to her waist, pulling her firmly into his arms, despite David's presence, his body hard and firm against hers, as his unexpected action caused her to fall heavily against him, her breath tangling in her throat.

'That's twenty-five minutes too long.' His free hand moved against her nape, the words feathered across her forehead.

Emma was aware of David muttering something about having to go, and hurrying past them. It must have been the jolt to her system of finding herself so suddenly off balance that was playing havoc with her pulses, she thought faintly, trying to stem the flooding tide of weakness flowing through her. There was a dangerous enchantment in being held like this . . . in being wrapped in concern; in being cosseted and cared for by strong male arms.

With a jerk Emma brought her thoughts under control. What was the matter with her; was she losing her mind? How could she possibly believe even for a second that Drake Harwood's arms offered security and warmth? He was merely acting a part . . . merely pretending to care about her . . . although as yet she did not know why.

'Let me go.' She pushed a bunched up fist against his chest, trying to reinforce her plea with physical force, but trying to match her strength against his was laughable. Indeed he was laughing; she could feel the sound rumbling deep in his chest, and when she raised her eyes to meet his, they were a dense dark green; gleaming with mockery and amusement.

That he should dare to laugh at her was like a lighted match applied to the fuse paper of her temper; badly frayed during the build up to the wedding, her taut nerves suddenly seemed unable to take any more.

'Don't you dare laugh at me,' she told him tensely. 'Just what. . .?'

'Why did you refuse to take the television job?'

His eyes weren't amused any longer; they were cold and watchful, the crisp question taking the heat out of her anger; confusing her almost. Her mouth compressed into a firm line. She didn't have to answer his questions; let him answer them himself.

'Not going to speak? Well I know a remedy for that . . .'

Before she knew what he was doing Emma felt the warm pressure of his mouth on hers; not painfully or brutally—that she could have dealt with. No, his lips were caressing hers with a mobile, experienced sensuality that made her pulses jerk into confused awareness and her heart pound as idiotically as a gullible teenager's. It made no sense; there was no logical reason that she could think of why he should be able to arouse this reaction inside her; her intelligence told her that experience alone could not be the answer.

What he was doing to her was a true seduction of the senses, she thought hazily; he was using his

skill and her vulnerability as a weapon against her
and it was one which he wielded with deadly
accuracy. His tongue, warm and knowing, stroked
along the curves of her still closed mouth,
investigating the tensely held in corners, urging her
body without using words, to disobey the
commands of her brain. The scrape of his teeth
against her lower lip was intensely erotic; so much
so that she trembled visibly; knowing that if she
didn't give in she would soon be swamped with
sensations she would not be able to control.

Against his chest the hands she had curled into
fists uncurled and pressed flat as she tried to push
him away. Her neck felt as though it was going to
snap beneath the pressure he was applying to her
nape to keep her mouth still under his, but from
somewhere she found the strength to pull away
just enough to mutter thickly, 'All right, all right
... I'll tell you ...'

His eyes were incredibly dark, she realised as her
own locked with them; dark and hot; burning with
an intensity that poured rivers of heat under her
own skin. She had thought he was simply cold
bloodedly trying to dominate her, but the heat of
his concentrated study told a different story.

'Too late ...' The sound of the words
reverberated against her mouth as his own possessed
it, hotly and deeply, his hand at her nape, curling
into her hair and bending her back until her body
was as taut as a bow string, her breasts pressed flat
against his chest, her mouth vulnerable to any assault
he chose to make on it. She had to grip his shoulders
to stop herself from overbalancing; her senses
rioting out of control, her mouth warm and pliant
beneath his, betraying her commands in favour of

response to a deep rooted need that seemed to have
sprung up inside her.

He ended the kiss slowly, lingering over his
enjoyment of it, rubbing his thumb softly over the
swollen contours of her mouth as he released her.

His eyes were almost jade green; hot as a
tropical night, almost smothering her in a
sensation of heat and languor.

'Now tell me,' he murmured as she stepped
unsteadily away from him. 'Why did you refuse to
take the job?'

'Did you expect me to do anything different?'
Now that she was free and back in control of her
own body an irrational feverish anger possessed
her; that most of the anger should have been
directed against herself Emma couldn't deny; he
hadn't forced a response from her, she acknowledged; he had seduced it; and she fool that she
was had responded to that seduction. Her heart
was still pounding as though she had been
running; her skin hot and prickly. She wanted to
deny the effect he had had on her but it was there
in the aching tension in the pit of her stomach and
the shivering bewilderment of her body.

'How could I take it?' she stormed on, trying to
ignore the vulnerability he had revealed to her,
and which she had never suspected herself capable
of. 'How could I sign a contract, knowing what
you intended to do. . .?'

'So instead you cheated on our bargain, by
refusing the job, believing that I wouldn't use the
photographs if you weren't employed by the
studio?'

He was watching her closely, but Emma was too
angry to pay much attention.

'No!' she told him vehemently. 'It wasn't like that at all. You can do what you like with them . . . humiliate *me* as much as you care to . . . but it will just be *me* you humiliate, not Emma Court Newsreader, I won't be manipulated in that. I won't be used in your publicity war against a rival magazine . . .'

'And your present job?' He said it quietly, still watching her and Emma had the distinct impression that he already knew.

'I've handed in my notice.'

'So at the present time you're out of a job. . .'

'That's right . . . but no doubt I'll be offered plenty once your magazine comes out . . . When. . .?' Her throat closed up and she had to swallow hard to appear unconcerned as she asked coolly, 'When will my photographs appear?'

'That's up to you.' He was watching her carefully, 'But it isn't something I care to discuss right now. We'll talk about it tonight. You've surprised me you know,' he told her as he stepped away from her and down the stairs, and the way he said it told Emma that he wasn't used to being surprised by her sex. 'Nine of ten women would have signed that contract and left others to cope with the ensuing uproar. . .'

'Then it's no doubt unfortunate for us both that I happen to be the tenth isn't it?' Emma said tautly. She heard footsteps on the stairs behind her and glanced up to see Camilla coming down. Her sister ignored her, and instead smiled at Drake, dimpling him a flirtatious smile.

'Drake, you are very naughty, turning up like this,' she teased, linking her arm with his. 'Poor David is terribly jealous.'

'Is he?' Emma could have sworn there was derision and even faint contempt in the green eyes as they rested on her sister's face. 'Have you told him what happened yet?'

Flirtatiousness gave way to alarm as Camilla withdrew from him. 'No ... and neither must you,' she exclaimed hurriedly. 'Promise you won't...'

'I've already given that promise—to your sister,' Drake said coolly ... 'We struck a bargain over it, and I've no intention of reneging on my side of it ...' His eyes met Emma's over Camilla's head. 'I'll pick you up for our dinner date at seven,' he said to Emma, and there was a warning implicit in the words that told her she would be unwise to try to evade him.

It was just gone six and Emma had just reached home. Her father and Uncle Ted were closeted in the study, reminiscing, and perfectly content with one another's company. As she turned to go up the stairs Emma tried to control her erratic pulses. Dinner with Drake... If only she didn't have to go. She was behaving like a gauche adolescent, she scorned herself; where was her self-control; her poise? Neither had proved inviolate.

She had lost them when Drake kissed her, she acknowledged wryly. In retrospect it seemed impossible that a mere kiss should have such a devastating effect on her, and she was inclined to think she had overreacted; something brought on by her quarrel with Camilla and the stresses and strains leading up to the wedding. It seemed a much more plausible explanation than to admit that sexually at least she found Drake Harwood overwhelmingly attractive. That she could respond to someone so intensely on a purely sexual level, had been something she had never considered or experienced before, and it was a touch disconcerting.

She dressed for their dinner date almost automatically. Her wardrobe wasn't extensive; unlike Camilla she wasn't a clothes-aholic and she pondered on what to wear, ultimately selecting a new Caroline Charles outfit she had purchased in a fit of extravagance. The slim black silk skirt clung to her hips, the white jacket cut to mould itself neatly to her body emphasising her narrow waist. The jacket buttoned at a military angle and although simple, the outfit could be dressed up or down as the occasion demanded. Black silk stockings and high heeled shoes completed the outfit, and after scrutinising herself carefully in her mirror Emma decided that she had chosen correctly. The plain black and white of her suit gave off a formal, even faintly austere impression she decided, not seeing in the way the silk clung to her body a sensuality that was not immediately obvious but which held an allure that would linger long after the more obvious had been forgotten.

Drake arrived exactly on the dot of seven. She heard the Ferrari long before she saw it. Monster, she thought tetchily, glancing out of her bedroom window, as it stopped outside. A bright gleaming red, it certainly caught the eye, she decided cynically—exactly right for the type of man who liked to be noticed; to cause a ripple of interest when he appeared.

She dodged back away from the window, as Drake got out and walked up the path. She was in the hall by the time he rang the bell, opening the door to him with cool pleasantness. That was the best way to treat him she had decided, with a certain amount of tolerant disdain.

He raised his eyebrows as he studied her and pronounced, 'Very nice . . . In fact very, very nice.'

For some reason his compliment angered her. She felt like rushing upstairs and ripping the suit off. *That* was it, she decided as she gave him a cool smile, it was his air of believing that she had dressed specifically to please and attract *him* that infuriated her; that and his lordly bestowal of the compliment—a bone for a trained performing dog, she thought waspishly, following him out to his car.

Contrary to her expectations he was a controlled and considerate driver. Almost as though he realised her disdain for his car, he flicked a glance at her as he drove and said whimsically, 'This car is the embodiment of all my boyhood dreams—it's something of an anachronism in these days of petrol shortages and fuel conserving cars, but . . .' He shrugged and then added, 'I sense a certain amount of disapproval. Is it for the car . . . or for me?'

'A car is an inanimate object,' Emma responded coolly.

'Ah, so it is for me . . .'

'You can hardly expect me to be thrilled by the way you've turned up out of the blue and forced this dinner date on me,' Emma told him.

'But surely you expected some response? You must have known I wouldn't let your actions go by unremarked upon?'

'I didn't do it as an attention seeking exercise,' Emma told him curtly, infuriated by the intimation

behind his words that she had deliberately set out
to entice a response from him. 'I did it because my
own code of ethics prevented me from taking the
job when I knew that by doing so I would be
causing a good deal of potential embarrassment to
my employers . . .'

'Yes. It's very strong, isn't it, this code of ethics
of yours? First it leads you into protecting your
sister, and then to protecting your would-be
employers. I wonder if it could be extended to
embrace me as well.'

'You?' Emma turned scornful eyes toward him.
'And what would you need to be protected from?'

'Oh you'd be surprised,' he told her softly,
forestalling any further questions by adding, 'but
we'll discuss it over dinner. Here we are . . .' As
he turned into the George's narrow car-park
entrance, Emma fell silent so that he could
concentrate on manoeuvring the car. He parked it
deftly and then helped her to alight. He had all the
old-fashioned gentlemanly courtesies at his fingertips she had to give him that . . . but that didn't
change the fact that he was still a wolf . . . and as
rapacious and dangerous as any of that breed,
despite any sheep's clothing he might choose to
assume.

Emma could tell by the deference of the waiters
that they, like her, were aware of his aura of power
and self-confidence. Their table was slightly
secluded from the others; by a window, which in the
already fading daylight gave pleasant views over the
George's garden. Once an old-fashioned coaching
inn, the hotel had gardens which stretched down to
the river, and in summer the restaurant was often
packed with out of town visitors who had heard of

its charm and excellent chef.

'Well,' Emma pounced the moment they had given their order. 'What do you want to talk to me about that couldn't be said this afternoon.'

'Let's eat first.' His lazy drawl, and the laconic way he smiled at her increased Emma's impotent fury. He seemed determined to reinforce the fact that *he* was the one in control; that he held the whip handle. 'If you pick a fight with me now it will only ruin your digestion,' he added accurately reading the intention in her tense posture. What was it about this man that drove her beyond the limits of all reasonable caution; that practically willed her to behave in a way that was in direct contradiction of the standards she normally set herself?

'I don't have the slightest intention of picking a fight with you,' she lied coldly. 'I'm not a child Drake; and besides,' she added tauntingly, 'what makes you think you're so immune?'

She had wanted to prick his ego a little, to bring home to him the fact that he too was only human, but all he did was laugh and say lazily, 'Discipline ... I'm a very disciplined man, Emma. I never waste either time or energy if I can help it. Unlike you I have no desire to fight ... on the contrary...'

The look he gave her reminded Emma forcibly of the way he had kissed her on the stairs that afternoon. A warm, golden heat slithered disturbingly along her veins, but she forced herself to ignore it, to ignore everything but the food in front of her. Disciplined was he, she thought bitterly, glancing surreptitiously at him. Well she should show him what discipline was.

It was torture not to demand that he tell her exactly why he had sought her out, and by the time they had reached the coffee stage of their meal Emma was ready to burst with ire and impatience.

Even so she was determined not to say a word. She would wait for him to speak.

He had been served with a brandy before he did so, Emma having refused a liqueur. She had already drunk quite enough for one day, what with the champagne this afternoon and now wine with her meal. Something told her that she was going to need her wits about her to contend with Drake Harwood successfully.

Her self-control, hard won though it had been, hadn't deceived him. He smiled at her as he warmed his brandy glass in his palm and remarked softly, 'Very well done Emma... You know I find myself admiring you more and more all the time.'

'Then don't,' Emma said shortly. 'Save your admiration for those who want it.'

'Like your silly little sister, do you mean. You know,' he ruminated slowly, 'I'm surprised at her new husband, he'd have been much better off with you.'

'David happens to love Camilla,' Emma told him stiffly. Despite her own doubts concerning the marriage, she wasn't going to let anyone else get away with such a provocative statement, especially when it implied a criticism of her sister.

'I hope to God he isn't expecting a virgin bride.'

The comment stunned her.

'Oh come on,' he was patently amused, 'don't tell me you can't see that he's the type who would, but unlike you my dear, Camilla is anything but virgin. And no, I'm not speaking from personal experience,' he added laconically before she could say a word, 'but certain things speak for themselves, and just as there is that about you that tells me that you have had no lover; there is that about your sister that tells me she has.'

Emma thought of several retorts and banished them all in favour of what she hoped was a coldly repressive silence.

'What's the matter? Shocked because I've guessed the truth? Are you really so ashamed of it, Emma?'

'Neither ashamed or proud,' she told him with a coolness she was very proud of. Some deep seated instinct warned her against lying; he would know immediately what she was doing and it would be humiliating to be taxed with *that* on top of everything else. 'It is simply that as yet I have not met . . .'

'Met a man you want to go to bed with,' Drake finished for her. He was regarding her with open amusement. 'At least you hadn't, until recently isn't that it, Emma?'

His audacity took her breath away. Too intelligent to pretend she didn't know what he meant, Emma fought down the angry tide of colour threatening to run up under her skin and said freezingly, 'Your ego must be mammoth Drake. Believe me I have no desire whatsoever to . . .'

'Go to bed with me?' He said it for her, laughing openly at her expression.

On the verge of reinforcing his statement with a heated denial Emma decided to show more caution. She shrugged aside his comment with what she hoped was aplomb and said instead. 'Look, why did you want to see me. . .? Was it to tell me when the photographs will appear?'

'Only sort of.' He pushed aside his brandy glass and leaned towards her, watching her carefully, all evidence of his earlier bantering mockery gone. 'I have a proposition to put to you Emma. Let me explain it to you if you will before you make any comments. Now, are you ready?'

When she nodded her head mutely he said. 'Very well. As you may know the magazine came into my hands as part of a package when I took over its controlling parent. It hasn't been doing all that well and I confess that initially I thought it might be worthwhile trying to boost circulation but now I'm having second thoughts. For the most part my business interests lie in a different field.' He paused and looked across at her. 'At the present time I'm in negotiation to sell off the magazine to someone else. Negotiations have reached a very delicate stage. He wants the magazine but he's not prepared to meet my price or terms, and I'm not prepared to sell until he does. Most importantly I want to ensure security for all the staff on the magazine before I sign anything, and that's proving something of a sticking point.

'My prospective purchaser is an American, I met him and his wife last year while I was in the States—although she wasn't his wife then.'

Something in the way he said it alerted Emma, unable to keep silent she asked waspishly, 'What was she then—your girlfriend?'

'Something like that . . . Let's just say we were . . .

good friends. However, Giles was prepared to offer marriage and I wasn't, so Bianca married him.'

He glanced down at the table and frowned. 'Giles is an extremely jealous husband . . . very much older than Bianca too. It appears that she is very keen to resume the relationship we once had . . . I, on the other hand feel that it would be extremely unwise to do so, especially if I want to exact the best possible terms I can from Giles.'

'Yes indeed,' Emma agreed sardonically. 'I can quite see that he wouldn't be inclined to be particularly generous if he found out that you'd been having an affair with his wife, but I can't see what all this has to do with me?'

'Can't you?' He smiled wolfishly at her, 'Then perhaps I'd better explain. Bianca is threatening to blackmail me into resuming our relationship by revealing to Giles that we were once lovers. If he knows that he will immediately assume that I still want her. He's that sort of man, and almost obsessed with Bianca to the extent that in his eyes she can do no wrong, so I thought I might try a little blackmail myself . . .'

Emma didn't know what he meant, but cold fingers touched her skin as she looked into his eyes.

'If I promise not to publish those photographs of you Emma, would you agree to pose as my fiancée for the duration of their visit?'

Her first instinctive question of 'but why ask me. . ?' was answered immediately by her own senses, a cynical smile curving her mouth as she answered herself. 'But of course . . . with me you won't have the additional worry of being blackmailed into a genuine marriage by your fake fiancée.'

'Very astute,' Drake agreed. 'That was something that taxed my mind when I first decided a fiancée was what I needed to keep Bianca at bay and Giles . . .'

'Unsuspicious?' Emma supplied contemptuously. 'I won't do it Drake,' she told him, making to get up, but he grasped her wrist as she did so and forced her to regain her seat. 'I thought you might say that,' he drawled easily, 'but my dear have you really thought the whole thing through? Already your family and friends know you're involved with me. Once those photographs are published they'll assume that we've been lovers and that I've dumped you. This way at least you can have the satisfaction of ridding yourself of *me* when the charade is over. Besides, I can hardly believe that either your father or your new brother-in-law would relish the thought of you appearing in . . .'

He had her in a corner and he knew it Emma thought bitterly. She could see no way out. This man was a master when it came to manipulating people. But he couldn't succeed in controlling his ex-mistress, she thought, so he wasn't completely invulnerable.

'Well?'

'I don't have much choice do I?' Emma said tautly. It would be a relief to know that those photographs of her would never be published. Could she trust him in that regard? Instinct told her that she could. They were of scant use to him now and would be of even less value once he had sold the magazine. She could hardly think that this Giles whoever he was would be remotely interested in half a dozen or so shots of some English girl no one had ever heard of.

'Not really.' His smile was amused and that amusement stung Emma's pride.

Lifting her head challengingly she said, 'There is just one thing though—won't your ... friend ... think it strange that you're engaged to me?'

When he looked blank, she added acidly, 'After all I'm scarcely up to your usual high standard of glamour ... and of course, as you remarked yourself earlier, I am still a virgin.'

As she watched the skin tighten over his facial bones Emma knew she had made a dangerous mistake.

'Luckily for you Bianca isn't all that astute where her own sex is concerned. She sees what she wants to see. Don't try needling me Emma,' he warned her drily as the waiter brought their bill, 'you might not like the results.'

CHAPTER FIVE

ONCE he had set his mind on a course, Drake obviously pursued it with a single mindedness that confirmed his adherence to discipline Emma reflected, staring bleakly at the elegant, solitaire diamond ring glittering on her left hand. He had arrived with it this morning, having spoken to her on the telephone the previous evening to warn her of his arrival.

It was just over a week since the wedding and she hadn't seen him once during that period although he had rung her every day. Emma had known that her father was waiting for her to say something; to mention Drake's presence in her life, and at last, last night knowing it could not be put off any longer she had gone to him and told him that she and Drake were getting engaged.

'I didn't want to say anything before because I didn't want to steal Camilla's thunder,' she had told him awkwardly, hating the lie and the man who had made it necessary.

A little to her surprise her father had accepted her explanation quite easily. 'You won't want a long engagement I don't expect, and to judge from what I've seen of him, neither will your young man. You always did have a good deal more fire beneath the surface than most people give you credit for, Emma,' he had added, further surprising her and making her tense in remembered shock as she recalled how her body had leapt with sexual excitement when Drake touched her.

She could only pray that their engagement was of short duration. She wished she could appear totally indifferent to him, because she sensed that her rage against her response to him amused him, and she would not put it past him to deliberately encourage it because he was amused by her reaction. Now she knew how a wild animal felt when it was caught in a trap she reflected, pretending she was studying the awesome glitter of her ring, while in reality what she was doing was avoiding the speculative curiosity in Drake's eyes.

He had arrived just under an hour ago, and with an old fashioned courtesy she thought both unnecessary and overdone in the circumstances, had insisted on speaking privately with her father.

When they had emerged from his study both men had been laughing. Her father wouldn't laugh if he knew the truth Emma thought angrily, but then neither would he automatically blame Drake—that wasn't his way. He would have to analyse and consider the situation before apportioning blame. She sighed fretfully, wishing for once she might have a less objective and more emotional parent. A lot of people thought she was like him, coolly weighing the pros and cons of a situation before acting, but in reality she was not. She had only learned through bitter mistakes to force herself to do so, to take the long cool view of things before reacting.

For the first time in years Emma turned her keen intelligence inwards on herself and was mildly shocked to discover how long she'd been playing a part; been adopting a character that wasn't really hers . . . or at least was only in part hers. In two short interviews Drake Harwood had stripped away far too much of that adopted character, to reveal the passionate intense woman who hid behind it, and Emma suddenly felt thoroughly frightened by that discovery.

It was the searching intensity of his glance, rather than his words that brought her out of her reverie, but she stood stock still, tense with the shock of knowing he was about to deliver another blow as she heard him saying. 'Yes . . . it is rather a nuisance. I'd have preferred them to come over here, but he's insisting that I go there, and since he's the piper in this case I'm afraid I'll have to pay the tune. We'll only be gone a fortnight or so though . . .'

Gone? Gone where? He must have read the question in her eyes before she could voice it, because he turned towards her and said mildly, 'I was just telling your father, darling, that we won't have time for an engagement celebration because we have to leave for New York at the end of the week. Giles has too many business commitments to leave the States right now and Bianca has very kindly suggested that we can stay with them for the duration of our visit . . .'

Caution warned Emma to wait until they were alone to question him. She went through the ritual of having a celebratory drink with her father and Drake in an angry state of tension. Why had Drake changed his plans, and why hadn't he consulted her first?

'If you'll excuse us, I'd like to take my new fiancée out to lunch,' Drake said at length, standing up. Emma rose automatically herself, flinching with barely concealed temper as Drake put out a hand to touch her arm, very much the solicitous fiancé. She hated him touching her, she boiled inwardly, she hated this deceit she had been forced to enter into ... she ... red hot darts of awareness arrowed along her nervous system from the point of contact with his hand. She badly wanted to pull away, but with her father looking on it was impossible.

The lunch date had been arranged before Drake arrived, to give them an opportunity or so Emma had thought to finalise the arrangements for Giles and Bianca's arrival. She had already half prepared her father for her absence.

A realist and comparatively broad-minded, she knew he would make no objection from a moral point of view, but there was still the smooth running of the parish and the vicarage to consider and with this in mind Emma had engaged Mrs Johnson, who came in occasionally to help them out, on a full-time basis.

Emma got into Drake's car in a stony, angry silence, not speaking, not wanting to speak until she could trust herself not to let her rage boil over and swamp her.

When she felt she had some measure of self-control she turned to him and said coolly. 'What's all this about our going to New York?'

'Bianca's decision,' Drake told her tersely. 'So don't go thinking it's some clever plan of mine. I suppose I ought to have expected it. Bianca's a master tactician and knows as well as I do the advantage of being on one's home ground so to speak. I'll warn you now she'll try everything she can to cause trouble between us.'

'She knows about our engagement then?' Emma spoke cynically. 'What a brave man you are Drake, hiding behind a woman's skirts.'

'On the contrary,' he told her drily, 'I prefer to consider it as fighting fire with fire. Besides, Bianca on her own I can handle. . .'

'By doing what? Going to bed with her? But of course you can't do that with her husband around and likely to find out can you?'

'Snappy this morning aren't we?' he commented laconically. 'You know you're a better actress than I thought, for a moment you almost managed to inject a tinge of jealousy into your voice. Keep that up and Bianca will be in no doubt as to the reality of our relationship.'

For a moment Emma was too furious to respond. She *had* been jealous she realised on a wave of self-contempt, bitterly, hotly jealous; imagining him making love to the unknown Bianca.

'All she has to do is to tell her husband that you and she were once lovers,' Emma reminded him.

'She won't do that . . . Giles is a very wealthy man. No, what Bianca wants is the sense of power that being able to force me to do what she wants gives her. A lot of women are like that although they cloak their greed for power in other emotions . . . usually fake. Mind you, I suspect that Bianca hasn't given up completely.'

'How very flattering for you,' Emma commented waspishly. 'What am I supposed to do about it? Lie outside your bedroom door like a devoted guard?'

'Would you?' A wicked grin slashed across his face, his eyes sparkling deeply green as he glanced at her. 'Of course there is an even better way you could protect me . . .'

Watching her frown, he said softly, 'You could share my bed.' Her body tensed automatically and obviously, and Drake's derisive laughter grated across sensitive nerves. 'Don't worry my little virgin. I'm not about to demand the ultimate sacrifice.'

'Don't *you* worry,' Emma snapped back, through closed teeth. 'Because you aren't about to get it.'

Drake's rich chuckle worried her, but she strove to hide her anxiety from him. It sounded so lighthearted . . . and . . . and self-confident, she thought anxiously, almost as though he knew quite well just how easy it would be for her to abandon the moral code she had lived her life by and slake herself with almost feverish greed on the purely physical pleasure his body could offer hers. And that's all it was; simply a physical need that he brought to life inside her. Deep, strong and very intense, but completely without any finer feelings or emotions to temper it.

Perhaps that was why it was so strong, Emma pondered inwardly; perhaps like a weed it needed no nourishment to grow, as love and caring did. She was shaken by the thought, shaken and cautious, so much so that she kept quiet during their meal, speaking only in monosyllables until Drake raised his eyebrows and said mockingly, 'What's the matter? Surely you aren't frightened?'

That depended, Emma thought bitterly to herself. Certainly she was frightened of the feelings he aroused inside her, what sane person would not be?

'Of Bianca or of you?' she asked coolly. 'I'm not a fool Drake. Of course I'm frightened. Most people are when they're confronted by ruthlessness so intense and self-motivated that it smashes everything in its path. I should have thought you and Bianca would be well suited. So far everything you've told me about her makes me think she's possibly the only woman alive who'd be a match for you.'

'You think so?' The smile he gave her sent prickles of awareness shivering along her spine. 'Well there are matches and matches. However, when the time comes for me to settle down it won't be with a woman of Bianca's calibre. By the way,' he added briskly, 'before we leave I want you to come and spend a couple of days in London. I've booked you into the Inn on the Park. You'll need some new clothes ... a new hair-do perhaps, and ...'

The way he was studying her made Emma itch to hit him. 'I'm sorry if my looks, my clothes and my hair, don't meet your exacting standards,' she told him seethingly, 'but they suit me, and I won't change them and furthermore if they don't suit you then I suggest you go and look somewhere else for your bogus fiancée.'

'Temper, temper.' His voice was mild, but his eyes so totally amused that Emma longed to throw something at him. 'I didn't say they didn't suit me,' he told her eyeing her in a way that made her skin tense over her bones and her muscles ache. 'Personally I can't think of any way I'd rather see you than without any clothes at all and all that glorious red hair spread out around you on my pillow ... but it was you I was thinking of. New clothes, a new hairstyle, they all help to give a woman confidence—armour if you like . . .'

'And I'm going to need it against Bianca aren't I?' Emma murmured, seeing the sense of his words, and too anxious to forget the images his earlier ones had conjured up to take him too much to task. There had been a photograph very like the mental picture he had just painted of her among the batch Pat had taken and her skin crawled in revulsion as she thought about him looking at it . . . studying her naked body . . .

'No, I didn't,' he said calmly breaking into her thoughts. For a moment Emma simply looked blankly at him. 'I didn't look at the proofs Pat sent to me. They're locked in my safe in the same envelope they came to me in.'

'Insurance against my good behaviour,' Emma said bitterly, not wanting him to see how relieved she was. 'I'm surprised you don't know each one off by heart.'

It was an inflammatory thing to say, and it was born of her own aching humiliation that they had been taken at all.

'I'm no voyeur, Emma,' he told her curtly, 'we both know that if I wanted to see your naked body, it would be relatively easy for me to see—and touch—the real thing. Stop taking what happened so personally. It wasn't. At that time I was hoping to boost the magazine's circulation. You arrived opportunely—for me, and had you taken that job I should have published the photographs perhaps three or four months from now, when your face was known, and who knows I might have found the magazine profitable enough to retain. As it is . . .' he shrugged and added warningly, 'Don't push me too hard. Some allowances I am prepared to make, but you fight every inch of the way don't you?'

Too stunned by his comment about seeing and touching her, Emma could only marshal her thoughts sufficiently to say bitterly, 'Commodities, that's all people are to you isn't it? You don't give a damn about their feelings.'

'Perhaps because the people I'm dealing with don't give a damn about mine, and you're wrong you know. I cared enough about yours to employ—at considerable expense I might add—a woman photographer. I could simply have sent you along to the sort of studio my rival uses—but I didn't, did I?' he said grimly.

What he was saying was true. Emma remembered how relieved she had been when she saw Pat but her pride ached too much for her to acknowledge the truth of his comment.

'Stop worrying about it,' he told her curtly. 'Once this is over and the magazine is sold, you can burn the damn things and forget all about it.'

'I might be able to burn them,' Emma told him in a voice taut with self-loathing, 'but how can I burn my memories, how can I forget. . .?'

'There are times when we all have to do things we don't want to,' Drake cut in harshly. He had gone curiously pale and Emma wondered if perhaps he cared more about Bianca than he was letting her see. It seemed curious to her that a man as strong and hard as this one couldn't cope with an importuning woman. Perhaps he was frightened that he might not be as indifferent to Bianca as he was trying to pretend. It was disturbing to discover how much her body ached at that thought.

*   *   *

Her two days in London passed in a whirl of activity. She did visit a hairdressers, but only to learn how to dress her long hair in several more sophisticated styles. It was far too attractive and healthy to cut, the stylist told her firmly, and Emma was relieved.

At first she had felt uncomfortable spending Drake's money, but her new clothes were all part and parcel of the role she was to play he told her.

Even so, she spent carefully. Bianca would expect her to be worldly and sophisticated and she chose accordingly, half surprised herself to discover how easy it was to alter her appearance.

Drake didn't ask to see what she had bought and she didn't show him. On the second day of her stay he had arranged to have dinner with her at the hotel.

She was waiting for him in the cocktail bar when he arrived and frowned in astonishment over the large box he gave her.

'Get someone to take it up to your room for you.'

'What is it?' Emma questioned.

He smiled wryly at her. 'Something I suspect you'll have forgotten. Now, are you ready to eat.'

When he chose to be he was an entertaining companion. A little to her surprise, he didn't as she had expected him to do, scorn women's views and opinions as of being of no importance and they talked for some length on current issues, Emma finding it exhilarating to pit her wits and views against his. She was surprised when he glanced at his watch and commented that if they were to be ready in time for the Concorde flight in the morning they ought to be thinking of calling it a day. It was just gone ten, she realised, looking at her own watch, and as Drake left her just by the lift, and she watched his tall back disappearing in the direction of the foyer she wondered if he was really planning on an early night or if he had a date with someone else . . .

She still smarted from his remark that he could look at and touch her body if he wanted to, the more so because she knew irresistibly that it was true. She wanted him to make love to her; and that was half the reason she found his company so exhilarating. Tonight listening to him talk at one point she had glanced at his hands and had immediately pictured them touching her skin. As she got in the lift she shuddered slightly. She had to stop thinking of him in that context. For them to become lovers would do nothing but complicate the situation still further. She didn't love him, she reminded herself, she simply wanted him physically.

As she got out of the lift and unlocked the door to her room it struck her rather ironically that she had come a long way from the woman who had considered herself so immune to physical desire—and in a very short space of time.

She had forgotten the box Drake had given her until she saw it lying on the bed. Curiously she undid the wrapping, glancing at the name written on it. It wasn't one she recognised but to judge from the quality of the box, it belonged to an expensive and exclusive establishment.

At first the layers of tissue paper obscured its contents from her view but as she moved them her hand stilled, her heart racing painfully.

Drake had bought her underwear; expensive, exclusive underwear, all of a highly sophisticated design—underwear such as the women in his life must wear, she decided, studying the beautiful detail on a cream satin bra. In all there were half a dozen sets of underwear; all expensive and understated; not bridal as Camilla's had been, or deliberately provocative, and yet somehow because of their very sophistication and the fact that he had chosen them, acutely but subtly sexy.

She wanted to send them back to him, but common sense warned her not to. She wouldn't put it past him to find some highly embarrassing and pointed way of ensuring that they were returned, and besides he was right; she *had* forgotten about underwear, and if Bianca was half as formidable as he had intimated she would pounce on and use to her own advantage any hint at all that they were not really engaged.

Although she tried hard not to show it, Emma was extremely excited about the thought of her Concorde flight. Normally such a luxury would have been completely out of her reach, but now Drake, albeit for reasons of his own, was making it possible for her, and she was determined to enjoy it.

Enjoy it she did, at least until she caught Drake eyeing her with an amused and comprehending smile. When she saw it she tried to feign cool indifference, turning away from him, angry with herself for appearing so gauche.

His hand covered hers as they lay folded in her lap, the firm squeeze he gave them making her turn her head quickly to look at him.

'I wasn't laughing at you,' he drawled; as always, infuriating her with his astuteness. 'It's extremely refreshing to see someone genuinely enjoying something. You're as prickly as a little hedgehog aren't you . . . I can see we're going to have some fireworks ahead of us . . . especially if you keep on glaring at me like that,' he added in a soft murmur. 'Remember we're supposed to be in love.'

'*We're* supposed to be,' Emma asked cynically, 'or I am.'

He studied her for a moment. 'Women generally show their feelings more openly than men, but I promise you while we're staying in New York you needn't have any worries about me fulfilling my role Emma. Just see that you fulfil yours.'

The flight was uneventful; their arrival in New York smooth and well organised, and not for the world would Emma have wanted Drake to see as they drove out of the city in their hire car, just how nervous and tense she was. However, as always, his ability to read her thoughts and see into her mind made any subterfuge on her part a mockery.

'Stop worrying,' he told her laconically, negotiating the busy freeway traffic with an ease that Emma could only envy. 'I'm the one who should be doing that.'

'What will you do if Giles won't buy the magazine?' she asked, wondering for the first time what would happen in that event.

'Run it down,' he responded crisply, 'although I'm loath to do that because it will mean people losing their jobs. From a personal point of view it isn't an asset that particularly appeals. I wanted the parent company because it fits in nicely with the rest of my organisation, but I don't have the time or the inclination to work on the magazine to build it up to what it should be. Contrary to what you seem to think owning a girlie magazine does absolutely nothing for me Emma,' he added drawlingly. 'I much prefer the real thing.'

'Yes, I'm sure you do.' Emma flicked him a disparaging glance as she studied the busy traffic. During their flight out she had done some careful thinking. She was vulnerable to him sexually and they both knew that, but she would be a fool to allow that vulnerability to undermine her to the extent that she became physically involved with him. He could have virtually any woman he wanted; if he did make love to her, it would simply be on the impulse of the moment, and she was beginning to have the uneasy suspicion that apart from severely damaging her pride and self-respect to be simply another casual affair in his life would not be enough.

At this stage she wasn't prepared to take her line of reasoning any further. It was enough that she had seen the warning light flashing.

The Fords' home was in New York State, imposing and extremely gracious. They had had to announce themselves to the guard on the gate before they were admitted; and the long drive, that eventually swept round to end in a small circle adjacent to a porticoed entrance was certainly impressive. Even so, Emma did not think she would care to live in such splendid isolation, so cut off from the world, guarded against it.

A manservant opened the door for them, nodding a grave recognition to Drake.

'Drake darling . . .'

The hard tip-tap of high heels along a tiled floor alerted Emma to her presence long before their hostess stepped into the ornate black and white tiled hallway.

Blonde and tall, she was so immaculately groomed and made up that she looked almost unreal Emma thought wonderingly, suddenly conscious of her own creased skirt, and no doubt tacky make-up. No wonder Drake had insisted on that hurried shopping spree. This woman looked as though she spent a fortune on her face and figure. Older than she was herself, Emma guessed; she was nonetheless extremely beautiful; almost impossibly so, every blonde hair in place, her silk dress clinging to her model-thin figure.

Her heavy, oriental perfume embraced Emma at the same time as its wearer embraced Drake.

There was no mistaking the sensuous way in which she draped herself along his body, carmine finger nails pressing into the thick darkness of his hair, her mouth raised for his kiss.

'Oh come along darling,' Emma heard her purr. 'I'm sure your little fiancée won't mind you kissing me.'

Emma took note of the derogatory 'little', and said coolly, surprising herself, 'On the contrary, I should mind very much indeed.'

It didn't take much acting to let her eyes shoot cold sparks in Bianca's direction, nor to move closer to Drake, her fingers gripping his arm so that he could not return Bianca's embrace.

For a moment Emma could not define the expression in his eyes as he looked at her and then she realised it was surprise. So she had surprised him for once had she? She was just beginning to recover from the shock of her own behaviour and realise what a ridiculous picture they must present, the two of them clinging like limpets to the one man, when she heard other footsteps, more measured and heavy than Bianca's, coming down the hallway towards them. Bianca released Drake immediately, but not before she had flashed Emma a challenging, glittering glare.

'Ah, there you are darling,' Emma heard her saying gaily. 'Our guests have arrived.'

The man who came to greet them was in his late fifties. Tall, with a shock of white hair, he must once have been handsome and still retained that powerful aura of attraction many older men possessed. He smiled warmly at both Emma and Drake, shaking Drake's hand and studying Emma with warm eyes.

'Well you've really surprised me this time Drake,' he said at last. 'When Bianca said you were bringing your fiancée with you, I must admit I was surprised, but now that I've seen her I can only applaud your choice. You're a very lucky man.'

'I think so.' Drake's smile caressed her flushing skin, his fingers interlinking with hers, as he raised them to his lips and then slowly kissed each one. Emma was totally flabbergasted. She wanted to snatch her hand away, but the sensation of his mouth against her skin was too blissful to resist. As always when he touched her the power of her response to him was unnerving. She wanted to melt into him, to touch his hair, his skin, to lose herself completely in him.

'Anyone can tell you're only very newly engaged,' she heard Giles laughing. 'It's a long time since Bianca looked at me the way Emma's looking at you Drake. I envy you old man.'

Emma was so scarlet she felt her skin was

burning off her bones. How could she have been
so stupid. She dared not look at Drake. However,
Bianca created a diversion, her voice shrill and
bitter as she said icily, 'But then you're not Drake
are you, darling?'

There was a small, unpleasant silence, which
Drake filled by saying calmly, 'I wonder if we
could go to our rooms. Very unsociable of us I
know, but it's been a hectic day.'

'Of course you can.' Giles was instantly the
concerned host. 'I'll get Bates to take up your
bags. Why don't you both rest until dinner time.
You're here for a fortnight, so we've plenty of time
to discuss business.'

The room Emma was shown to was magnificent.
Overpoweringly so, and she detected the hand of a
professional interior designer in the mixture of
fabrics and colours. She had her own bathroom;
and a walk-in wardrobe room, far too large for the
clothes she had brought with her. So this was how
the very rich lived, well she didn't envy them . . .
Despite Giles' money there seemed precious little
harmony or happiness in this house. She had seen
the way his mouth tightened and his eyes grew
bitter when Bianca made her acid statement. She
herself had had no need to act; she had been too
startled by the other woman's comment to hide
her surprise. What made it even more surprising
was that she should say it in front of the woman
her ex-lover was going to marry. Drake had been
right; she was a very very formidable woman—and
an extremely dangerous one Emma suspected.
Dear God if she were genuinely engaged to Drake
and in love with him she doubted if she would
have stood a chance. At least she was free from the

burden of emotional involvement with him and therefore immune to most of Bianca's poisonous darts.

She glanced at her cases, thought about unpacking and then remembered that the house was staffed. Better to start off by giving Bianca as little ammunition as she could. She wasn't going to allow the other woman to make her feel gauche or unsophisticated and if no one came to unpack for her she could always do it herself later.

Dinner tonight would be an extremely tense affair she suspected, wondering what to wear. If she was too dressed up she would feel uncomfortable and embarrassed, and yet she didn't want to let Drake down by not dressing as his fiancée would be expected to.

Another door in the wall behind the bed caught her eye, and she glanced at it. There was a key in it on her side, and she walked over to it, trying the door. It was unlocked. She wondered if she and Drake had been given connecting rooms. It seemed highly likely, not that she needed to worry about that. She had the key, and Drake would be far too busy keeping Bianca at bay to have any time to spare for her.

Perhaps she ought to ask for his advice about dinner, and she had better do it now, she decided, just in case he was going to have a rest. Knocking briefly she turned the handle and walked through. The room was very similar to her own, and Drake was over by the window, staring out of it, hands in the pockets of his pants, his jacket lying discarded on a chair.

'Drake?' He turned round as he heard her, and she saw that he was frowning. 'I was just wondering about tonight,' she told him. He had removed his tie, and unfastened several of his shirt buttons. She could see the dark tangle of hair shadowing his chest and her own seemed to tighten suddenly, strangling her voice. 'I'm not sure what I ought to wear . . . I don't want to don my full formal regalia, if . . .'

'Umm . . .' His frown deepened suddenly and he lifted his head staring towards the door on to the landing. In half a dozen lithe strides he had crossed the distance that separated them, and as Emma protested heatedly he pulled her into his arms, his fingers locking in her hair and holding her mouth a prisoner beneath his as he kissed her deeply and almost roughly.

Robbed of breath, Emma struggled to fight free, furious with him for his behaviour. His free arm clamped her against his body and she could feel the deep thud of his heart against her; the steely strength of his thighs.

A weak tide of need poured through her, destroying her resistance. She made a sound beneath his mouth, half protest, half plea and then her arms were round his neck, her body melting into his. She wasn't aware of the approaching footsteps, only of Drake's hand moving from her back to her breast, exploring its firm contours. A tug and her silk shirt came free of her skirt. Drake's palm felt warm against her midriff. She was overwhelmed by a need to feel his skin against hers and she trembled wildly, drowning beneath his kiss.

'Good heavens! Drake darling I need to see you alone for a few minutes. Perhaps your little fiancée . . .'

Bianca's voice chilled the heat in Emma's blood.

She tensed automatically, but Drake didn't release her, merely lifting his mouth from hers to turn his head and say in a softly slurred voice. 'Not now Bianca . . . can't you see that I'm busy . . .'

Emma looked at the other woman wondering at her hardiness. In her shoes, she suspected that she would have crawled out of the room if Drake had spoken to her like that, but instead Bianca merely smiled tightly and raised thin eyebrows to say sweetly, 'Darling you *have* changed . . . Since when has sex been more important to you than business?'

Emma didn't have to fake the tide of angry colour sweeping over her skin. Bianca really was a first-class bitch she thought, stunned by the other woman's persistence.

'Sex might not be,' Drake returned in an even drawl, 'but love certainly is.'

'Love?' At last Emma saw Bianca change colour, her eyes wild with rage as she glared from Emma to Drake. 'Are you trying to tell me that you love her, Drake?'

'I'm not *trying* to tell you anything,' he said calmly. 'I'm simply stating a fact. And now if we could please have a little privacy. I was very dubious about staying here,' he added coolly, 'in fact I think it might be an idea if we left and booked into an hotel, although of course Giles will want to know why.'

With another furious glare at Emma, Bianca opened the door. 'You might think you can deceive me, Drake,' she said softly, 'but you can't. I don't know what game you're playing, but you're not as indifferent to me as you're pretending, and before you leave here I'll prove that to you *and* your little fiancée.'

CHAPTER SIX

EMMA sat through dinner in a haze, feeling more like someone observing the behaviour of actors involved in a TV play rather than a supposed participant in what was going on.

If she hadn't still been tussling with the effects of Drake's ability to arouse a hitherto unknown sexual hunger deep inside her she might have been able to be almost amused by Bianca's behaviour. The woman was pure bitch, Emma reflected without malice. The fact that her husband was watching and listening to her attempts to draw Drake's attention to herself and keep it there, appeared to concern her not in the least. Towards Emma when she did have occasion to speak to her, her manner was both off-hand and distinctly contemptuous.

Once or twice Emma thought she saw a look in Giles's eyes which indicated that he was not quite as besotted by his wife as she seemed to think, and it occurred to Emma that Bianca suffered from a dangerous degree of over-confidence. In many ways she reminded her of Camilla and her blood ran chilly to think that her young sister could, in time, turn into another Bianca.

When dinner was over, and Emma noted that for differing reasons neither she nor Bianca had done justice to the excellent food, Giles suggested that they all retire to the drawing room.

'No business talk tonight,' he said with a smile,

to Drake. 'I believe in fair play, and as I know to my cost transatlantic flight is particularly draining.'

'But darling.' Bianca's voice dripped venom as she poured the coffee. 'You forget how much younger than you Drake is.'

There was a moment's awkward silence and then Drake interposed smoothly, 'Younger maybe, but I quite agree. Besides,' he glanced at Emma, and her cheeks caught slow fire from the sexual appreciation of his look, 'there are other reasons why I'd appreciate an early night . . .'

Emma had no need to fake her blush or her confusion. Bianca's laugh seemed particularly high and false. 'Good heavens Drake,' she said shrilly, 'where on earth did you find her, she's positively Victorian!'

'Ignore Bianca, my dear,' Giles counselled Emma in a kind voice. 'Like a good many men with something of a reputation where women are concerned, when it comes to his own woman, Drake appreciates rarity value.'

While half of her was inclined to object to the blatant derision of his remark, Emma couldn't help responding to the pain in her host's eyes as they rested on his wife's tautly bitter face. 'I'm afraid Bianca has grown too used to being the centre of male attention to appreciate the company of another woman, especially one as attractive and feminine as yourself. Drake is known as a shrewd businessman, and I can see he's been equally shrewd in his choice of future wife.'

Bianca who had caught the last part of her husband's comment said bitchily, 'Oh I quite agree, Giles. What is it they say? If a man wants to be securely married he should choose a plain wife.'

Had she in reality been engaged to Drake, there was just enough truth in that comment to cause real pain, Emma thought wryly. She knew quite well that she was no true beauty; certainly not as she suspected Bianca judged her own sex, and she only had to think of the beautiful women Drake had escorted publicly over the last twelve months to admit that she herself was way, way out of their league, but she was not engaged to Drake; she was not emotionally involved with him, therefore she was completely safe from Bianca's vitriolic comments. So why this feeling of acute pain; why this need to glance uncertainly at Drake as though needing his support and reassurance?

Confused by her own reactions Emma was unaware of Drake moving until she felt the hard reality of his arm round her waist, her body responding irresistibly to the warmth and security of his—so irresistibly that her breath caught in her throat, her eyes focusing blindly on his face as she tried to come to terms with the emotions rioting inside her. You should have been an actress my girl, she told herself hardily, you certainly have a gift of throwing yourself wholeheartedly into your part.

'Emma has a beauty of spirit and personality which has far more appeal than anything manufactured by cosmetic surgeons and beauticians,' Drake responded calmly.

His defence of her was everything that, as his fiancée, she could have wished for. From the look on Bianca's face it was plain that the older woman was furious, and Emma wondered about Drake's remark. Bianca's features were so perfect that they could owe more to a good plastic surgeon than to nature, and for the first time she felt something akin to pity for the older woman. She had a loving husband; everything that his wealth could buy and still she wasn't happy. Nor ever would be Emma thought intuitively, even if that husband was Drake; Bianca would always want what just lay over the next hill ... the next man. Almost as though she sensed her pity the older woman glared at her, and Emma knew that she had made an enemy; not just because she was Drake's 'fiancée', but in her own right.

Shortly after that they said their good nights. Emma wasn't sorry to be leaving the drawing-room, which for all its elegance and expensive furnishings was a cold, unwelcoming room.

As she hesitated outside her bedroom door, Drake's hand on her wrist stopped her from opening it, and she allowed herself to be guided in the direction of his own door. Once inside he closed it behind them, and as he turned she saw that he was frowning; the strain of the evening plainly showing in his face.

'Thanks for your support downstairs,' he said, tossing the words casually to her over his shoulder as he discarded his evening jacket. 'God what a bitch that woman is, she was determined to create as much havoc as she possibly could.'

'Yes, I think if we were really engaged, we'd be in the middle of an extremely destructive row right now,' Emma agreed tiredly, remembering some of Bianca's bitchy remarks about Drake's previous womenfriends. Every remark she had made to Emma had been carefully designed to undermine her self-confidence, to throw in her face the fact that Drake was an extremely desirable and highly sexual man—as if she didn't already know.

'A row?' Emma could see Drake through the dresser mirror. The fine silk of his white shirt emphasised the muscular lines of his body. Of its own volition her body responded to its masculinity, her pulse rate increasing fractionally, the muscles in the pit of her stomach tightening. It really was amazing; the logical side of her nature retained enough control to tell her how illogical it was that she should respond so quickly and so intensely to a man who, on the face of it, was everything she most detested. Oh the perversity of human nature. Thank goodness, this was all simply a charade, and that she had the good sense to see exactly what sort of man lay behind the smooth urbanity with which he had countered Bianca's attacks on her tonight.

'Umm, Bianca is proving even more troublesome than I had envisaged.'

'Perhaps she does genuinely love you.'

It was a comment she had not intended to make and from the frown scoring between Drake's eyebrows it was not one he had expected to hear. 'Love?' His eyebrows straightened and lifted. 'My dear Emma, don't be naïve, that woman doesn't love anyone other than herself...'

The contempt he felt towards Bianca was quite plain to hear, and Emma echoed his frown although for different reasons. 'Are you always so contemptuous of the women you sleep with?'

For a moment Drake checked, and then he answered in a laconic drawl, 'If they merit it, then yes.'

'A psychiatrist might be curious to know why

you choose women you can only despise to share your life.'

'Meaning that I myself must be inadequate in some way?'

He was quick, Emma had to give him that. 'Not necessarily so. I suspect the majority of men are looking for a woman who combines perfect features and figure with a perfect nature. It can hardly be held to be our fault that Mother Nature rarely sees fit to wrap all three in the one package.'

His cool mockery and taunting dismissal of her sex stung Emma into retorting, 'If men weren't always so keen to debase and exploit physical beauty in women perhaps they might . . .' She broke off angrily when she heard Drake's soft laughter.

'If Bianca could see you now she wouldn't be in such a hurry to dismiss you as a nonentity. There's an awful lot of passion lurking beneath that cool surface, isn't there?'

'I'm a normal, intelligent human being,' Emma responded, calming down a little, 'and like other intelligent human beings, I'm capable of having strong feelings on a variety of subjects.'

'So I've noticed. What a pity one of those subjects can't be me, Emma mine, something tells me that you and I could be very good together.'

He had moved as he spoke and was now standing directly behind her. Emma could feel the heat of his body filling the small distance that separated them. She badly wanted to lean back against him and to feel his arms come round her, his hands caressing her body. The intensity of her desire shook her, forcing her to fight to banish it from her mind.

'Any involvement between us will only prejudice

your business discussions,' she managed to respond crisply.

'You think so? Very well. But we *will* be lovers, you and I, Emma,' he warned her softly, as he stepped away from her. 'Maybe not now, maybe not here in New York, but ultimately your body will surrender its secrets and its passion to mine, and you're a liar if you deny it.'

How calm, and dispassionate he was, Emma thought, listening to him. While her body shook and trembled at the visions conjured up by his words, he remained unmoved, but then how many women had heard those words, or ones like them from him before? His body was no stranger to desire, to wanting, unlike hers ... and yet she knew that in all honesty she could not deny what he had said; that some small masochistic part of her didn't even want to deny it. She didn't know what it was about her that made him want her; she wasn't like his other women. Perhaps that was it; perhaps it was the challenge she represented; the novelty value of her virginity.

She was trying to whip up inside herself a resentment against him but although her mind might revolt against his arrogant words, her body reacted to them as surely and undeniably as though it had been programmed to do so. Her body was her real enemy, not Drake, Emma acknowledged, because it was her body that would ultimately betray her with its craving to satisfy its need to be possessed by his. There was no logical explanation for what she felt; no learned or reasoned arguments that could be applied against a force so great that she literally shook with the intensity of it.

She moved towards the connecting door, knowing that he would not stop her.

'Leave the door unlocked,' he warned her as she opened it. 'We don't want Bianca leaping to any conclusions, and I wouldn't put it past her to have given the staff instructions to spy on us and report back to her.'

'Surely she must see that you don't want her?' Emma queried.

'Bianca is a woman who thinks her beauty entitles her to everything she wants from life. Facing the fact that that isn't so, means facing up to the fact that her beauty is not the powerful, invincible weapon she has always believed and that's something she'll fight strenuously against doing, because it's all she has.' There was no pity in his voice only contempt, and as though he read her mind, he quoted softly, 'Those who live by the sword, my dear Emma. Bianca has not cared who she has hurt in her greed and self-conceit; witness her attitude towards Giles tonight. Now she is a candidate for the shrink's couch,' he added referring to their earlier conversation, 'but don't under-estimate her, Emma. She's a very dangerous woman, in the way that a person who's obsessed can be.'

'Meaning she's obsessed with you?'

'Not specifically. What she's obsessed with is getting her own way; with proving to her own satisfaction that she has the power through her looks to compel men to give in to her, I just happen to be the man she wants at this particular moment in time.'

Initially inclined to dismiss his comments as callous; to brand him as an egotistical male far too

ready to see in Bianca an all too convenient Eve,
Emma was compelled to hesitate and re-assess her
own judgment. In many ways Drake was right and
in admitting this she was forced to concede that he
was a shrewd, almost intuitive, judge of character,
and that, combined with what he had said to her
about wanting her was sufficient to increase her
tension to the point where it was almost a physical
reality.

It would be hard enough simply to battle against
his desire to possess her, but she had to fight the
added hazard of her own feelings.

It was a long time after she had left Drake
before she managed to fall asleep. Her feelings
towards him were constantly changing; her
judgments almost hourly having to be amended.
He was so complex a character that fresh sides to
him were constantly being revealed to her. She was
like a child, fascinated by fire, Emma told herself
wryly, on the edge of sleep; she knew that contact
with it would hurt and yet, irresistibly, she was
drawn towards the bright glitter of its heat.

'Good heavens, what time is it?' Emma struggled
to sit up as a uniformed maid arrived with a tray
of coffee and biscuits, fearing that she had
overslept so badly that she had disrupted the
household.

'Just after eight,' was the smiled response.

In answer to Emma's anxious enquiries about
breakfast she was told that the two gentlemen
would be having theirs in the breakfast room at
nine o'clock, and that she could either join them or
have breakfast in bed, as her hostess was
apparently doing.

How the rich lived, Emma thought humorously, declining the latter. Now that she was awake, she was too keyed up to simply lie in bed. Would Bianca's behaviour prejudice Drake's hopes of selling the magazine to Giles?

The latter had seemed a shrewd man to Emma, but even the shrewdest of men could sometimes have their weak points and his was definitely Bianca. Emma had not missed the look of pain in his eyes at some of his wife's more contemptuous comments, and it didn't take a degree in human behaviour patterns to guess that like any other human being he would be more inclined to blame an outsider for his wife's indifference to him than to blame her. Emma had sensed that Giles respected Drake, and yet that respect must be tinged with some envy. Drake was a young man in the full power of his maleness, looking forward to life while Giles was looking back.

Showered and dressed Emma made her way downstairs, thanking the maid who gave her directions for the breakfast room.

Once a conservatory, it was massed with plants, its decor as carefully planned as that of the rest of the house. Drake and Giles were both there before her. Drake stood up as she walked in, the brief hard pressure of his hand on her arm and his mouth against her skin sending pulses of awareness jolting through her body.

There was a certain degree of tension in the air, Emma could feel it, and as she glanced questioningly at Drake, Giles greeted her, saying, 'It looks as though Drake and I won't be able to get down to any business today. My secretary is off sick, and I wanted notes taking of our discussions. I don't like using agency girls, and I positively loathe those infernal recording machines.'

He looked rather like a little boy, scowling ferociously as he admitted to this weakness. Although she hid it from him Emma was faintly amused that a man who was the head of a multi-million dollar empire couldn't bring himself to use a dictating machine. He was not alone; Emma had come across this phenomena before—and often from men who had insisted on computerising whole departments. Their excuses were normally almost childish.

Without pausing to think she offered impulsively, 'Could I stand in for your secretary? My shorthand speed is quite good, and . . .'

Before she could finish Drake had picked up on the suggestion. 'Great idea,' he approved, without giving Giles a chance to object. 'Emma my love, you're a real treasure. What would I do without you?'

After that the morning flew by so quickly, Emma could not believe it when the maid came in to tell them it was time for lunch.

Tactic, and counter-tactic, thrust and counter-thrust; as two skilled combatants in the same field Drake and Giles had put forward their differing viewpoints. As a fascinated observer, Emma could almost feel the point where the tide began to turn in Drake's favour, and Giles began to give ground slightly.

By lunch-time Drake had won his agreement to retaining all the existing staff for a probationary period of six months, if they were able to conclude all their other negotiations satisfactorily and the business did eventually become his.

Emma had listened closely to everything that had been said and on a couple of occasions had been able to insert a deft comment of her own.

During lunch the business discussion continued, with Giles making one or two comments to Emma. At one point he turned to Drake and said admiringly, 'You've really picked a winner here Drake; beauty, brains and femininity.'

'The three graces,' Drake responded, smiling at Emma. When he smiled at her like that she had difficulty holding on to her commonsense. She was almost grateful to Bianca for the small explosion of sound she made, her expression derisive, as her mouth twisted in bitterness.

'Be careful darling,' she said acidly to Giles. 'Your little heroine might not be as sure of Drake as you think. She might be lining you up as a substitute. A role you should be used to playing by now. I'm going out,' she added, standing up abruptly. 'We're dining out with the Carltons tonight. It will be a rather formal occasion,' she added to Emma. 'I do hope you've brought something suitable with you. Unfortunately, I can't lend you anything, all my clothes would be much too small.'

Much too small? A size at most, Emma guessed, but she didn't say anything merely smiling politely. She wasn't here to get upset or offended, she was here simply to act as a form of protection for Drake, and personal feelings of her own weren't allowable.

'I must apologise for Bianca,' Giles murmured uncomfortably when she had gone. 'She's been going through a difficult time recently. The drugs she's taking for the depression she's been suffering from sometimes have an adverse effect on her. I suppose all beautiful women go through a similar thing as they get older.'

He was asking her to make allowances for his wife, and Emma smiled again, and said truthfully, 'I'm just sorry we're here at such a difficult time for you.'

'Don't let it put you off marriage,' Giles cautioned Drake on a lighter note.

'It doesn't.' The look he gave Emma literally made her toes curl and all her commonsense warnings to herself go up in sheets of flames. The man was as lethal as dynamite, she told herself. If it was possible to do such a thing he was making love to her just by simply looking at her. The sensation was an unnerving one.

After lunch the men continued to discuss business while Emma made careful notes. It was gone five before they finally called it a day, and she was stiff from so much unaccustomed sitting still. A long soak in a hot bath was definitely called for she decided as she made her way to her room. There was also the question of what to wear tonight. Out to dinner Bianca had said, and Emma preferred the elegance of being slightly under-dressed to going for over-kill.

After inspecting the contents of her wardrobe she decided on a simple silk jersey Jean Muir dress in a misty shade of lilac. At first she had been uncertain about the dress because of the colour of her hair, but the shade was one that did wonders for her Celtic skin and eyes, giving the latter a faintly purple depth that made them seem twice their normal size.

Having decided on her dress, she went into the

bathroom to run a bath. She doubted that they
would go out much before eight, which gave her
ample time to rest and then get ready. She had
brought a couple of paperbacks with her and
taking one with her she wandered through into her
bathroom.

An expensive range of toiletries had been
provided for her use but after uncapping and
sniffing the bath oil Emma rejected it in favour of
her own Chanel. The perfume reminded her too
much of Bianca; it was heavy and sultry, and not
to her own taste at all.

The bath was enormous and the water piping
hot; the paperback she had bought on impulse a
good choice. Time went by and Emma was lost in
another world, lifting her eyes from her book
occasionally to add more water and push away
thoughts of guilt at her self-indulgence. At home
there was never enough time for a long soak; or
when there was Camilla was in the bathroom.

'Emma?'

She was so lost in her book that it was several
seconds before she registered the sound of Drake's
voice calling her name, and it was only when he
called her name again, his voice closer this time,
that she was galvanised into action, calling out
breathlessly, 'Yes, I'm here Drake ... I...' Her
voice was strangled in her throat as Drake pushed
open the unclosed door. The towel she managed to
snatch up was barely large enough to wrap round
herself, her face pink with indignation as she
glowered at him.

'Umm, Number 5.' His voice was light, amused
almost, but there was nothing amused about the
long slow tour his eyes took of her body still damp

from her undignified scramble to get out of the
bath, and very inadequately concealed by the small
towel.

'You should have stayed outside,' Emma
protested wrathfully. 'Why . . .?'

'*You* should have let me know before that you
were in here. I called out at least three times, for
all I knew you could have drowned in here.'

Giving him a scathing look Emma started to
skirt round him. He was standing between her and
the protection of her robe. He made no effort to
help her, merely picking up the paperback where
she had dropped it and glancing as though
extremely interested in it, at the printed pages.

'Will you please go away and let me get
dressed.' The words were gritted through Emma's
teeth as embarrassment gave way to anger.

'What? And deny myself the alluring picture of
my fiancée . . .?'

'I am not your fiancée.' Emma snapped the
words at him, glaring at him angrily. 'This is
simply a business arrangement—remember? And it
does not entitle you to come walking unannounced
into my bathroom.'

'Oh but I was announced——'

'Will you please go away.'

'What are you so frightened of Emma?' His
voice was soft, dangerously so, his scrutiny
thorough as he studied her thoughtfully. 'You're
far more adequately covered now than you would
be on a beach for instance.'

What he said was true; she wasn't frightened so
much as far too aware of the contrast between his
masculinity and her own femininity and her
vulnerability towards him.

'You scared me,' she said at last, admitting only a portion of the truth, 'I had no idea you were there.'

'I came in to talk to you about tonight. There was something I forgot to mention before we left London, and Bianca's bitchy remarks at lunch reminded me.'

Emma longed to tell him that whatever it was could wait until she was dressed, but every feminine instinct she possessed warned her that to do so would be to concede him a very definite advantage.

She was standing within two feet of him, with her robe lying behind him on a chair, and he stood between her and the door. 'If you'll just give me a minute to put on my robe we can talk about it,' she suggested lightly, hoping he wouldn't guess at her tension. The smile that curved his mouth told her that he had, his eyes mocking her.

'I like you the way you are,' he told her smoothly. 'And I like it even more knowing that my liking it disturbs you Emma. Oh yes it does,' he said softly before she could deny it. 'When you're disturbed about anything your eyes turn almost violet. What worries you so much? Is it the fact that I might do this?'

There was no way she could evade his arms imprisoning her, holding her tensed body against the relaxed outline of his. He laughed softly deep in his throat when she glared at him. 'Relax tigress,' he commanded her as he bent towards her, 'I'm not going to hurt you.'

The moment he said the words Emma knew that he was lying to her. Oh, he wasn't going to hurt her physically right enough, but emotionally . . .

So intense was the sense of self-revelation she suffered that her body shuddered with the force of it. Somehow without her being aware of it she had become dangerously vulnerable to him; a vulnerability that could only spring from the deepest kind of emotional involvement and yet there was none between them. Her feelings for him were purely and simply physical; weren't they?

She was so deeply involved in her own thoughts that it took his fierce, 'Emma ... don't try and escape from me that way ... Look at me,' to focus her attention on the darkly tense expression in his eyes.

'Where were you then?' he demanded. 'Where were your thoughts?'

'On my sister,' Emma lied valiantly, 'I was ...'

'Forget her,' Drake advised her. 'Think only of this.'

The heat of his mouth searing hers shocked her body first into frozen immobility and then into fierce, heated life. As if governed by an inner force that could not be controlled by her brain, her hands lifted to his shoulders, seeking for and finding the firm curve of his nape and the thick hair that grew there. Her mouth parted at the insistence of his, not making any attempt to resist his sensual invasion, her body shuddered, alight with a fierce, deep hunger as his hand slid from her waist to her breast, cupping it through the softness of the towel, his thumb unerringly finding the burgeoning tautness of her nipple.

Aching waves of pleasure spread through her body, radiating outwards from his seductive caress. Unable to stop herself from shuddering deeply in response Emma closed her eyes. It was a mistake. Instantly she was transported to a world where the senses ruled. Behind her closed eyes images of Drake danced; his body supple and male, and completely nude.

Fire shimmered across her skin, the aching in the pit of her stomach intensifying. She was barely aware of the firm tug Drake gave her protective towel, knowing only that as it fell away and his hands moved over her back into the curve of her waist, holding her against him, she was consumed by a fierce need to have him go on touching her, holding her, caressing her, loving her. . .

It took her several seconds to react to what she had unwittingly betrayed to herself; seconds during which she drowned beneath the sexual expertise of his touch, intoxicated to the point of madness by the feel and smell of him, recovering only when her brain forced her to acknowledge the danger she was courting.

Why should she want his love? Sex was all he could offer her; and sex was all she wanted from him, wasn't it?

When she stopped returning his kiss Drake lifted his mouth from hers, brilliantly jade eyes studying the smoky, aroused grey of her own.

'Second thoughts? It's too late for them now Emma, and besides they'd be a complete waste of time. You want me,' he told her arrogantly, and it was the sureness in his voice, the male conceit adding victory to his eyes that gave her the courage to move slightly away from him, her body tense as she responded coolly, 'Yes, of course I do, Drake, but sexual wanting isn't enough I'm afraid at least not for me.'

She saw him frown and bent to retrieve her

towel, hoping he wouldn't notice the way her body reacted to his careless appraisal of it. When she stood up and re-secured it, he was still frowning and Emma knew she had to take what small advantage she had gained and use it against him before he guessed the truth.

'You surely don't suppose you're the first man I *have* wanted?' She managed to inject a small thread of amused mockery into the words and had the satisfaction of seeing his eyes harden, his mouth tightening slightly as he moved a step back from her. 'I'm twenty-six years old Drake,' she shrugged smoothly. 'Of course I've experienced physical desire before, but I made myself a promise years ago that I wouldn't succumb to it unless it was teamed with something else. You see,' she told him proudly, hoping he wouldn't challenge her; that he wouldn't guess that no man had ever aroused her to the fiery heights he had taken her to, 'I'm not prepared to settle for the second rate; for sex on its own.'

'You want "love" as well is that it?' he interrupted harshly, his mouth and tone openly derisive. 'People have wasted their lives looking for that elusive state,' he told her sardonically. 'What makes you think you'll be any more successful? You're so smug and secure locked away behind your own principles aren't you Emma? What do you expect me to do? Admire you for them? Well I don't find them admirable, I think they're the mark of a coward; a woman who won't allow herself to come down to earth and enjoy life as it is. There's nothing morally wrong about enjoying sex for sex's sake; rather the opposite. The love you dream of is an elusive, non-existent state of mind.'

Every word he was saying to her was driving the pain deeper into her heart. She had known right from the start what manner of man he was; it was pointless to cry aching tears inside now because she loved him and she knew that love would never be returned. 'What is it you want from me Emma?' he demanded explosively. 'What is it you want me to say? That I love you?' His mouth twisted. 'I thought better of you; I didn't think you were the kind of woman who demanded lip-service paying to a set of outmoded customs . . .'

'Stop it Drake.' The words came out huskily, betraying to herself her intense pain. 'Whatever you say to me won't make any difference. I want to give and to receive love; I want to share my body with a man for whom I feel more than just sexual desire.'

'*Just* sexual desire?' She could hardly bear the derision in his eyes. 'Oh Emma how you deceive yourself. Just ten minutes ago that same "mere sexual desire" had you going mad in my arms; hungry for my complete possession. Lie to yourself if you must,' he added curtly, 'but don't lie to me. Just remember when the ache of your body keeps you awake at night what you could have had and what you still can have, if you come and ask me nicely.'

'Never.' The denial exploded from her tense throat, earning a cynical grimace.

'You're chasing after rainbows Emma; looking for pots of gold that don't exist. You're the first woman I've ever met who I find as stimulating mentally as I do sexually. We could be very good together you and I, and the pity of it is that by the time you're ready to admit as much it will be way, way too late.'

'Meaning that you'll already have moved on to the next woman; the next challenge,' Emma retorted bitterly. 'I'm sorry Drake, but I want more from a man than a few weeks' sexual pleasure and then goodbye.'

'Well you know what they say.' His smile was cruelly hard. 'Either you use it or you lose it.'

He was gone before she could add another retort and childishly Emma followed him to the connecting door locking it behind him although she knew he would make no attempt to walk through it. Drake wasn't that kind of man. He didn't need to be, with women like Bianca around she thought wryly, asking herself derisively if she had locked the door not so much to keep Drake out, but to keep herself in; to stop herself from weakening and going to him.

It made no difference that she spent most of the evening telling herself that she had made the right decision. Every time she looked up from the meal she was barely tasting to find Drake deep in conversation with one or other of their fellow female guests she was pierced with a jealousy so acute that she could hardly contain it.

To make matters worse Bianca kept on watching her; like a cat at a mousehole Emma thought muzzily, aimlessly pushing a piece of steak round her plate.

Giles's friends were a couple in their mid-forties, the husband brash and too forceful for Emma's taste, the woman relentlessly flirtatious, brittle in a way that made Emma shudder inwardly and pray that she herself never found herself trapped in a life-style that necessitated such behaviour.

It was something she ought to take as a timely

warning, she told herself later on as they were driven back to the house. Marriage to Drake, if such a thing by some miracle were ever to come to pass would be a constant effort to be the woman Drake wanted her to be and she too would develop that fretful, anxious look, she had seen so clearly betrayed on Rita Vanguard's smoothly made up face. No, that wasn't for her. She wanted a mate she could share her life with; laugh with; love deeply and intensely. Which was one of the reasons she was still single, she reminded herself sardonically. Perhaps Drake was right, perhaps she was living in a fantasy world.

They were back at the house almost before she realised it, so deeply engrossed in her thoughts that it came as something of a shock to hear Bianca saying tauntingly, 'I think our love birds must have had a quarrel. Never mind my dear,' she said to Emma, 'they do say a double bed is a great place for making up and Drake was always at his best between the sheets or so I've heard.'

Bianca was playing a dangerous game Emma thought, chancing to see the deeply bitter look crossing Giles's face. She was playing with fire and if she wasn't careful she was going to get badly burned.

'Thanks for the testimonial.' Drake sounded laconically unconcerned by Bianca's remarks. 'Our apologies, if we've both been somewhat subdued this evening,' he apologised to Giles as they entered the house. 'Jet lag catching up on us, I suspect.'

'I know the feeling. Bianca should have been a little more thoughtful and given you a couple of days to recover before arranging anything. It always takes me at least forty-eight hours to get anything like back to normal.'

'Yes, but darling, you're at least thirty years older than Drake,' Bianca murmured sweetly as they walked into the house. Emma almost cringed for the other woman's unkindness. Although he fought hard not to show it, Giles had winced away from her cruel words. Drake's mouth was a hard line as he refused a nightcap, and as Emma turned towards the stairs he followed her, catching hold of her elbow to bend his head and murmur, 'Still believe in the magic potency of "love", after witnessing that little débâcle?'

'I doubt that Bianca ever loved Giles, as I conceive it,' she responded shortly, 'although it's obvious that he adores her.'

'And a relationship with love on one side and not on the other, isn't what you'd go for, I take it? It would be against all those high-minded principles of yours?'

'It would be a recipe for disaster,' Emma responded shortly, hating herself for the unruly thoughts he was arousing inside her; the insane desire to turn to him and tell him that she loved him; and that so long as he was a part of it, she could take any relationship he cared to offer her.

Was she completely mad, she asked herself as she paused outside her room. She had seen tonight, with her own eyes, the effect marriage to a sexually dynamic man could have on a woman. She personally might have found John Vanguard brash and insensitive to his wife's needs, but she had recognised instantly the powerful sexual aura he gave off, and it hadn't needed Drake's murmured remark that John had probably slept with every single woman at the dinner table apart from herself, to underline the man's sexuality. Drake had made the remark to torment her, but Emma had instantly looked at his wife, and had seen past the carefully lifted and made up forty-odd-year-old face and had seen the agony of the woman behind it; a woman still deeply in love with a husband who no longer fully had that love. Was that what she wanted for herself?

'Where do you go to when you get that look in your eyes? And don't tell me you're thinking about your sister again,' Drake demanded, roughly grasping her arm.

'I was thinking about John Vanguard,' Emma responded truthfully without thinking, gasping out loud in sharp pain as Drake's fingers hardened on her skin. 'Damn you,' he cursed violently. 'Just what in hell are you trying to do to me?' His voice was thick and unfamiliar, sending frissons of corresponding sensations curling down her spine. 'I've been going mad all evening with wanting you, aching so much that I can feel it in every bone; every muscle,' he ground out at her, 'and then you throw John Vanguard in my face as calmly as you please. I thought Bianca was the original bitch, but I'm beginning to revise my opinion. What were you wondering about just then? How good he is in bed? Why don't you ask Bianca?'

'Why not,' Emma agreed coolly, fighting against the flood of emotions his angry words had aroused. She badly wanted to tell him that he was mistaken but she daredn't. If she gave way now she would spend the night in his arms; in his bed, and tomorrow morning she would bitterly regret her folly. 'I'm sure she'd be only too glad to give me a blow by blow description; of your technique as well as his.'

The expletive that burst into the tense silence between them made Emma shrink. Used as she was to TV technicians' colourful language, this was something else. The fingers Drake had clamped round her arm tightened until they were bone white, a look in his eyes that made her regret to the depths of her soul her hasty words.

'Why bother getting the information second-hand.' His voice was a thick, angry grate against over-sensitised nerves. 'I'll give you a personal demonstration.'

The violence with which he thrust open her bedroom door was a shock to her already over-tense system. Panic flooded through her body at the anger she seemed to have built up inside him. Drake was no carefully controlled product of a middle class public school like most of the other men she knew. He had grown up in a rough, tough atmosphere and it had left its mark on him.

Instinct told her to take the course of least resistance and so she remained completely passive beneath the bruising pressure of a kiss designed to hurt and degrade. His teeth against her skin hurt and drew blood forcing an involuntary gasp of pain that gave him the leverage he had wanted, his mouth brutalising the soft sensitivity of hers.

'Fight me, damn you.' His voice was harsh and strange against her ear, her whole body trembling nervously with a mixture of tension and reaction. 'Show me that you're capable of some feelings at least ... or is your lack of sexual experience merely a cover for the fact that you're completely incapable of feeling *anything*, Emma?'

It was so brutal that she had no way of shielding herself from the pain. She could feel the blood draining out of her body; the agony of having her own deepest most private fears revealed with all the brutality of newly formed skin being ripped away from a wound. The pity of it was that until she had met him she would not have been able to refute the taunt. It had taken him to show her the true depths of her own sexuality; to show her that she was indeed capable of feeling deep passion; intense sexual hunger and for a moment she was driven almost to the point where she wanted to abandon everything she had fought for and show him all the hungry need she felt. But she couldn't do that. Drake was an intelligent man, once his anger had cooled he would start to analyse her reactions and it wouldn't take him long to guess the truth. That was the one thing she could not bear. Always an intensely private person, Emma could not carry the double burden of loving him and knowing that he knew of that love and probably pitied her for it. Instinctively she searched for a means of self-defence and found it slotted away neatly in her mind.

'You said you wouldn't touch me again,' she reminded him huskily, 'you said you would wait until I came to you.' Slowly her confidence returned and she was able to look him in the face, knowing that all he felt for her was sexual desire and the look she could see in his eyes; almost savage in its intensity could only be sexual frustration.

For what seemed to be an endless span of time they simply looked at one another, and then Drake broke the tense silence to say rawly, 'Damn

you Emma, damn you for the cold-hearted,
unfeeling bitch you are.'

He was just on the point of turning away when
Bianca came up the stairs. Emma knew the older
woman must have seen the swollen bruised
contours of her lips because her glance lingered
glitteringly on them before she said tauntingly to
Drake, 'My goodness Drake what on earth have
you been doing to your little fiancée. She looks as
though she's been mauled by an animal.'

'Jealous, Bianca?'

It was a sign of just how much his control had
slipped that he should reply the way he had,
Emma thought, shivering a little as she saw the
look that passed between them; an intense, bitter
hunger on Bianca's part which she had no
difficulty in interpreting at all, and an angry
curtness on Drake's which was harder to understand.

She could appreciate that he could be suffering
from sexual frustration; after all wasn't she
herself? Hadn't she too experienced the sharp
claws of need his earlier caresses had unleashed
inside her; but Drake was an experienced man not
someone who had never known the full force of
sexual desire before and surely it took more than
the brief caresses they had shared to arouse him to
the point where frustrated desire had to be turned
into the sort of anger he was exhibiting?

'Why should I be?' Bianca had recovered some
of her poise, her red mouth curling into a taunting
smile. 'It's already obvious to me that your fiancée
can't satisfy you Drake. But I can.' Ignoring
Emma completely she moved closer to him placing
her hand on his wrist, smiling invitingly up to him.

Emma was completely stunned. It was the sort of behaviour one expected to read or to see on celluloid, but certainly not to experience in real life. Bianca was totally ignoring her, treating her as though she simply did not exist. Remembering the agreement she and Drake had made and her supposed role, Emma thought frantically, wondering how she ought to react. Easy, an inner voice mocked her, just follow your instincts and scratch her eyes out.

Effective, but hardly what Drake would want. She was Drake's fiancée at least as far as the rest of the world was concerned, and no matter what had passed between them privately, Drake had given her no indication that he wanted that to change; or that he might welcome Bianca's advances. When it came down to it, his business interests were of far more interest to Drake than any woman. Her mind made up, Emma acted. Placing her hand on his arm she moved closer towards him, noting that she had no need to fake the faint trembling that seemed to have invaded her, even to the extent of infecting her voice.

'Drake, what's going on? Why does . . .'

'I'll tell you what's going on,' Bianca shrilled back interrupting her. 'Drake's trying to fob me off by producing you. He's just using you because he doesn't want Giles to know the truth.'

It came so close to the mark that for a moment Emma was stupefied.

'You're becoming hysterical Bianca.' Drake had recovered his control, his voice cool and icily dismissive. 'The fact that you and I were briefly lovers long before you met Giles is no secret to Emma, and you're only storing up humiliation and

pain for yourself by constantly trying to resurrect
something that was never truly alive.'

'You wanted me.' If anything Bianca's voice was
even shriller and Emma found it in herself to feel
sorry for the other woman no matter how badly
she was behaving.

'Did I?' Drake sounded bored. 'I seem to
remember that the boot was somewhat on the
other foot. You were the one who did all the
running, Bianca,' he told her cruelly.

She went white and gasped out loud releasing
his arm. 'You . . . you . . .'

'Bounder?' Drake supplied wryly for her. 'I
never did pretend to be a gentleman, Bianca, and
it seems to me that was what you liked about me
as I remember it.'

'All right, marry her if you want to,' Bianca
snapped back viciously. 'Take her to bed and
make love to her, but if you think Giles will go
ahead with that magazine deal when I tell him the
truth, you've got another think coming.'

'If Giles had any sense the only action he'd take
once you've revealed all to him would be in the
direction of the divorce courts,' Drake responded.
'The only reason I've put up with your tricks,
Bianca, is that I don't want to hurt Giles, but I've
come to the end of my patience. Tell him what the
hell you like.'

CHAPTER SEVEN

SHE had never in her life experienced so much tension as she was experiencing now, Emma thought wearily as she studied her face in her bedroom mirror.

The atmosphere in the house since Bianca's outburst three nights ago, had been virtually intolerable. The only positive thing to happen was that Drake and Giles were continuing to negotiate the sale of the magazine. Giles's secretary was now fully recovered and back at work, and having chatted to the older woman on several occasions, Emma had found her warm-hearted and intelligent. She also suspected that Marti was in love with Giles. Life was a constant series of almost macabre jokes, she reflected unhappily, and Drake was probably right, love was an impossible to reach nirvana; a hoax thought up by unkind and mocking Gods to torment lesser human beings.

Bianca was in a mega-sulk, which although in many ways easier to bear than her constant vitriolic outbursts made for a very uncomfortable atmosphere, but Bianca's behaviour wasn't the sole cause for her tension, Emma admitted to herself. There was also Drake; and her own awareness of him; her body's awareness of the fact that he slept in the next room; her imagination's cruelty in relaying to her night after night tormenting images of his body, powerful and sleek, capable of arousing her own to the very

heights of human experience. But in the trade off
to reach those heights she would be giving up so
much ... She would always have her memories, a
traitorous voice persuaded her; many women
married for friendship; for children; for calmer,
surer waters than those represented by Drake.

That way was not for her ... It was unfair and
weak. Better to spend her life completely alone ...
So why not take what was offered to her now; why
not allow herself the pleasure Drake could give her
and leave payment of the price for the future?

On and on the inner arguments raged exhausting
her mentally and physically, and Drake wasn't
helping. Every time he touched her or looked at
her, he turned the screw a little tighter, increasing
her hunger for him, wearing away her resistance.
Since that night outside her room he had had
himself completely under control. Which was more
than she could say for herself, Emma thought
ruefully. Today he and Giles had gone to see
Giles's lawyers and would be gone for most of the
day, which was probably why she felt so restless.

At last unable to endure the confining, stifling
atmosphere of the mansion any longer Emma
decided she would go into New York and do some
window shopping. She hadn't visited the city
stores once during her stay and it would be a way
of passing time.

Giles had said on several occasions that if she
wanted to go anywhere she had simply to tell
Barnes their major domo who would organise a
car for her, and without giving herself time to
change her mind Emma sought him out.

Although he expressed doubts as to the wisdom
of Emma going into the city centre alone, she

eventually overruled him, and an hour later was seated in the back of Giles's luxurious limousine travelling towards New York itself.

The sheer pace of life in the heart of New York was something that had to be seen to be believed Emma decided exploring the fashion floors of Macy's Department Store. American women possessed a panache and style that took Emma's breath away and yet she didn't envy them. Somehow in their search for perfection, of face, figure and lifestyle they had developed a hungry, almost desperate look of strain that made her wonder if at the end of the day the frenetic pace of life was really worthwhile. I must be getting old, she told herself ruefully looking round for a coffee bar where she could sit down and catch her breath. She hadn't bought anything; for one thing she had neglected to bring any money out with her, fully alive to the dangers of carrying cash in the city centre and neither did she have the credit card Drake had given her. She had hoped that getting away from the claustrophobic atmosphere of the mansion might bring her back down to earth; put her in touch with reality again, but all it had done was to emphasise the wide gap that lay between Drake and herself. Here in New York, as in any other international city, he would be completely at home, whereas she preferred the relative peace and simplicity of country life. Why was she bothering to convince herself of their incompatibility, she derided herself an hour later, stepping out into the heat and bustle of the New York streets; she was perfectly safe from Drake; he would not approach her again; the ball was now in her court; all she had to do was to withstand her own feelings.

Easier said than done Emma thought, blinking in the harsh sunlight. The sidewalk was crowded with people and she felt someone jostle her from behind, thrusting painfully into her side. She turned automatically to object, the sound strangled in her throat as she saw the man's raised fist, and realised too late what was happening. Fool, fool she chided herself mentally in the instant that it dawned on her that she was the victim of a mugger's attack. *Why* had she turned round, why hadn't she realised what was happening and simply let him snatch her bag; there was little enough in it. So many thoughts chased through her mind in the few seconds it took for the hard blow to knock her to the sidewalk that later she was to find it impossible to believe a greater time had not elapsed.

She was aware of pain exploding in her head, of her arm being wrenched excruciatingly, of noises all around her, slowly dying away as she became engulfed in a tide of unconsciousness, her last thought a panicky fear of simply being left here to die while all around her life went on. New Yorkers were notorious for their non-involvement in the violence that went on around them every day.

'Emma?'

The voice was familiar, but the anxiety in it wasn't, and Emma struggled painfully to analyse why the anxiety should be so perplexing.

'She's not speaking.'

There was something else joining the anxiety now, a harshness that was more familiar under-writing the masculinity of the voice. It was a voice that belonged to a man who knew what he wanted from life, and who took it regardless of any opposition. Oddly enough it was also a voice that reassured her; that made her feel safe and secure.

'Give her time. She's had a bad knock, there's bound to be an element of concussion. To be honest we'd prefer to keep her here for observation for twenty-four hours.'

There was a hint of disapproval in the other male voice which Emma now recognised as American, as though this had been a point of conflict at an earlier discussion. She badly wanted to say that she didn't want to be left behind; that she wanted to go with the first speaker wherever he wanted to take her.

'Emma?' She knew he had bent closer to the bed, because she could feel his breath fanning her skin. She forced her eyes to open and a sensation like a massive shock wave jolted through her system. She had never seen such darkly green eyes, was her first dazed thought, followed quickly by the knowledge that she *had* seen these particular eyes before.

'Emma . . . are you all right?'

There was that anxiety again and now that she could focus on him properly she could see it mirrored in his eyes; evident in the taut stretch of skin against facial bones.

She lifted her hand and was bemused for a second by the brilliant flash of light from the diamond on her engagement finger. Something in her expression must have given her away because he said thickly, 'It's mine,' and Emma had the distinct impression that what he was really saying was, '*You* are mine.' The thought made her feel secure and safe and she looked trustingly up at him.

'We're engaged?'

'Don't you remember?' He was watching her closely and Emma shook her head; she had several muzzy impressions of pain and then falling; and slightly dimmer ones of a huge house which for some reason she didn't want to return to. One thing was clear to her and that was that they were visitors to America, because neither of them had American accents, but why they were here she could not remember.

'What can you remember, Emma?' His voice was stronger now, firmer and yet still carrying an undertone of anxiety.

'Very little,' she told him truthfully. 'Just pain and then falling.'

'Temporary amnesia,' she heard the other voice interjecting curtly. 'That's one of the reasons we'd prefer her to stay here.'

Watching him frown, Emma felt panic well up inside her. 'Don't leave me here,' she begged, fighting back weak tears. 'Please . . .' His eyes narrowed as she reached out towards him, and she wanted to tell him that he was the only familiar thing there was; the only person who could provide reality in the strange empty world she suddenly seemed to have entered.

'I have no intention of leaving you, Emma mine.'

'Drake . . . I've just heard the news, how is she . . .' The man who burst into the room was vaguely familiar, older by far than her fiancé and yet still very attractive. The feeling she felt on seeing him was a strange one; a combination of liking and pity, but yet she couldn't understand the reason for those feelings.

'Still very groggy,' Drake responded. 'I don't want to leave her here alone and yet it's too soon to fly her back to England.'

'Good God you can't do that. No, she must come back to the house. We'll get a nurse ...'

'No! No ... I don't want anyone.' It was to Drake that she appealed, wanting to tell him that he was the only person she wanted; the only person she needed. The doctor was frowning again. 'This is all very irregular,' he began, but Emma over-ruled him. 'Please ... I want to go with my fiancé.'

'Very well, but only on the understanding that you ring us if there should be the slightest change in her condition.' He was speaking to Drake not to her Emma realised. 'If she becomes sleepy or listless, we want to know about it. At the moment she's suffering slight concussion but if it should get worse.'

'What about her memory?'

'That will return once the effects of the blow and the anaesthetic wear off. She's bound to feel very muddled for at least forty-eight hours. You've been one very lucky young woman,' he told Emma severely.

'What happened?' Emma asked shakily, 'I remember falling. . .'

'You were mugged,' Drake answered curtly for her, 'but luckily for you a policeman saw what had happened and he brought you here. Again luckily, you had enough identification in your bag for the hospital to trace me.'

'And even more luckily, the gash in your head, although messy, was little more than a surface wound,' the doctor interrupted. 'We've stitched it

for you which is one of the reasons you're feeling
so groggy—after-effects of the anaesthetic. Some
people are more susceptible to it than others, but
you're also suffering a degree of concussion from
the blow. Didn't anyone warn you about the folly
of walking alone in New York?'

There were several formalities to be gone
through before the hospital would release her, but
at last Emma was free to accept Drake's help out
into the open air. The Mercedes limousine he took
her to was vaguely familiar. It belonged to their
host Drake explained when Emma checked
slightly. They were staying with an American
associate of his while he conducted some business
negotiations with him, he further told Emma once
they were all in the car.

'That's right,' Emma was told by the American
who joined them in the car and who Drake told
her was their host. 'We were in the middle of a
meeting with my lawyers when we got the news.
I've never seen Drake so uptight in all the time I've
known him.

Emma was instantly remorseful. 'Oh I'm so
sorry,' she apologised ... Drake was frowning,
and at first she thought it was because she had
upset his day, but his mind must have been on
other things because he simply shrugged and asked
her how she was feeling. In point of fact she was
feeling almost light-headed, and muzzy. It seemed
so strange to have lost part of her life. She knew
who she was; she knew she had a father and a
newly married sister, Drake was familiar to her
although she couldn't remember how they had met
or how long they had known one another, and yet
she knew that she loved him and that the thought

of being parted from him even for one night was almost unbearable.

She listened to Giles talking to her on the drive back to his house, telling her that there was no point in panicking and that her full memory would return in due course.

The house was vaguely familiar, which was reassuring, but the way in which Giles enquired as to his wife's whereabouts sent prickles of alarm racing down her spine, which she couldn't explain.

Drake had insisted on carrying her inside. To judge from the reaction of her senses to being in his arms, they could not have known one another long Emma judged hazily; such intense sexual excitement at merely being held against his body, feeling the steady beat of his heart did not suggest a long-standing relationship. She wanted to question him but felt too tired. Tomorrow they could talk, she thought sleepily as he opened a door and carried her over to a large double bed.

'Don't fight it,' he advised her, pulling back the cover and then tucking it round her. 'They gave you a shot to make you sleep. Best medicine in the world.'

As he tucked the cover round her, he turned to leave and Emma reached out to detain him, clutching his arm. The look in his eyes as he gazed down at her was one she found it hard to define. It was a combination of pain and a certain wry self-mockery she was at a loss to understand.

'Stay with me,' she pleaded, 'I feel so strange and disorientated . . .' She essayed a brief smile. 'Am I always this clingy . . .? Somehow it doesn't feel like me.'

'It isn't,' he assured her with a wry smile. 'In

fact you're almost infuriatingly independent, hence today's contretemps.' He disengaged her fingers and stood up.

Emma frowned. 'Don't I get a kiss?'

'Are you sure you really want one?'

It seemed a strange thing to say to her and Emma was puzzled by it. 'Is there any reason why I shouldn't?'

Before he could answer there was a brief tap on her door and Giles walked in. 'Sorry to interrupt but there's a transatlantic call for you Drake.'

'I'm coming now,' Drake responded. 'Try to sleep and I'll come up and see you later,' he told Emma, as he walked across to the door.

For some reason that comment worried her, but before she could discover why, sleep was washing over her in unavoidable waves, dragging her down into its warm darkness.

CHAPTER EIGHT

EMMA woke up dry-mouthed and tense, disturbed by a confused and somehow frightening dream, whose details she could not remember but which left her feeling unhappy and confused.

Her room was in darkness and she fumbled for a lamp switch, crying out in alarm as she knocked something off the bedside table. As she started to scramble out of bed a door was thrust open sending an oblong of light to illuminate the room.

'Emma, are you all right?'

She felt almost weak with relief at the sound of Drake's voice.

'Fine,' she assured him shakily, 'just a mild case of blind panic. I woke up and couldn't remember where on earth I was for a second.'

He came to the side of her bed and eyed her thoughtfully. 'And now you can?'

'Just about.' Her voice was rueful as she fought against the dizzying flood of awareness just having him standing close to her brought thundering through her veins. 'But that's as much as I *can* remember I'm afraid.' She looked up at him and frowned as she realised he was wearing a robe and that he must have been in bed. As she looked at the door he had opened she realised it must belong to an adjacent bedroom and her frown deepened.

'Something wrong?'

'Why are we sleeping in separate rooms?' The words were out before she could check them.

'Don't you know?'

His question threw her. Was it because their hostess, who she couldn't remember and who she had not yet seen since her return from the hospital, disapproved of couples sleeping together before they were married?

'Is it because Giles's wife would object?' she hazarded a guess.

'That's one reason.'

One reason? Emma shivered. Despite the warmth of the room and acting purely on primaeval instinct she said hesitantly, 'Drake please stay with me tonight. Giles's wife needn't know.' Her face flamed as he continued simply to look at her. 'What I mean is if she disapproves of the fact that we're sleeping together before we're married, you could be back in your own room by morning. I just don't want to be alone tonight.

'If I come into your bed, it won't be simply to sleep.' The blunt warning was reassuring. For a minute she had begun to wonder if they had quarrelled perhaps.

'I need you tonight,' she said simply, not knowing how else to convey to him how much she needed the security and comfort of his warmth beside her.

'Have we been lovers long?' she asked shyly as he slid off his robe and pushed back the covers.

'What makes you ask that?'

She had instinctively averted her eyes from the satin gleam of his shoulders, caught off guard by the tight spiral of excitement building up inside her; an excitement that was spiked with something approaching fear, an emotion akin to the sensation she had experienced as a child when doing something she knew she ought not to do. Quite ridiculous really. She reached out to switch off the lamp and the light from it fractured against the diamond of her engagement ring.

'Leave it on.' Drake's voice was rough, sending prickles of alien sensation across her tender nerve endings. 'I want to see you when I make love to you, and no, we haven't been lovers long, why do you ask?'

He was watching her so closely Emma felt sure he must be able to penetrate the protection of the bed-clothes and see the wave of colour washing up over her body.

'It's simply the way I react to you,' she replied helplessly, unable to fabricate a lie.

'Meaning?'

He was lying on his side, his head propped up on one hand, the soft glow of the lamp emphasising the tanned healthiness of his skin. She wanted to reach out and touch him but she felt too shy, inhibited almost. It must be something to do with her amnesia Emma thought uncertainly.

'Meaning,' he prompted again.

Groping to find a lucid explanation for sensations and emotions she could only half grasp herself Emma said hesitantly, 'It's just that I find you so . . . so sexually overwhelming,' she told him honestly, 'almost shatteringly so. It unnerves me,' she admitted. 'It seems as though such a reaction is alien to my personality.'

'In many ways it is. You're a very private, independent person Emma, and I suspect that part of you deeply resents finding me "sexually overwhelming".' When he quoted her own words there was a gleam in his eyes that made her skin turn to goosebumps. She reached out to touch him and then withdrew, puzzled by her own behaviour, confused by the conflicting signals it was giving her. One part of her said touch him, love him, the other said don't, withdraw, hide. Perhaps it was simply a side effect of her concussion and the anaesthetic, bringing to the fore emotions she normally kept hidden.

'Why are you looking at me like that?'

His question caught her off guard, and she answered it honestly. 'Because I want to touch you and yet part of me says I mustn't.'

'Ignore it.' His breath fanned her skin as he bent over her, tracing the line of her jaw with tiny teasing kisses. 'Ignore it Emma,' he muttered hoarsely against her skin. 'Ignore it and make love with me.' His lips found the delicate lobe of her ear, his touch sending dizzying frissons of pleasure spiralling under her skin. Her fingers were stroking his body, exploring the hard maleness of his shoulders, her senses urging her to abandon herself to the rip-tide of pleasure surging over her. It seemed impossible to believe that she had felt this before; that she had touched him like this before and that he had touched her and yet she could remember nothing about it.

In some strange way it made her almost greedy to absorb every sensation he aroused inside her, as though she was motivated by some deep-seated need to imprint them on her consciousness in a way which could never be erased.

She was still wearing her underwear and the gown they had given her in hospital—the same clothes in which Drake had carried her upstairs to bed on their return—and at the first touch of his fingers against her skin as he untied the robe she moaned with feverish pleasure, hungering for the feel of his hands and mouth against her skin with an urgency that assured her that whatever else she had forgotten she had not been mistaken in remembering how much she loved her fiancé.

As though in some way the small sounds of pleasure and need she made deep in her throat enticed and excited him Drake shuddered deeply as he released the catch on her bra, pushing back the duvet so that the lamp glow fell directly across the aroused curves of her breasts revealing skin the colour and sheen of mother of pearl tipped with rose pink crests.

It was impossible and unnecessary not to arch invitingly beneath the openly aroused caress of his eyes, the sound of her name, thick and slurred as though he had difficulty in enunciating it, causing the muscles in her lower stomach to contract achingly.

'Kiss me.'

Her mouth opened eagerly and hungrily beneath the onslaught of his, spasms of pleasure rippling through her body when his hands cupped her breasts. She opened her eyes dizzily, feeling her own sensual response to the sight of his tanned skin against the paleness of her own. Like her he was naked, and her pulses leapt and jolted erratically as she looked down the length of their entwined bodies. She ran her fingers lightly down his spine and felt him respond, his teeth nipping the soft inner skin of her mouth, the smothered sound of pleasure he made as her hand moved from his spine to the hard thrust of his hip all the incitement she needed to shape the male firmness of his buttocks.

His reaction was instantaneous, his mouth leaving hers with a smothered sound of pleasure to ravish the tender curve of her throat, the light touch of his thumb brushing tormentingly across the aroused peak of her nipple an ache that could only be appeased by the moist dragging heat of his mouth and the erotic pressure of his teeth.

Emma cried out with pleasure arching feverishly beneath him, her nails raking the taut flesh of his back, her body on fire with desire for him. His tongue stroked her skin, teasing and tormenting; his hand splayed across the smooth skin of her stomach. She ached with an intensity that held her in thrall, and he was teasing her, Emma thought feverishly, her teeth closing protestingly on his skin and making him growl deep in his throat.

His hand moved lower, filling her with a sexual heat that burned through her veins like fire. Unable to stop herself Emma arched against him in supplication, gasping in aching pleasure when his hands grasped her hips lifting her and holding her against the aroused heat of his thighs. Without even being conscious of what she was doing Emma ground her hips rhythmically against him, crying out to him feverishly when his hands cupped her bottom and he moved thrustingly against her.

Above her his face looked dark and unfamiliar and a spasm of fear shot through her. Almost as though he sensed it, he stroked his tongue against her lips, teasing her with light kisses, slowing down the pace of their lovemaking, coaxing the wholly unexpected panic from her.

She reached out blindly to return his caresses, stroking him feverishly until he muttered her name thickly and moved against her in a way that commanded her response. The weight of his body against hers, the heat and pressure of his thighs, invoked a compulsion that couldn't be denied. Emma cried out in a mixture of pain and pleasure as he entered her; the pain unexpected but almost totally lost beneath the intensity of sensations his possession aroused.

He filled her body, taking it and making it a part of his own until she was mindless with the ache of pleasure he was arousing, urged on to some peak she could sense was there, but was unable to reach. She felt the spasms contracting his body and knew from the way he cried out her name that he had reached that peak without her. Disappointment shivered through her; disappointment and a feeling of self-reproach, but before she could question it she could feel herself sliding deep down into heavy layers of sleep massed like thick clouds, supporting and comforting her, dulling the unfamiliar ache and stilling the quivering shivers racking her exhausted body.

She woke up in the night comforted by the warmth and presence of Drake beside her, curling her body into his and snuggling up against him. She had thought that he was asleep but he murmured thickly, 'Keep on doing that and neither of us is going to get any sleep tonight.'

His voice brought her fully awake, a vivid sensation of self-disappointment sweeping over her as she remembered their lovemaking. She felt as though she had failed not only him but herself as well. She wanted to talk to Drake about it but something held her back.

'What's wrong?' He seemed to sense instinctively that she was restless although she hadn't moved.

'You tell me.' Her voice was faintly self-derisive but instantly he picked up on what was distressing her. His arms came round, curving her more intimately into his body.

'Emma, we ought to talk,' he began slowly. 'There's something . . .'

'Wrong with me?' she concluded for him bitterly. 'Do you think I don't realise that. I can't understand it.' Her body ached and she moved restlessly, ill at ease with herself. Were she and Drake experiencing sexual problems; had he concealed the truth from her? Could *that* be the reason they had separate rooms?

'Something wrong with you?' She thought he sounded faintly stunned but was at a loss to understand why. She could feel him tense against her and then suddenly the tension went as he said in a different tone. 'Ah yes . . . I think I understand. There's nothing wrong with you Emma,' he told her softly.

'Then why?'

'Shush . . .' The warmth of his mouth against hers silenced her protests his skilled hands soon coaxing her body to abandon itself completely to him. This time their lovemaking was slower paced, more sensual than urgent, her body responding to his caresses as indolently and instinctively as a flower opening to the sun.

'Still think there's "something wrong with you",' he teased with lazy amusement as she floated down from the stars he had taken her to.

She was too dazed and satiated with pleasure to respond, content simply to lie in his arms and let sleep claim her.

*　　*　　*

'How do you feel this morning?'

Drake was dressed; frowning slightly as he looked down at her. 'Okay,' Emma assured him.

'No signs of returning concussion. No further memory lapses.'

'None at all,' Emma responded, remembering with perfect clarity the pleasure of his body possessing hers. This morning she felt languorous and lazy, content to simply lie and doze like a satisfied cat. It was an effort simply to move.

'Stay in bed this morning,' Drake advised her. 'I'm going with Giles to see his lawyers. We should get everything tied up and then this afternoon . . .' he broke off as a uniformed maid walked into the room carrying a breakfast tray. 'See you later,' he told Emma, bending to kiss her cheek. 'We'll talk then.'

Talk? What about, Emma wondered curiously sensing that the words concealed some hidden emphasis. Although losing her memory was only a temporary thing it was intensely annoying, almost depressing in some ways. Still there was no need to panic. Drake could tell her all she wanted to know and they had been most definite at the hospital that her muzziness and confusion was unlikely to last more than forty-eight hours.

Too restless to sleep she got up and showered. The morning stretched emptily ahead of her. She missed Drake. This feeling of insecurity she was suffering from must be something to do with her concussion she mused as she did her make-up.

She saw the door opening in the mirror and her heart thudded violently with pleasure as she anticipated Drake's early return. But it wasn't Drake who walked into her room, it was a vaguely familiar woman.

'Well, well, no need to ask how *you* are this morning. Drake's a first-rate lover, isn't he?'

Bianca! Memory returned with a sickening thud as Emma recognised the other woman.

'It won't last though,' Bianca told her, 'Drake will use you for as long as it suits him and then he'll go on to the next woman. That's his way.' She glanced down at Emma's engagement ring and laughed tauntingly. 'Oh, I know all about that. Drake is using you to hide the truth from Giles. He doesn't want Giles to know that we were once lovers, and would be again if it wasn't for the fact that he's so desperate to conclude this deal. He might have deceived you, but he can't deceive me.' She laughed again. 'Drake would never involve himself with a woman like you for real, you're not his type.'

Emma felt the well of blackness opening up treacherously beneath her. She was dimly conscious of Bianca's face, its beauty marred by the two ugly patches of colour darkening her cheekbones, but then mercifully the blackness engulfed her and she was alone and safe.

'Emma?'

She recognised his voice instantly but refused to respond to it. What was the point? She had been awake when he walked into the room but had feigned sleep, buying time, wishing only that he would go and leave her alone with her humiliation. The first thing she had known when she came round from her faint was that Bianca had been telling the truth. She was *not* really engaged to Drake, but she had not admitted as much to the other woman. Frightened by her collapse, Bianca

had sent for her housekeeper who had fussed and
fussed until Emma was on the point of screaming.
Desperate to be alone she had volunteered to go to
bed and rest, but there had been precious little rest
to be found. Instead her thoughts had gone round
and round, trapping her in a mill-race of self-
betrayal and contempt. Her memory had returned
completely, but twenty-four hours too late.

Dear God, when she remembered how she had
behaved last night. Even knowing that Drake was
watching her she was unable to stop herself from
shuddering with self-loathing. But Drake *had*
known, she reminded herself bitterly, Drake had
known and he had still . . .

'Hey, don't I get a kiss?'

His duplicity infuriated her. She wanted to lash
out at him almost physically to make him ache
with pain as she was aching, but in reality she felt
forced to admit that she had no one to blame but
herself. She had thrown herself at him and he,
being the man that he was had simply taken what
she had offered. It was as simple and basic as that.
Now, despite the pain building inside her pride
compelled her to find some means of protecting
herself; of concealing from him how deep her
feeling for him actually went.

'I hardly think so Drake.' She was proud of the
crisp cool sound of her voice. 'I've regained my
memory,' she added coolly. 'Unfortunately several
hours too late.'

She was surprised by the dark colour burning
along his cheekbones and by the anger she saw
blazing in his eyes.

'I see. Hit you hard has it, the realisation that
that moral code of yours wasn't quite as inviolate

as you had believed. We're all of us only human
Emma, you're no exception to that rule.'

'What are you trying to say? That I didn't know
what I was doing?' She was torturing herself but
was unable to stop doing it, unable to stop
scorning herself for her own self-betrayal.

'Oh you knew what you were doing all right.'
The mockery in Drake's voice made her skin burn.
'You were doing exactly what you've wanted to do
ever since we met, however much you might want
to deny it.'

'And I hate myself for it,' Emma told him
bitterly, watching the way his face closed up and
his eyes grew bitter, without understanding the
reasons for them doing so.

CHAPTER NINE

USING a will-power and self-control she hadn't known she possessed Emma managed to endure the remainder of her stay in New York. She had agreed to pose as Drake's fiancée for as long as it took to conclude the negotiations safely, and she was determined that she was not going to give Bianca the satisfaction of seeing her run away.

Not that it was easy. They stayed on for a further week while Drake and Giles wrapped up all the final details, and during that week Emma not only had to cope with the anguish of her love for Drake, and the continual strain of hiding it from him and pretending a curt indifference she could never feel, but she also had to endure Bianca's vicious verbal attacks which ranged from outright statements that Drake could not possibly love her to more subtle and sometimes more painful innuendoes which luckily she managed to totally ignore.

None of it was easy, but at last the final details of the contract were agreed and both parties had signed. Since she had confronted him with her return of memory Drake had been controlled and wary whenever they were together. Was he frightened that she might demand the traditional virgin's recompense for loss of her virginity? she wondered acidly on one such occasion. But then she reminded herself that he had known of her inexperience, had *known* of it, and deliberately

ignored it simply to appease his own megalomania.
That was what she found hardest to forgive; to
understand; that he had known the truth but that
he had quite callously ignored it.

On the few occasions he had attempted to bring
the subject up; to talk to her about it, Emma had
cut him off abruptly stating that it was not
something she wished to discuss.

'What's wrong?' he had demanded on one such
occasion. They had been deeply involved in the
final details of the contract all morning and she
had been able to see the exhaustion drawn into the
fine-grained texture of his skin. Not only that but
he was also distinctly tense and on edge, the
mocking indolence she had grown to associate
with him, displaced by a bitter wariness she could
only assume sprang from her discovery of the
truth before he had been able to exploit the
situation to the full. When he had told her with
such arrogant self-assurance that they would be
lovers, she had not dreamed he would go to such
lengths to fulfil his boast. And the pitiful thing was
that it would not have been necessary. One smile;
one false word of love and she doubted that she
would have been able to resist him for much
longer.

'What is it?' he had persisted. 'Disillusioned to
discover that after all your body's capable of
disobeying you and enjoying sex without love?'

It had hurt so much to hear him say the words.
For one aching moment she had been tempted to
tell him the truth, to blurt out that there might not
have been love on his side, but there certainly had
on hers, but she had restrained herself, telling
herself that if nothing else she could retain some

degree of pride. He obviously didn't realise that she loved him, and he never was going to realise, she had told herself firmly.

'Is it?' She could still remember the way his facial muscles had tensed as she spoke, almost as though in anticipation of some mortal blow. 'We obviously have vastly differing memories of what happened,' she had continued blightingly. 'Enjoyment was certainly not the word I would have used.' She had almost broken down then, but had forced herself to remain cool and unmoving in the face of his angry retort, closing her eyes to blot out the sight of his tight, too pale face and glittering eyes.

It was over now, she reminded herself, opening her bedroom door. The contract was signed and this evening they flew back to London. As far as she was concerned she could not get home fast enough. She was tired deep down in her bones; in her very soul really. Tired and broken; aching with the pain of her love and yet knowing there was no surcease for it.

Even if they had not quarrelled, even if they were still lovers the pain would still be there. She didn't just want Drake's desire; she craved his love; wanted and needed it so that it was a sickness in her soul; a pain that absorbed all her energy and will-power.

They scarcely spoke to one another on the long flight back to Britain. Emma was glad. Her self-control was at such a low ebb that she didn't believe she could have said a word without bursting into tears. It was only as they were actually landing that Drake said tersely, 'Emma, look we must talk, there's . . .'

'Nothing we have to say to one another really,' she responded quickly, not wanting to hear his protestations, his glib explanations of his behaviour. 'We made a bargain. I stuck to my side of it, and now it's over.'

'Meaning that *I* did not stick to mine?' he demanded bitterly.

Emma could not bring herself to look at him. Her mouth twisted slightly as she told him, 'In your own eyes I'm sure you did. After all you did warn me that you intended us to become lovers.' At last she managed to raise her eyes to his, using all the contempt and anger she felt at the sheer callousness of his behaviour to give her the courage to do so. 'It simply never occurred to me that you meant you would use any and every means at your disposal to do so. What's the matter Drake?' she asked mirthlessly. 'Are you so insecure; so uncertain of yourself as a man and a human being that you *have* to cheat?'

'You *wanted* me to make love to you.'

Now she couldn't look at him, and the hoarse tension of his voice made her stomach clench in bitter protest. The emotion he was projecting sounded so real, but she knew the truth.

'So I did. When I thought you were my fiancé; when I believed that we were in love.'

'You accuse me of deceiving others Emma,' he retorted brutally, 'but when it comes to deceiving yourself you're an expert. Do tell me,' he invited cuttingly, 'how was it you were able to persuade yourself so easily that you loved me enough to accept me as your fiancé; as your lover in fact?'

Another second and he would be guessing the truth Emma thought frantically, panicked into

saying bitterly, 'I don't know. I only wish to God I
did, because on a scale of nought to ten it rates a full
one hundred as the worst experience of my life.'

After that he had said nothing, but she could tell
from the angry white lines carved either side of his
mouth that he was furious with her.

They went through Customs in a tense bitter
silence, which was broken only when Drake
commandeered them both a taxi.

It was already gone ten at night, but when he
suggested that she stay at his apartment for the
night Emma shook her head curtly, her scathing,
'No thanks,' drawing patches of dark colour to
stain his cheekbones and add a curiously
vulnerable appearance to his face, which somehow
looked thinner, drawn almost.

He didn't try to argue with her, for which
Emma was deeply thankful, but it was only when
he had got out of the taxi that she finally felt able
to breathe properly.

Knowing she would not be able to get rail
connections all the way home at this hour, she
decided to hang the expense and go all the way
home by cab. She was just too weary to wrestle
with the problem of finding cheap accommodation
in London at this time of night and anyway she
wanted the security and comfort of home; like a
wounded animal she longed for the protection of
the place she knew best, she thought tiredly closing
her eyes and leaning back against the leather seat.

As she had expected when she got home the
vicarage was in darkness. When he was not out,
her father went to bed relatively early. She let
herself in with her key, dumping her suitcase in the
hall before making her way up to her own room.

It was so deeply familiar that she could scarcely believe how much had changed since she last saw it; first the realisation of her love for Drake; then trying to cope with it; to fight against his blatantly expressed desire for her, which had all been a complete waste of time, she reminded herself bitterly as she climbed into bed. Tomorrow she would have to start re-thinking the course of her life, but that was tomorrow, right now all she wanted was sleep and oblivion; and the longer it lasted the better.

The first problem she had not anticipated was her father's concern over her supposed 'broken engagement'. Over breakfast she told him simply that they had discovered that their personalities clashed, and while on the surface he had accepted this, she could sense him turning the matter over in his mind and carefully weighing it.

'You know you surprise me,' he told her at length. 'I should have thought your personalities would have meshed extremely well. Unlike Camilla, you need a man who can be strong enough to over-rule you on occasions. You don't respond to weakness Emma; probably because your own character is so unswerving.'

Emma tried to shrug nonchalantly. 'A broken engagement isn't the end of the world these days.' She put down her cup and faced her father. 'I was wondering if that post with David Carter was still open.'

Although he regarded her thoughtfully her father made no comment other than a calm, 'I think so. Would you like me to find out?'

'It might be an idea.'

'Running away Emma, that isn't like you.'

She could hardly tell her father that Drake was most unlikely to come looking for her with a view to persuading her that they were after all suited, so she took refuge in a brief shrug. She knew that if she told him the truth he would not stand in judgment, but talking about what had happened was still far too painful for her to discuss it with any third party. She never had been a person who found surcease in discussing her problems with others. No, all she could do was to keep herself so busy that there simply wasn't time to think or brood.

In the afternoon once she had unpacked she decided to walk through the village and up to the Manor. Sooner or later she would have to see Camilla. How was her sister settling down to married life, she wondered as she set out. She knew from her father that she and David had returned from their honeymoon the previous week, although her father had not yet seen Camilla.

Laura opened the door to her brief knock, beaming with pleasure when she saw her. 'Back from New York so soon?' Her eyes rested briefly on Emma's left hand, and swallowing the anguish burning in her throat Emma said lightly, 'Yes, it didn't work out as we hoped, so we decided to cut our trip short.'

Accepting Emma's philosophical attitude at face value she stood to one side to let her walk into the hall. 'Well these things happen,' she agreed. 'Have you come to see Camilla?'

Grateful for the fact that she hadn't asked any awkward questions, Emma nodded.

'She's in the sitting-room. I'll go and organise some coffee for you.'

Camilla was glancing through a magazine when Emma walked in. She threw it down the moment she saw her sister, and Emma's heart sank a little as she saw her petulant expression.

'You look marvellous,' she began placatingly, 'What a wonderful tan. I really envy you. How was Barbados?'

'Oh all right,' Camilla shrugged. 'Not as exciting as New York though I'll bet. Where's Drake?'

'I don't have the faintest idea.' Emma accompanied the cool words with a brief smile. 'The engagement is off.'

Camilla stared at her. She seemed about to say something, and then the door opened and David walked in. He went straight to his wife's side, kissing her warmly.

'God I never realised how dull estate work could be, or how distracting it is to have such a lovely wife.'

The adoration in his eyes as he looked at her sister made Emma's heart ache with jealousy. If only Drake felt that way about her. Something in her expression must have betrayed her because she heard Camilla saying with genuine concern. 'Emma are you all right, you've gone quite pale.'

'I'm fine,' she lied. In point of fact for a moment she had felt quite dizzy. It was an unnerving sensation making her remember the American doctor's warning about concussion. 'Jet lag I expect,' she added by way of explanation. 'I only got back late last night.'

'Emma's engagement's off,' Camilla remarked to her husband. 'What happened exactly?'

While David gently chided his wife for her brutality Emma made herself shrug and say as she had done to her father. 'Oh nothing very dramatic we simply discovered that we were poles apart in our outlook on life.'

'I could have told you that myself.' There was a certain degree of satisfaction in her sister's voice, and Emma remembered that Camilla had always liked to be the one in the limelight; and that she had always resented anyone up-staging her.

'So it's all over. What will you do now then?'

'I'm hoping to get a summer job working with Professor Carter.'

Camilla pulled a face. 'God how boring. No wonder you and Drake didn't suit. At least he knows how to have a good time.'

Emma was conscious of a sudden tension in the atmosphere. David glanced at his wife and frowned. Camilla's expression was tinged with a faint smugness and Emma felt herself tense in response to the heavy silence. Camilla always had enjoyed baiting David, and normally he was slow to respond, but this time she seemed to have succeeded. He looked very angry.

'I thought you didn't know the man all that well,' he said curtly.

'Oh no . . . well I don't,' Camilla agreed lamely, 'but one only has to read the newspapers. Oh do stop being such a jealous bore darling,' she chided him. 'Emma I'm afraid we're going to have to throw you out. We're going out to dinner with some friend's of Mama's this evening and we really ought to be getting ready.'

'There's plenty of time yet, Camilla,' David interrupted, still frowning. 'Emma is your sister and . . .'

'And I have to get back to the vicarage,' Emma broke in calmly. 'Enjoy your dinner party.'

As she walked home she wondered about her sister's marriage. Was Camilla growing bored already, or was it simply that she enjoyed making David jealous? And for so little reason. Her sister could be swimming in dangerous waters, Emma thought. She had rarely seen David look as angry as he had when she mentioned Drake's name. She wouldn't put it past her irresponsible sister to pretend that there had been more between herself and Drake than there had been simply to torment David.

Reminding herself that her sister's marriage was none of her affair Emma continued on her way home.

Over dinner she discovered that the post with Professor Carter was indeed still open; mainly because there were so few people qualified to fill it who were willing to work for the extremely small salary he was able to pay. She could live in at Cambridge, and the change of scene would do her good she told herself. There would be no memories of Drake there to torment her.

Several days later Emma reflected that she had forgotten that one took one's memories with one. It seemed impossible that she could have lost nearly half a stone in so short a time, but that was what had happened. When she looked in the mirror she barely recognised herself in the fine-drawn, almost haunted woman who stared back at her. The work itself was interesting; the pace of life in Cambridge with most of the graduates gone for the summer recess, drowsy and timeless, which probably accounted for her increasing restlessness,

Emma decided, trying to deny to herself that her restlessness sprang from the fact that she was missing Drake's dynamic presence.

She had telephoned Camilla on a couple of occasions but her sister had been abrupt almost to the point of rudeness to her which made it all the more surprising to arrive at her rooms one afternoon to find a message waiting for her saying that her sister wanted to speak to her urgently.

She got through to the Manor straight away. Laura answered the 'phone and, while she waited for her to find her sister Emma ran through all the possible reasons why Camilla wanted to speak to her.

'Emma?'

'Yes, it's me,' she confirmed. 'What's wrong?'

'It's David,' Camilla told her flatly, causing Emma's heart to drop. 'He's being so unreasonable.'

'What about?' Emma had long ago learned that there was little point in reasoning with Camilla until the full story was known. Camilla was not above enjoying a little self-dramatisation, and Emma waited patiently for the story to unfold.

She was not disappointed. 'He's got this crazy idea that I was involved with Drake. He's furious about it Emma,' Camilla continued when Emma didn't respond. 'He's practically accusing me of being unfaithful to him with Drake that time I was in London. Of course I've told him he's being ridiculous,' Camilla complained petulantly, 'but he just won't listen to me. You've got to help me.'

'By doing what?' Emma asked. 'If he won't listen to you why should he pay any attention to me?'

'He would if he thought you and Drake were back together again,' Camilla astounded her by saying.

For sheer selfishness her sister really took the biscuit Emma thought, too stunned to speak.

'Emma? Emma are you still there?' Camilla's voice sharpened with anxiety. 'Look Emma you've got to help me. It's really serious. I'm afraid that he might even divorce me . . .'

'Oh Camilla, don't be so ridiculous,' Emma started to say, but Camilla broke down in noisy sobs, interrupting her.

'You don't understand,' she wept. 'I think I could be pregnant, and we'd already planned that we wouldn't have a family just yet, David will probably start thinking the baby isn't even his, the way he's acting at the moment. I'm so miserable about the whole thing Emma . . . I've even thought of abortion.'

'No . . . no Camilla you mustn't do that.' There was genuine panic in her sister's voice and Emma remembered that Camilla had always had a deep-rooted fear of childbirth. Recently it had not been mentioned and Emma had thought she had got over it, but obviously she was wrong. Her sister was highly strung and emotional enough to cause problems for herself and the baby she carried, if she was not cosseted and cared for all through her pregnancy, and if David genuinely did believe that she had been involved with Drake . . . while her mind fought to grasp all the ramifications of what might happen, Camilla was still crying.

Fighting for self-control Emma spoke quietly, soothing her into mere sobs.

'You will help me won't you . . .? God Emma

I'm so scared.' She wasn't acting, Emma cou...
hear the fear in her voice.

'What can I do? Do you want me to talk to
David?'

'No . . . no that won't do any good.' Camilla was
almost feverish in her anxiety. 'No Emma, the
only thing that will work is for him to see you and
Drake together.'

'But that's impossible,' Emma protested, her
stomach muscles contracting painfully at the mere
thought of seeing Drake again. 'Our engagement is
over,' she reminded Camilla, 'I could hardly go to
Drake and ask him to pretend that we're still
together. Besides, David would never believe it . . .
he knows that we've decided to go our separate
ways.'

'You could make him believe it.' Camilla was on
the edge of hysterics, Emma could feel it, and her
own fingers tightened tensely round the receiver.

'Camilla, please . . .' she began placatingly, but
her sister would not be soothed.

'You *won't* help me will you?' she sobbed
angrily. 'You want David to divorce me. . . .
You've always hated me . . . I . . .'

'Camilla, Camilla stop it, please,' Emma begged
fighting against panic and the knowledge that she
would have to give way. 'Try to relax . . .'

'How can I relax, when David is virtually on the
point of demanding a divorce? Emma I'm so
frightened . . .' It was a little girl wail and Emma
responded automatically to it.

'All right Cam, I'll do what I can . . .'

'You'll get in touch with Drake and get him to
come down here then?' Now that Emma had given
way, Camilla was curiously practical. 'We're

ıng a dinner party next week, if you could just
ıng him to that . . .'

'Oh Camilla . . . I . . . Surely David will guess
the truth when he realises we aren't still
engaged . . .'

'He won't know will he,' Camilla said impatiently. '*You're* working in Cambridge; Drake's
in London, he'll just assume that you've made it
up and . . .'

'And what? You can't preserve the fiction of our
engagement for ever.'

'I won't need to. Once he's got over this
ridiculous jealousy and I've told him about the
baby, everything will be all right, I know it will.
Oh Emma, I promise you I'll never ask for your
help again if you just do this for me.'

What could she say? If it hadn't been for the
fact that Camilla was pregnant she might have said
no, but she couldn't rid herself of her fear that her
impulsive, over-emotional sister might do something very silly if she turned her down.

'Very well,' she said quickly, 'I'll telephone
Drake and ask him if he will come to this dinner
party with me, but Camilla,' she cautioned her
sister. 'You must remember that he could refuse.'

She rang him at his apartment that night.
Although he was ex-directory he had given her his
number during the days of their 'engagement' and
for some reason she had kept it. 'For some
reason', who was she kidding; she derided herself.
She knew quite well why she had kept it; because it
was a last link between them that she had not been
able to bring herself to destroy.

He answered almost immediately, and it struck

her as she announced herself that he didn't sound in the least surprised; quite the opposite. It was almost as though he had been expecting her call. Sheer nerves, she told herself, fighting against an impulse to hang up. Her stomach was alive with nervous butterflies. Was he alone she wondered or was there someone with him ... Another woman...? Stop it, she warned herself, you're doing this for one reason and one reason only—to help Camilla.

'Emma ... how delightful to hear from you. What can I do for you?'

'I need your help,' she said baldly, cursing herself seconds later as she heard a sound that could have been a muffled curse. 'Emma, you're not trying to tell me that you're pregnant are you?'

Humiliation washed over her in a burning wave. She almost hung up there and then. 'No, I *am* not,' she retorted through gritted teeth, 'and if I were you would be the last person I ...'

'Is that so? My goodness you have been busy since we came back to England haven't you?' he taunted. 'So if you're not ringing to break the news to me that I'm to become a parent, what do you want?'

He wasn't making it easy for her, but somehow Emma managed to outline the situation.

'And ...?' he questioned smoothly when she had stumbled into silence,

'And I have promised Camilla I'd do what I could to help,' Emma told him at last. 'She's giving a dinner party next week and she feels that if you and I attended it together it would ...'

'So you're ringing up to ask me out to dinner is that it? Emma, how delightfully modern of you.'

He was tormenting her deliberately, Emma knew that. Forcing down her panic and embarrassment she said curtly, 'I'm sure it isn't the first time you've received an invitation from a woman, Drake, so don't pretend it's so unusual.'

'Ah yes, but normally with an ulterior motive,' he responded softly. '*Is* that why you're telephoning me Emma? Because you want me to go to bed with you?'

Oh God, why was he doing this to her? She had a vivid and acutely agonising mental image of him as he had been that morning after they had made love. A surge of need and hunger swept through her body leaving her aching, shivering with the force of it; heartsick because she knew that nothing in her life would ever compensate her for not having his love.

When she didn't say anything he continued drily, 'But then of course I'm forgetting that making love with me isn't an experience you want to repeat, or so you say. That pride of yours must be a heavy burden to bear at times, Emma. It has to be appeased at all costs hasn't it? No matter what.'

His words forced her into retaliation. 'If you have to believe that quite simply I didn't find your love-making pleasurable enough to want to repeat the exercise, then by all means do so Drake,' she told him, holding her breath as she prayed to be forgiven the enormity of the lie. Her body still ran hot and tremulous now even at the thought of his hands upon it.

'Really? Permit me to tell you that you have the oddest way of signifying your lack of pleasure,' he told her sardonically, 'I have a distinct and very vivid memory of the way you cried my name when you abandoned yourself to me, Emma—and of the way you responded to me. But you aren't ringing me up so that we can discuss old times are you?' he continued smoothly before she could react. 'Very well Emma, I will come to Camilla's dinner party with you. What time do you want me to pick you up?'

She told him seven-thirty and, having thanked him formally for his assistance, hung up.

It was sheer reaction that made her dream of him that night, she told herself on waking; sheer chance that she had woken heavy-eyed and headachy, knowing that she had been crying in her sleep.

Don't be any more of a fool than you already have, she chided herself over breakfast. You're fathoms deep in love with the man; so much so that . . . that the mere thought of seeing him sent her into a tense panic. She could only pray that from somewhere she would find the strength not to betray to him how she felt. Cursing her sister, she finished her cup of coffee and reminded herself that she was here in Cambridge to work— supposedly the most powerful panacea there was.

Hours later, she admitted that either because of the strength of her love or the quality of her job it was a panacea that did not work for her. She could barely go five minutes without thinking about Drake; without aching for him. Fool, fool, she derided herself. Forget him, forget everything about him. But that was far easier said than done.

CHAPTER TEN

SEVEN twenty-five; just five more minutes to go. Emma paced the floor tensely, half of her praying that Drake would arrive soon and the other hoping that he would not. How was she going to live through the evening ahead? How could she, without betraying to him how she felt? You'll find a way, she told herself stoically, reflecting rather wryly that if nothing else, love was a great leveller; her present behaviour was rather more Camilla than Emma.

He arrived at seven-thirty on the dot; the sound of a car drawing up outside and then the door slamming making her stomach nerves clench in on themselves. She wasn't going to the window to look she told herself firmly; fighting against the impulse to rush to the door and open it before he knocked.

Seeing him brought a flood of pain and aching need. She wanted to touch him so badly that not doing so required a positive effort of will. He was dressed formally in a dinner suit, and he looked so urbane and polished that had she seen him like this at their first meeting she might have been deceived into thinking he was simply another smooth dilettante.

Watching him move towards her was an education though; how could she have forgotten that powerful economy of movement; in many ways he reminded her of a jungle predator forced to assume the guise of a domestic cat.

'Ready?'

Something glinted in his eyes as she moved towards him, almost in a state of trance. She had agonised for hours over what to wear—very unlike her—wanting to appear at her best and yet anxious not to give him the idea that she had dressed to impress him. In the end she had settled for a simple silk two piece, which was both elegant and restrained. It had also cost her far more than she had intended to spend, but it was worth every penny simply to see the masculine appreciation in his eyes as his glance lingered on her slender shape.

'You've lost weight.'

His observation startled her.

'Have I?' How tense and clipped her voice sounded. She shrugged casually.

'You're not suffering from a broken heart then?'

For a moment her heart almost stopped beating. She forced herself to look at him, determined to withstand the cruelty of his deadly barb and then realised as she met his eyes that his remark had simply been a casual comment. There was no special knowledge or mockery in his eyes as they rested on her pale face; no indication that he knew exactly why she had lost weight; in fact if anything he too looked thinner, Emma reflected, at liberty to study him at close quarters for the first time since his arrival.

'Well?' The harsh grittiness of his voice startled her.

'Well what?' she asked lightly.

Instead of responding he touched her face lightly; holding it so that she couldn't avoid his eyes. The mere brush of his fingers against her skin burned like fire, she wanted to pull away; to treat before she humiliated herself completely by turning her lips into his palm and betraying exactly what she was suffering from.

'Don't play games with me Emma,' he warned her, his voice still faintly harsh. You know exactly what I mean. Have you actually found a man to whom you can give both your heart and your body?'

He sounded so tauntingly derisive that she was betrayed into immediate retaliation.

'Yes,' she told him simply, forgetting for a moment how much she had to be on her guard against him, and remembering only how he had mocked her for wanting to love and be loved by the man with whom she shared her body.

Her response seemed to throw him slightly. His hand dropped away from her face, a frown creasing his forehead.

'Camilla will be wondering where on earth we are,' Emma said brittly into the tense silence. 'We'd better be on our way.'

'By all means, let's not keep Camilla waiting.'

The tension inside the car was something that could almost be felt, Emma reflected silently, wondering what on earth it was she had said to provoke Drake's almost bitter withdrawal.

It didn't take long to reach the Manor. Camilla greeted them half sullenly; it was almost as though she resented their being there Emma thought in some surprise, which was ridiculous when she remembered that Camilla had been the one to suggest their meeting.

David welcomed her with an awkward hug and a brief kiss, before turning to shake hands with Drake. Her brother-in-law was masking his

suspicions well, she thought watching the sma..
inter-change. There were no signs of jealousy o.
distrust on David's face as he led the way into the
drawing-room, and it occurred to Emma that as
always her sister could have been guilty of some
degree of exaggeration.

On the pretext of offering to help with the meal
she left the two men together and followed Camilla
into the kitchen. Her sister was talking to Mrs
Berry when Emma walked in. She frowned
petulantly when she saw Emma.

'Mother isn't at all pleased about tonight,' she
told Emma crossly. She wanted us to go out to
dinner with her—with some old friends who could
help David if he decides to go ahead and enter
local politics.'

Who was doing whom the favour here? Emma
wondered wryly surveying her sister's flushed and
tense face. Stepping out of earshot of Mrs Berry
she said coolly, 'Tonight wasn't my idea, Camilla.
You were the one who begged me to get in touch
with Drake to assuage David's jealousy—remember?'

'Oh that was only because . . .'

'I can't promise to hold this soufflé for much
longer.' Mrs Berry's faintly anxious voice cut in to
their conversation.

She would have to try to speak with her sister
later on Emma promised herself, heading back to
the drawing-room. Camilla was behind her, urging
the men to head for the dining-room. Neither of
them looked particularly hostile to the other.
David was obviously a better actor than she had
imagined. Local politics would probably be his
metier Emma thought cynically.

A little to her surprise the dinner table conversation flowed quite freely. She had drunk two glasses of wine before she realised that David was pouring her a third. Nervous tension she decided, sneaking a brief glance at Drake, and wishing she hadn't, as he became aware of her scrutiny, his eyes locking with hers. Dark colour burned up under her skin, and she turned away, shivering slightly, becoming aware as she did so that David was launched on one of his favourite hobby horses.

'A woman's place *is* in the home,' Emma heard him saying, 'and there's no getting away from that fact, especially when she has children . . .'

'I'm afraid I can't agree with you.'

Emma was startled to hear Drake speak so categorically. 'Some women work through necessity and would love nothing more than to be at home with their children; other women although excellent mothers, need the stimulation of a career.'

'That's all very well in theory, but would you let your wife work?' David demanded quite heatedly.

'I doubt it would be a question of "allowing".' Drake shrugged his shoulders. 'In my book, a good marriage is a true partnership and if my wife felt the need to have a career independent of me then I would support her in that decision. After all, I would scarcely expect her to demand that I gave up my career or my interests.'

'But if you had children,' Camilla put in, 'surely then you would want their mother to be at home with them.'

'I should *want* it yes,' Drake agreed equably, 'but only if that was what she wanted too.'

'And yet Emma's given up her television career,' David broke in glancing half triumphantly at Drake.

Emma was conscious of three pairs of eyes all focused on her. Drake's responses to David's questions had caused her both pleasure and pain. Pleasure that he could be generous and open-minded enough to give the woman he loved the freedom to make her own choices in life, and pain because she would never be that woman.

Of the three of them only Drake knew the real reason why she had given up her television career, but if she was Drake's wife would she have wanted to continue with it? Facing the question honestly Emma spoke slowly. 'I have to admit that I'm pulled two ways. Half of me would want to devote my time to my husband and family and yet the sense of self-worth one gets from succeeding in something outside that small world can be very important. Perhaps I'll be one of those women who return to a career once the children are teenagers.'

'I hope not.' Drake's firm denial startled her. She looked at him with unguarded eyes for a moment, quickly turning away when she realised what she might be betraying.

'Emma has an excellent brain which I would hate to see atrophy,' Drake spoke succinctly. 'I would very much like to persuade her to work alongside me as my assistant. It can be hellish lonely and vulnerable at the top of a large corporation; and there's nothing like sharing that burden with the person closest to you.'

'Oh I've never believed that a married couple can work together successfully,' David said stuffily.

Emma wasn't really listening to him. She was fighting against a growing tide of emotional havoc. Did Drake really not know what he was doing to her when he talked so evocatively of a future she knew they would not share? How could he know, she reminded herself; she had taken good care to make sure that her love remained a secret from him. More and more she admired and respected him; she liked him as a person; a fellow human being; as well as loving him as a man. It was a combination that would be pretty hard to beat; maybe even impossible. She stared moodily at her half finished meal, startled to tense irritation when David exclaimed, 'My goodness Emma, that's your third glass of wine. No point in asking you if you want a brandy. What's got into you? You're normally very abstemious?'

'Well perhaps tonight I feel like leaping out of my rut,' Emma told him curtly. She did feel quite light headed; more because she had not been eating properly for the last few weeks than because she had consumed three glasses of wine, but it irritated her to be treated like a child and by David of all people, 'and I should like a brandy,' she added, 'a large one.'

By the time they were saying their goodbyes to Camilla and David, Emma was beginning to regret her bravado. She felt distinctly light-headed and wobbly, and she had not had an opportunity to question Camilla further about David's reaction to Drake. In fact as they left she had the distinct impression that Camilla was out of charity with them both, which was ridiculous when they were the ones doing her the favour.

She said as much to Drake as they walked

towards his car, and was surprised by the small
grin of amusement he gave her, but she felt too
muzzy-headed to question it.

Once she was in her seat with the belt fastened
she leaned back and closed her eyes, wishing the
earth would not spin in quite such a violent
manner.

It was some time later when she opened them,
totally disorientated by the thick darkness outside.

'Where are we?' As she asked the question she
glanced at her watch and frowned. They had been
driving for just over two hours.

'Drake where are we?' she persisted, when he
said nothing. 'We've been travelling for over two
hours.'

'I'm taking you home with me,' Drake told her
calmly, 'I want to talk to you.'

His cool manipulation of events stunned her,
rendering her almost speechless. 'But I don't *want*
to go home with you,' she managed at last, the
alcoholic affects clearing fast as she tried to come
to grips with what he was saying.

'Too bad,' he responded laconically, 'because
you don't have much choice.'

He was right there, Emma reflected mentally,
subsiding back into her seat. And what on earth
did he want to talk to her about so urgently that it
required this draconian action? Perhaps he wanted
to offer her a job? The thought ran through her
mind as she remembered the dinner table
conversation, but why should Drake offer *her* a
job? Perhaps he was still hoping to persuade her
into an affair with him? But why should he do that
now when he had been content to ignore her for
over three weeks?

Emma was still trying to solve that puzzle when Drake drove into a narrow turning. Gravel crunched beneath the car tyres; the dark shapes of bushes lining the drive. He stopped the car in front of a floodlit Tudor farmhouse of rambling proportions, and said drily, 'Home sweet home— out you get Emma. Or would you prefer me to carry you?'

'I can walk.' She managed to inject a certain dignity into her voice, but it was something she was far from feeling. The thought of him touching her body made her shiver with mingled pleasure and dread. Idiot, she derided herself; he doesn't love you; you know that; stop tormenting yourself.

His choice of home half surprised her. She would have expected something more regal and impressive. This half timber, rambling black and white building looked comfortable and welcoming. It wasn't hard to picture it filled with children and dogs. This impression was reinforced when she stepped into the attractive irregular-shaped hall-way. The walls glowed soft cream, the exposed beams mellow and dark.

'Please go into the study and make yourself at home,' Drake told her. 'I just want to go upstairs and change. Dinner suits aren't my favourite clothes.' He grimaced faintly as he spoke, tugging impatiently at his bow tie. Emma felt weak with the longing to go up to him and press her lips against his skin. but she managed to suppress it long enough to stumble blindly through the open door he had indicated.

His study was lined with bookshelves; a comfortable, masculine room slightly untidy and obviously well used.

Too tense to sit down she was studying book titles idly when she heard a sharp brief cry. Instantly alarm tingled through her body. She waited to see if the sound was repeated and when everything remained silent she walked back into the hall and called out tentatively, 'Drake, are you all right?'

There was no answer, and reasoning that he must not have heard her Emma called again. Still there was no response. Now a primitive deep rooted anxiety spread through her body, enmeshing and immobilising her reason with pure fear. What had happened to Drake?

Before she knew what she was doing Emma was hurrying upstairs. When she reached the landing she stared about herself, her eyes finally alighting on an open door.

'Drake?' She walked through it tentatively, her throat so tight that her voice was little more than a croaky whisper.

Drake was sitting on a large bed, minus his shirt, the room smelled sharply of masculine cologne.

'I knocked it off the dresser,' he told her briefly and it soaked my shirt. God,' he grimaced slightly, 'This room reeks of it.'

'I think it's quite pleasant.' Emma spoke automatically, all her senses too intent on registering the magnificence of Drake's naked torso, to concentrate on mere speech.

'Do you?' He got up and came towards her reaching her before Emma had time to think properly.

'Heaven help me Emma, but I want you.' His voice was thick, slurred almost, as though *he* had

been the one drinking and not her. His fingers
punished the feminine sensitivity of her upper
arms, the heat coming off his bare skin engulfing
her in a tide of sexual awareness that drowned out
every other emotion.

'Emma!' He groaned her name, his hands sliding
down to her wrists, pinning them behind her back
as he bent his head and touched his tongue
tentatively against her lips.

Emma tried to strangle an involuntary moan of
pleasure that rose to her lips, but they were
already parting traitorously, eagerly seeking the
tormenting exploration of Drake's tongue.

Time and reality both ceased to exist. They were
simply two people bound up in the same spell;
bound by a need so intense that no mere human
will-power could overset it.

Emma wasn't aware of Drake sliding the clothes
from her body; only the delirious relief of feeling
his skin against her own as he lifted her on to the
bed and joined her there.

'Emma. God you're so beautiful. So perfectly
female. I thought I remembered every single thing
about you,' Drake muttered rawly, bending over
her to stroke long fingers over the curved outline
of her body. 'I thought I'd committed every last
detail irrevocably to memory, but memories are
nothing—starlight to the strength of the sun—
when you compare them to the real thing.'

'Starlight is kinder,' Emma responded, the
words hard to utter as her senses responded
passionately to the intensity with which he was
studying her.

'Perhaps in that its failure to mimic the sun
helps us to forget what we've lost. My memories

didn't do you justice Emma. Nothing could re-create the special silky smoothness of your skin; the way you tremble when I touch you; the way your body responds to mine.'

His mouth silenced the response she would have made, the fierce intensity of his kiss obliterating any ability to think. As she slid her arms round his neck and encountered the male heat of his skin Emma knew she was lost; drowning in water so deep that it was pointless to even think of fighting against its insidious pull.

The lightest brush of his fingers against her skin set off explosive bursts of pleasure so intense that they shook her body, causing Drake to mutter thick words of encouragement and praise as he witnessed her response to his caresses.

Need, anguish, love; all became one fierce torrent of emotion that would not be denied. Her fevered response to him seemed to have a cataclysmic effect on Drake. His mouth burned against her skin; fierce in its possession, the boundaries of his self-control dissolving in the heat of their mutual need.

When Emma arched instinctively beneath him he cried out her name; the male thrust of his body against and within her own so deeply welcomed by her senses that Emma could not conceive how she had existed without him.

Her body starved of his touch and proximity; incited and seduced, betraying instincts Emma hadn't known she possessed. The first time they had made love there had been pleasure it was true, but this ... this total giving of herself ... this heady power of knowing that Drake was as powerless to resist the lure of her body as she was

his, seemed to unite them in a way that made them
truly equal partners.

'Emma!' She felt Drake tense and tremble
slightly against her, his eyes almost black, his skin
so hot to the touch that it almost burned.

'Emma, dear God, what you do to me.' His
body shuddered in release against hers, setting off
explosive surges of pleasure that increased in
volume until she was crying out his name, relishing
the fierce drag of his teeth against her nipple.

Later lying sated and relaxed in Drake's arms it
was too much of an effort to move; or to think
about what she was doing. Her eyes closed and she
curled instinctively into the warmth of Drake's
body.

It was light when she woke up; knowing before
she opened her eyes that something was wrong;
but not knowing what it was. Her body felt
pleasantly lethargic; she stretched automatically
without opening her eyes, pushing back the bed
clothes to uncurl her body with an instinctive
sensuality.

'You look exactly as a woman should when
she's well and truly been loved.'

Drake's voice jolted her back to instant reality,
her body freezing tensely as she reached quickly
for the covers. Drake stopped her, the knowledge
of his proximity forcing her to open her eyes.
Unshaven, he was dressed in a brief bathrobe, his
eyes hard and unmerciful as they witnessed her
embarrassment.

'What's the matter Emma?' he taunted bitingly,
'Had a sudden attack of conscience? Perhaps that
man you've found, isn't the right one after all,' he
derided. 'To judge by the way you responded to

me last night you haven't found *physical* satisfaction with anyone else.'

'And of course that's all important,' Emma lashed back at him, too confused and hurt by the knowledge that what had happened between them last night was to him, merely the satisfaction of a physical urge, to think about what she was saying.

'It certainly helps,' Drake agreed, 'and don't try telling me that this man you've found can fulfil you sexually Emma, your body tells me a different story. It was starving for me ... *for me*!' he underlined humiliatingly, 'and don't bother trying to deny it ...'

'I was tipsy,' Emma muttered, turning away from him, desperate for any means of escape. Why oh why had she been betrayed into saying 'Yes' when he asked her if she had found a man whom she loved with her heart and her body? How long could she prevent him from realising just who that man was.

'That's my Emma.' His voice was angry, his eyes hard and cold. 'Make the facts fit her own preconceived ideas. You're not still tipsy this morning I trust?'

Emma shook her head, wanting only to escape from the bed and from him. 'Good, then we'll just put your little theory to the test shall we?' he suggested calmly.

As his meaning hit her she tried to squirm away but he was streets ahead of her, pinning her to the bed with one hand, while the other grasped her hair, forcing her to lie still. Just for a second she felt a tense spiral of fear convulse her body, but the moment Drake's mouth covered her own it was gone, smothered in a long slow surge of

...asure. She tried to fight against it, arching her
...ody, not in invitation but in angry rejection.

'Oh no you don't,' Drake told her thickly,
kneeling on the bed beside her, 'I'm going to make
you admit how good it is between us even if it
takes me all day. In fact I hope it does,' he added
with raw emphasis, 'because I'm going to enjoy
every single second of it.'

'Sex means nothing without love.' Emma almost
cried the words too wrought up by her body's
almost instant betrayal to use caution.

'To you? I don't believe that Emma.' Drake's
mouth was wry as he studied her flushed face and
angry eyes. 'You enjoyed every minute of what we
had together last night, but if your memory needs
jogging...'

The moment his fingers touched her skin Emma
knew she was lost. The slow circles he drew round
the aching peak of her breast were sheer torment,
and although she tried her best to resist him, it was
impossible not to move frenziedly against him,
inviting the erotic possession of his mouth against
her breasts, at first teasing and then arousing her
to the point where her body ached tormentingly
for the maleness of his.

'*Now* tell me you don't want me.' His voice was
thick, heavily slurred, his body as aroused as hers
Emma recognised shiveringly when he lifted his
head. 'You want me, Emma.'

'Not without love, Drake.' She moved her head
from side to side, fighting to deny her love for him
and regain some sense of reality. 'Please don't
make it harder for me than it already is?'

'Harder for *you*?' Drake swore violently, grasping
her wrists and forcing her arms down beside her

body. 'Just how the hell do you think I feel, Emma?' he demanded rawly. 'You're tearing my guts out. Believe me if there was some magic spell I could use to make you feel about me the way I feel about you, I'd move heaven and earth to find it. As it is . . . Well you can't deny that sexually you're responsive to me . . . Let me show you how good it could be for us Emma.'

'And when you're tired of me?' Emma asked achingly. 'I'm not like your other women, Drake, I just couldn't take that.'

'Tired of you?' His voice betrayed an aching pain she had never thought to see in him. 'Dear God, Emma don't you know yet that that will never be. When first you demanded to see me I'll admit I dismissed you without a second thought until it occurred to me that I could use you. And then I saw you——' he smiled in self-derision. 'I wanted you so badly it hurt. When you agreed to pose for the magazine I was glad; glad that you had a flaw. When I found out you'd turned down your job, I knew my first instincts had been right and that not only were you beautiful in body, you were also beautiful in mind and spirit. I had to see you again; to wipe the slate clean and start afresh, but I knew those photographs would always be between us, so I devised a way of blackmailing you into getting engaged to me. I thought if I put on enough pressure, worked hard enough at it, you'd be bound to . . .'

'Give in?' Emma supplied wryly. 'Well I did.'

'Yes,' Drake agreed bitterly, 'Have you any idea what it did to me when you thought we were really engaged; when you wanted me as I'd. . .' He broke off and shook his head wearily. 'I shouldn't have made love to you that night; I knew it at the time and yet I literally couldn't help myself.

'Why won't you give it a try, Emma? Let me prove to you that we *can* build something that will last on what we have.'

Hiding her surprise Emma studied him. 'I thought long lasting structures were something you made a point of avoiding,' she remarked drily.

'That was before I fell in love with you.'

He said it so simply that for a moment she couldn't speak, and then her opportunity to do so was gone as Drake continued urgently, 'This other man Emma, whoever he is, I don't believe you really love him. I know you. You'd never have responded to me the way you did if that were the case. I don't know who he is but . . .'

'On the contrary,' Emma interrupted coolly, fighting down a rising tide of pure, intense joy, 'you know him very well. It's you Drake,' she told him when he simply watched her. 'I love you.'

His instant withdrawal from her was not what she had expected. He half turned away from her as he said thickly, 'Emma if this is some sort of act of pity, forget it. I can take the fact that you don't love me, because I believe we can build a lasting marriage on what we have, but what I don't want are false promises; false hopes.'

'Drake.' She reached up cupping his face with her hands, smiling tremulously into his eyes. 'It's no act, and the only person I'm likely to pity is myself, because I've been through agony loving you and believing that you merely wanted me. When I talked about wanting love and desire I was talking about my wanting of your love as well as your desire.'

'I thought you meant that while you desired me physcially you didn't love me. In fact you said as much.'

'Because I was frightened that you'd guess the truth and that you'd use it to urge me into a relationship which ultimately could only cause me pain.'

'It's a very high opinion you have of me,' he murmured sardonically, 'but perhaps well deserved. If you marry me Emma, it will be for life . . .'

She smiled mischievviously at him. 'I shouldn't want it any other way.' He paused bending his head to kiss her. Against her body Emma could feel the deep, rapid thud of his heart. He loved her . . . Drake loved her . . . The knowledge pierced thrillingly through her.

'Just think,' she said dreamily as he lowered her back against the bed. 'If it hadn't been for David being suspicious of you and Camilla insisting on that dinner party we might never have learned the truth.'

Drake paused, removing his robe. The morning sunlight gleamed rich bronze on his body and Emma couldn't resist lifting her hand to stroke the satin smoothness of his skin. The ripple of pleasure that surged through him made her tremble in immediate response, but she froze in tense dread as Drake said quietly, 'I'm afraid I have a confession to make.'

What was he going to tell her? That his proclamation of love had been a trick all along? No, she didn't believe he could be so cruel.

'I coerced Camilla into going to you with that tale, by threatening to tell David about the night she spent at my house—with suitable embellishments of course. Naturally, I wouldn't have done so, but it was enough to make her come running to you, and to make you, with true sisterly loyalty come to me. You see I knew if I approached you, you'd run away from me and I was desperate for the sight and touch of you Emma. I told myself that somehow we'd talk but it just didn't work out that way. First you dropped your bombshell about finding someone you loved. I was almost mad with jealousy. I couldn't believe you could love someone else and yet have reacted so passionately to me. I told myself if I could just get you into bed; break down the barriers you had erected between us I could make you see that there was only one man for you—me. Hence the spilled cologne ... I hoped my crying out might bring you upstairs ...'

'Lazy beast,' Emma derided, 'after all the least I might have expected was to be swept up in your arms and carried off in true romantic fashion.'

'Umm, knowing you, you'd have kicked and fought all the way,' Drake told her. 'No, I knew I had to catch you off-guard ... to break down the barriers you'd put up against me.'

'Well you certainly succeeded in that.' She coloured faintly, remembering her abandoned response to his lovemaking.

'Umm, maybe, but you're not leaving this bed until I have your promise that you'll marry me.'

'You mean you'll trust my word?' Emma teased, rounding her eyes in mock amazement. 'Don't you know you should never believe anything someone says in the throes of passion?'

Drake shook his head. 'Wrong,' he said softly. 'When passion is combined with love, it's stronger than any truth serum ever invented. Last night it took every ounce of self control I had not to tell you how much I loved and needed you. You were right Emma,' he told her huskily, 'sex without love is a mere shadow of the real thing. Tell me you love me,' he demanded rawly. 'Let me hear you say it.'

Intuitive to his deep-rooted need to be sure of her Emma whispered the words against his ear. She also murmured them against his throat reinforcing them with soft kisses. She was still murmuring them as her tongue touched the flat plane of his belly, but it seemed Drake had heard them enough. 'Now tell me that you'll marry me,' he commanded thickly.

Emma needed no second bidding, but she continued to tease him with light kisses and caresses for several seconds before she did so, caught off guard by Drake's sudden transition from supplicant to aggressor as he rolled her away from his body and then began to tease and torment her as she had been doing him.

Quite when teasing gave way to passion Emma didn't know, she only knew that her body welcomed the surge of Drake's against it as though it had been fashioned just for it, the words of love he muttered into her skin finding a feverish response within her. Drake loved her. There was nothing more she asked from life. She already had it all safely encompassed within the confines of this bed; held fast to her with arms she knew would never let her go. Later they would talk and plan, right now was the time to feel and to share those feelings; to give and receive life's most precious gift of all. That of love.

CAPABLE OF FEELING

BY
PENNY JORDAN

WORLDWIDE BOOKS
LONDON • SYDNEY • TORONTO

*First published in Great Britain in 1986
Reprinted in Great Britain in 1993
by Worldwide Books, Eton House,
18-24 Paradise Road, Richmond, Surrey TW9 1SR*

© Penny Jordan 1986

ISBN 0 373 58952 2

99-9305

Made and printed in Great Britain

CHAPTER ONE

'DARLING, I do hope you're going to wear something a little more attractive than that for dinner. You know we've got the Bensons coming and he *is* one of your father's best clients. Chris is back by the way.'

Sophy had only been listening to her mother with half her attention, too overwhelmed by the familiar sense of depression, which inevitably overcame her when she had to spend longer than an hour in the latter's company, to resist the tidal flood of maternal criticism but the moment she heard Chris Benson's name mentioned she tensed.

They were sitting in the garden on the small patio in front of the immaculately manicured lawns and rosebeds. The garden was her father's pride and joy but to Sophie it represented everything about her parents and their life-style that had always heightened for her the differences between them. In her parents' lives everything must be neat and orderly, conforming to a set middle-class pattern of respectability.

She had spent all her childhood and teenage years in this large comfortable house in its West Suffolk village and all that time she had felt like an ungainly cuckoo in the nest of two neat, tiny wrens.

She didn't even look like her parents; her mother was five-foot-three with immaculate, still blonde, hair and a plumply corseted figure, her father somewhat taller, but much in the same mould; a country solicitor, who had once been in the army and who still ran his life on the orderly lines he had learned in that institution.

It was not that her parents didn't love her, or weren't kind, genuinely caring people. It was just that she was alien to them and them to her.

Her height, the ungainly length of her legs and arms, the wild mane of her dark, chestnut hair and the high cheekboned, oval face with its slightly tilting gold eyes; these were not things she had inherited from her parents, and she knew that her mother in particular had always privately mourned the fact that her daughter was not like herself, another peaches and cream English rose.

Instead, her physical characteristics had come to her from the half American, half Spanish beauty her great-grandfather had married in South America and brought home. Originally the Marley family had come from Bristol. They had been merchants there for over a century, owning a small fleet of ships and her great-grandfather had been the captain of one of these.

All that had been destroyed by the First World War, which had destroyed so many of the small shipping companies and Sophie knew that her parents felt uneasy by this constant reminder of other times in the shape and physical appearance of their only child.

Her mother had done her best ... refusing to see that her tall, ungainly daughter did not look her best in pretty embroidered dresses with frills and bows.

She had disappointed her mother, Sophy knew that. Sybil Rainer had been married at nineteen, a mother at twenty-one and that was a pattern she would have liked to have seen repeated in her daughter. Once too she . . .

'Of course, Chris is married now . . .'

Her mind froze, distantly registering the hint of reproach in her mother's voice. 'There was a time when I thought that you and he . . .' her voice trailed away and Sophy let it, closing her eyes tightly, thinking bitterly that once she too had thought that she and Chris would marry. Chris's father was a wealthy stockbroker and she had known him all through her teens, worshipping his son in the way that teenage girls are wont to do.

She had never dreamed Chris might actually notice her as anything other than the daughter of one of his father's oldest friends. The year he came down from university, when she herself was just finishing her 'A' levels, he had come home.

They had met at the tennis club. Sophy had just been finishing a match. Tennis was one of the few things she excelled at; she had the body and the strength for it and, she realised with wry hindsight, he could hardly have seen her in a more flattering setting.

He had asked her out; she had been overwhelmed with excitement . . . and so it had started.

Her mouth twisted bitterly. It was not how it had started that she was thinking of now, but how it had finished.

It hadn't taken her long to fall in love—she was literally starving for attention . . . for someone of her own and she had been all too ridiculously easy a conquest for him. Of course she had demurred when he told her he wanted to make love to her but she had also been thrilled that he could want her so much. Seeing no beauty or desirability in her own appearance, she could not understand how anyone else could either.

She had thought he loved her. She had wanted to believe it. She had thought he intended to marry her. God, how ridiculous and farcical it all seemed now.

Inevitably she had let him make love to her, one hot summer night at the end of August when they were alone in his parents' house . . . and that night had shattered her rosy dreams completely.

Even now she could remember his acid words of invective when he realised that she was not enjoying his lovemaking, his criticisms of her as a woman, his disgust in her inability to respond to him.

Frightened by the change in him, her body still torn by the pain of his possession she had sought to placate him offering uncertainly, 'But it will get better when we are married . . .'

'Married!' He had withdrawn completely from her, staring at her with narrowed eyes. 'What the hell are you talking about? I wouldn't marry you if you were the last woman on earth, darling,' he had drawled tauntingly. 'When I get married it will be to a woman who knows what it means to be a woman . . . not a frigid little girl. You'll never get married, Sophy,' he had told her cruelly. 'No man will ever want to marry a woman like you.'

Looking back, she was lucky to have come out of the escapade with nothing worse than a badly bruised body and ego, Sophy told herself. It could have been so much worse. She could have been pregnant . . . pregnant and unmarried.

'Darling, you aren't listening to a word I'm

saying,' her mother complained a little petulantly, 'and why do you scrape your hair back like that? It's so pretty.'

'It's also heavy, Mother ... and today it's very hot.' She said it patiently, forcing a placatory smile.

'I wish you'd have it properly styled, darling ... and get some new clothes. Those awful jeans you're wearing ...'

Sighing faintly, Sophy put down her book. If only her mother could understand that she could not be what she wanted her to be. If only ...

'I've told Brenda to bring Chris and his wife round to see us. She's a lovely girl, Brenda was saying. An American ... they got married last year while we were away on that cruise.' She looked across at her daughter. 'It's time you were thinking of settling down, darling, after all *you* are twenty-six ...'

So she was, and wouldn't Chris just crow to know that his cruel prediction all those years ago had proved so correct.

Not that she wanted to get married. She moved restlessly in her deck chair, unwanted images flashing through her mind ... pictures of the men she had dated over the years, and the look on their faces when she turned cold and unresponsive in their arms. She had never totally been able to overcome the fears Chris had instilled in her—not of the physical reality of male possession, but of her own inability to respond to him ... her own innate sexual coldness. Well it was something no other man was ever going to find out about her. It was her own private burden and she was going to carry it alone.

No male possession meant no children, though. Sighing once again, she opened her eyes and stared unseeingly at her father's neat flower border. Just when she had first felt this fierce need to have children of her own she wasn't quite sure but lately she was rarely unaware of it. She very much wanted children . . . a family of her own. But she wasn't going to get them, as Chris had so rightly taunted her. No man was going to want a woman who was physically incapable of responding to him sexually.

The sharp ring of the telephone bell on the wall outside the house cut through her despondent thoughts.

Her mother got up and hurried into the house via the french windows. Several seconds later she reappeared, beckoning Sophy, a frown marring her forehead.

'It's Jonathan,' she told Sophy peevishly. 'Why on earth does he need to ring you at weekends?'

Jonathan Phillips was her boss. Sophy had been working for him for two years. She'd first met him at a party thrown by a mutual acquaintance to which she had gone in a mood of bitter introspection having finally come to the realisation that the happiness and fulfilment of marriage and children would never be hers. She had also been well on her way to getting drunk. She had bumped into him on her way to get herself yet another glass of wine, the totally unexpected impediment of a solidly muscled chest knocking her completely off balance.

Jonathan had grasped her awkwardly round the waist looking at her through his glasses with eyes that registered his discomfort and shock at finding her in his arms.

She had pulled away and he had released her immediately, looking very relieved to do so. She would have walked away and that would have been that if she had not suddenly betrayed her half inebriated state by teetering uncertainly on her high heels.

It was then that Jon had taken charge, dragging her outside into the fresh air, procuring from somewhere a cup of black coffee. Both were acts which, now that she knew him better, were so alien to his normal vague, muddledly hopeless inability to organise anything, that they still had the power to surprise her slightly.

They had talked. She had learned that he was a computer consultant working from an office in Cambridge; that he had his orphaned niece and nephew in his care and that he was the mildest and most unaggressive man she had ever come across.

She, in turn, had told him about her languages degree—gained much to the disapproval of her mother, who still believed that a young woman had no need to earn her own living but should simply use her time to find herself a suitable husband—her secretarial abilities, and the dull job she had working in her father's office.

She had eventually sobered up enough to drive home and by the end of the next week she had forgotten Jonathan completely.

His letter to her offering her a job as his assistant had come totally out of the blue but, after discussing it with him, she had realised that here was the chance she needed so desperately to get herself out of the rut her life had become.

It was then that she realised that Jonathan was one of that elite band of graduates who had emerged from Cambridge in the late 'sixties and early 'seventies, fired by enthusiasm for the new computer age about to dawn, and that Jonathan was a world-renowned expert in his field.

Against her mother's wishes she had accepted the job and on the strength of the generous salary he paid her she had found herself a pleasant flat in Cambridge.

She went into the hall and took the receiver from her mother, who moved away but not out of earshot. Her mother disapproved of Jonathan. Tall, and untidy with a shock of dark hair and mild, dark blue eyes which were always hidden behind the glasses he needed to wear, he was not like the bright, socially adept sons of her friends. Jonathan never indulged in social chit-chat—he didn't know how to. He was vague and slightly clumsy, often giving the impression that he lived almost exclusively in a world of his own. Which in many ways he did, Sophy reflected, speaking his name into the receiver.

'Ah, Sophy . . . thank goodness you're there. It's Louise . . . the children's nanny. She's left . . . and I have to fly to Brussels in the morning. Would you . . .?'

'I'll be there just as soon as I can,' Sophy promised with alacrity, mentally sending a prayer of thanks up to her guardian angel.

Now she had a valid excuse for missing tonight's dinner party and inevitable conversation about Chris.

'What did he want?' her mother questioned as Sophy replaced the receiver.

'Louise, the nanny, has left. He wants me to look after the children for him, until he comes back from Brussels on Wednesday.'

'But you're his secretary,' her mother ex-postulated. 'He has no right to ring you here at weekends. You're far too soft with him, Sophy. He's only himself to blame . . . I've never met a more disorganised man. What he needs isn't a secretary, it's a wife . . . and what you need is a husband and children of your own,' she added bitterly. 'You're getting far too attached to those children . . . you know that, don't you?'

Mentally acknowledging that her mother was more astute than she had thought, Sophy gave her a brief smile. 'I like them, yes,' she admitted evenly, 'and Jon is my boss. I can hardly refuse his request you know Mother.'

'Of course you can. I wish you weren't working for the man. I don't like him. Why on earth doesn't he do something about himself? He ought to tidy himself up a bit, buy some new clothes . . .'

Sophy hid a smile. 'Because those sort of things aren't important to him, mother.'

'But they should be important. Appearance *is* important.'

Maybe for more ordinary mortals, Sophy reflected as she went upstairs to re-pack the weekend bag she had brought with her when she had come home, but the rules that governed ordinary people did not apply to near geniuses and that was what Jon was. He was so involved with his computers that she doubted he was aware of anything else.

At thirty-four he epitomised the caricature of a slightly eccentric, confirmed bachelor totally involved in his work and oblivious to anything else.

Except the children. He was very caring and aware where they were concerned.

As she went back downstairs with her case she frowned slightly. Louise would be the third nanny he had lost in the two years she had worked with him and she was at a loss to understand why. The children were a lovable pair. David, ten, and Alexandra, eight, were lively, it was true, but intelligent and very giving. The house Jonathan lived in had been bought by him when his brother and sister-in-law had died, and was a comfortable, if somewhat rambling, Victorian building on the outskirts of a small Fen village. It had a large garden, which was rather inadequately cared for by an ancient Fensman and the housework was done by a woman who came in from the village to clean twice a week. Jonathan was not an interfering or difficult man to work for.

'You're going then!'

Her mother made it sound as though she was leaving for good.

'I'll try and get down the weekend after next,' she promised, aiming a kiss somewhere in the direction of her mother's cheek and jumping into her newly acquired Metro.

Leaving the house behind her was like shedding an unwanted burden, she thought guiltily as she drove through the village and headed in the direction of Cambridge. It wasn't her parents' fault there was this chasm between them, this inability to communicate on all but the most mundane levels. She loved them, of course, and knew that they loved her . . . but there was no real understanding between them. She felt more at ease and comfortable with Jonathan, more at home in his home than she had ever felt in her own.

Of course it was impossible to imagine anyone

not getting on with him. He could be exasperating, it was true, with his vagueness and his inability to live in any sort of order but he had a wry sense of humour ... a placid nature ... well at least almost. There had been one or two occasions on which she had thought she had seen a gleam of something unexpected in his eyes. Best of all, he treated her as an equal in all respects. He never enquired into her personal life, although they often spent the evening talking when she was down at his home—which was quite often because, although he had an office in Cambridge, there were times when he was called away unexpectedly and he would summon Sophy to his side to find the papers he was always losing and to generally ensure that he was travelling to his destination with all that he would require.

It was through these visits that she had got to know the children, often staying overnight, and this was not the first time she had received a frantic telephone call from Jonathan informing her of some domestic crisis.

Her mother was right, she thought wryly, what he needed was a wife but she could not see him marrying. Jonathan liked the life he had and he appeared to be one of that rare breed of people who seemed to have no perceptible sexual drive at all. His behaviour towards her for instance was totally sexless, as it seemed to be to the whole of her sex—and his own; there was nothing about Jonathan that suggested his sexual inclinations might lie in that direction.

In another century he would have been a philosopher, perhaps.

However much her mother might criticise his

shabby clothes and untidy appearance, Sophy
liked him. Perhaps because he made no sexual
demands of her, she admitted inwardly. Her
conviction as a teenager that she was ugly and
plain had long been vanquished when she had
gone to university and realised there that men
found her attractive; that there was something that
challenged them about her almost gypsyish looks.
A friend had told her she was 'sexy' but if she was,
it was only on the surface, and by the time she had
left university she was already accepting that
sexually there was something wrong. When a man
touched her she felt no spark of desire, nothing
but a swift sensation of going back in time to
Chris's bed and the despair and misery she had
experienced there.

Just before she met Jonathan she had been
involved with a man she had met through her
father—one of his clients, newly divorced with two
small children. She had been drawn to him because
he was that little bit older . . . but the moment he
touched her it had been the old story and that was
when she had decided it was pointless trying any
longer. Mentally she might be attracted to the
male sex but physically she repulsed them.

When she brought her car to a halt on the
gravel drive to Jon's house, the children were
waiting for her, David grinning happily,
Alexandra at his side.

'Uncle Jon's in his study,' David informed her.

'No, he's not' Alex was looking at the house.
'He's coming now.'

All three of them turned to watch the man
approaching them. He was wearing the baggy cord
jeans her mother so detested and a woollen shirt

despite the heat of the day. His hair was ruffled, his expression faintly harassed.

He was one of the few men she had to look up to, Sophy reflected, tilting her head as he approached. She was five-feet-ten, but Jon was well over six foot with unexpectedly broad shoulders. She frowned, registering that fact for the first time, totally thrown when he said unexpectedly, 'Rugger.'

Her mouth fell slightly open. Previously she had thought him one of the dimmest men she had ever met when it came to following other people's thought patterns and that he should so easily have picked up on hers made her stare at him in dazed disbelief. It really was unfair that any man should have such long, dark lashes, she thought idly . . . and such beautiful eyes. If Jonathan didn't wear glasses women would fall in love with him by the score for his eyes alone. They were a dense, dark blue somewhere between royal and navy. She had never seen eyes that colour on anyone before.

It wasn't that Jonathan wasn't physically attractive, she mused, suddenly realising that fact. He was! It was just that he carried about him a total air of non-sexuality.

'Louise has gone,' Alexandra told her importantly, tugging on her hand and interrupting her thought train. 'I expect it was because she fell in love with Uncle Jon like the others,' she added innocently.

While Sophy was gaping at her, totally floored by her remark, David remarked sagely, 'No . . . it was because Uncle Jon wouldn't let her sleep in his bed. I heard him saying so.'

Conscious of a sudden surge of colour crawling

up over her skin Sophy stared at Jonathan. He
looked as embarrassed as she felt, rubbing his jaw,
looking away from her as he cleared his throat and
said, 'Uh . . . I think you two better go inside.'

It couldn't be true. David must have misunderstood, Sophy thought, still trying to take in
the mind-boggling implications of the little boy's
innocent statement.

She forced herself to look at Jonathan. He was
regarding her with apprehension and . . . and what
. . . what exactly did that faint glint at the back of
his eyes denote? Sophy mentally pictured Louise.
Small, petite with black hair and a pixieish
expression, the other girl had exuded sexuality
and, from the brief conversations Sophy had
exchanged with her, she had gained the impression
that the other girl had men coming out of her ears.

Jonathan hadn't denied his nephew's innocent
revelation, however. She studied him covertly,
suddenly and inexplicably granted another mental
image. This time it contained Jonathan as well as
Louise . . . a Jonathan somewhat unnervingly
different from the one she was used to seeing; his
body naked and entwined with that of the other
girl's.

Sophy blinked and the vision, thankfully, was
gone, Jonathan was restored to his normal self.
There was that strange glint in his eyes again
though but his voice when he spoke was familiarly
hesitant and faintly apologetic.

'I believe she had some strange notion about, er
. . . compelling me to marry her. She wants a rich
husband you know.'

Sophy's mind balked a little at taking it all in.
That Louise should attempt to seduce Jonathan, of

all people, into offering her marriage, seemed impossibly ludicrous. Surely she realised, as Sophy herself had, that he was immune to sexual desire . . . totally oblivious to it in fact.

Another thought struck her. 'And the other two nannies?' she asked faintly.

'Well they didn't actually go to Louise's lengths, but——'

Sophy was too amazed to be tactful. 'But surely they could see that you aren't interested in sex?' she protested.

The dark head bent, and she watched him rub his jaw in his familiar vague fashion, his expression concealed from her as he responded in a faintly strangled voice that betrayed his embarrassment.

'Uh . . . obviously they didn't have your perception.'

'Well next time you'll have to employ someone older,' Sophy told him forthrightly. 'Do you want me to get in touch with the agencies while you're away?'

'Er . . . no. We'll leave it until I get back. Can you stay with them until then?'

'Well yes . . . but why delay?'

'Well I'm thinking about making some other arrangements.'

Other arrangements. What other arrangements? Sophy wondered. As far as she knew, he was the children's only family. Unless—her blood ran cold.

'You're not thinking of abandoning them . . . of putting them into foster homes?'

'Of course . . . of course, it's always a possibility.'

Trying to come to terms with her shock, Sophy

wondered why she had the feeling that he had set out to say one thing and had ended up saying another . . . perhaps he was embarrassed to admit the truth to her. 'Surely there must be another way,' she said impulsively. 'Something . . .'

'Well there is,' he looked acutely uncomfortable. 'In fact I was going to discuss it with you when I came back from Brussels.'

'Well why can't you tell me now?'

There were times when his vagueness infuriated her and now was one of them.

'Well . . . this evening perhaps, when the kids are in bed.'

It was only natural that he wouldn't want them to overhear what he might have to say and so she nodded her head. 'All right then.'

It was nine o'clock before both children were bathed and in bed. Jonathan's case was packed, his documents neatly organised and safely bestowed in his briefcase. He had offered to make them both a mug of coffee while Sophy finished this final chore and she had urged him to do so. Up until then he had been hovering like a demented bloodhound in his study, frantically searching for some all important piece of paper which had ultimately turned up under the telephone. Gritting her teeth, Sophy set about tidying up. Talk about disorganised!

And yet for all his vagueness, Jon could be ruthless enough when the occasion demanded it, she mused, pausing for a moment—witness his dismissal of Louise.

She sat down in his desk chair, still half stunned that a girl as clever and as quick as Louise had honestly thought she could use her sexual allure to trap Jonathan into marriage. That must have been what she had thought. No girl as modern as the children's nanny had been could possibly have believed that any man would marry her simply because he had been to bed with her.

Getting up, she made her way to the sitting-room most used by the family. It caught the afternoon sun and she passed by the deeply sashed Victorian windows staring at the sunset as she waited for Jonathan.

'Coffee, Sophy.'

For such a large man he moved extremely quietly. Frowning as she turned round, Sophy was suddenly struck by the fact that Jonathan was altogether deceptive. She always thought of him as clumsy and yet when he was working on his computer he could be surprisingly deft. She had thought him too obtuse and involved in his own private thoughts and his work, and yet he was surprisingly perceptive where the children were concerned and this afternoon, when he had answered her unspoken question. He sat down on the ancient, slightly sagging sofa, the springs groaning slightly as they took his weight. Standing up he often looked thin and faintly stooping but he wasn't thin, she realised in sudden surprise as he took off his glasses and, putting them down on the coffee table, stretched his body tiredly so that she could see the way his muscles moved beneath his shirt, and they *were* muscles, too . . .

Still standing by the window she continued to watch him, faintly shocked to realise that in profile his features were attractively irregular and very masculine. Without his glasses he looked different from the normally aesthetic man he appeared to be. He ceased stretching and rubbed his eyes.

'What have you got planned for the children, Jon?'

She sounded more belligerent than she had intended and she half expected him to jump uneasily in apprehension as he was wont to do when she complained because he had upset her neat filing cabinets. Instead, he smiled at her glintingly.

'You sould like a protective mother hen. Come and sit down. I hate having to look up at you,' he added, smiling again. 'I'm not used to it.'

Knowing that she would not get a scrap more information from him until she did as he asked, Sophy took a chair opposite the settee. Beneath that vague exterior lurked a will of iron, as she already knew, but so far she had only seen it in force where his work was concerned.

Suddenly and quite inexplicably she felt tense and nervous, neither of them feelings she was used to experiencing in Jon's presence. To cover them she said quickly, 'Mother was saying only today that you need a wife, Jon, and I'm beginning to think she's right.'

'So am I.' He started polishing his glasses, something he always did when he was nervous, and yet his nervous movements were oddly at variance with the tense determination she could almost feel emanating from him.

'But not Louise surely?' she began faintly, only to realise that it was hardly any of her business. And yet the thought of the pert, dark-haired young woman as Jon's wife was oddly distasteful to her. She bit her lip and looked up. Jon was looking at her and it was hard to analyse the expression in his eyes. All she did know was that it was unfamiliar to her.

'Not Louise,' he agreed gravely, suddenly looking away from her, his voice once again faintly husky and nervous as he cleared his throat and said, totally out of the blue, 'As a matter of fact, Sophy, I was rather hoping that you . . .'

Her? Jonathan was trying to say that he wanted to marry her! Oh no, surely she must be imagining things. She must have misunderstood. She looked across at him and saw from the hopeful, hesitant look he was giving her that she had not.

'You want to marry me?' she asked disbelievingly, just to be sure. 'You think we should get married? But that's totally out of the question.'

She had expected him to accept her refusal immediately; even to be faintly embarrassed and perhaps a little relieved by it. After all, he could have no real desire to be married to her . . . but to her dismay he shook his head, and plunged on quickly.

'No, no . . . listen to me for a moment. You love the kids.' He paused and while she said nothing Sophy knew she could not deny it. She heard him clearing his throat again and held her breath slightly. 'And, er . . . well . . . that is . . . you don't seem to have a . . . er . . . a boyfriend at the present time.'

'I don't want to get married, Jon,' she broke in firmly. 'Not to you nor to anyone else.'

'But you want children, a family.'

There was no hesitation in his voice this time and once again she was astounded by his perception.

'I need a wife, Sophy,' he continued, 'someone to look after the children and to run my home but not someone to . . . to share my bed.'

The words sank in slowly.

'You mean a . . . a marriage of convenience?' Sophy asked him uncertainly. 'Is that legal . . . is . . .?'

'Perfectly, since no one will know the truth apart from ourselves.'

'But Jonathan, it's crazy! Just because Louise . . . is that why you want to marry me?' she asked, staring at him. 'To stop——'

'It's amazing the lengths some of your sex will go to, to secure what they consider to be a wealthy husband and I'm afraid I am wealthy, Sophy.'

She knew that, and while it had never particularly concerned her she could see, now that he had mentioned it, that he would be quite a financial catch for a woman wanting to marry only for money. Suddenly she felt quite protective towards him.

'The children need you as well, Sophy,' he told her. 'They love you. With you they would be secure.'

'If I don't agree, what will you do . . . put them in some sort of institution?'

Her mouth went dry at the thought. It was true, she thought bleakly, feeling the pain invade her heart. She did love them . . . perhaps all the more so because she knew she would never have any of her own.

She watched Jonathan shrug uncomfortably and get up to pace the room. 'What else can I do?' he asked her. 'You know how much time I spend away. It's not fair to them. They need a settled background. They need you, Sophy. *I* need you.'

'To protect you from the likes of Louise.' Sophy agreed drily, adding teasingly, 'Is the thought of an attractive young woman wanting to seduce you really so very repulsive, Jon?' She knew the moment the words left her lips that they were the wrong ones.

Slow colour crawled up under his skin and he turned away from her saying, in a faintly stifled voice, 'I must confess, I do find such determined young women . . . er . . . intimidating. I had a very domineering mother,' he added almost apologetically.

Busy drawing the inevitable Freudian conclusions it was several seconds before Sophy observed the faintly risible gleam in his eyes and then it was so brief that she decided she must be imagining it. After all what could Jon be laughing at? It was no laughing matter for a man to have to admit he was frightened of the female sex. After all, didn't she herself hold an almost equal fear of his own, albeit for different reasons. Temptingly the thought slid into her mind that as Jon's wife she would be safe for all time from her own fears about her lack of sexuality. There would be no uncomfortable reminders in her unwed state about her inability to respond to his sex nor any fear that others would discover it and mock her for it as Chris had done.

Chris! No one would ever want to marry her, he had said. She took a deep breath.

'All right then, Jon. I agree. I'll marry you.'

The moment she heard the words she regretted them. Had she gone mad? She couldn't marry Jon. She couldn't but he was already coming towards her, grasping her wrists and hauling her to her feet.

'You will? Sophy, that's marvellous. I can't

thank you enough!' He made no attempt to touch
her or to kiss her. Then again, why should he? She
wouldn't have wanted him to.

Panic set in. 'Jon . . .'

'I can't tell you what this means to me, to be
able to keep the children.'

The children. They would be her family. Already
she loved them and found them a constant source of
delight. She would have this house, its vast
sprawling garden . . . a whole new way of life which
she knew instinctively would delight her. She was no
ardent career woman and it was a fallacy these days
that housewives and mothers degenerated into
cabbages. She would have the constant stimulation
of the children's growing minds.

But to marry Jon of all people. She glanced at
his tall, slightly stooping frame. Wasn't Jon the
ideal husband for her, though? an inner voice
asked. Jon, whose lack of sexuality would always
ensure that he never learned of her humiliating
secret. With Jon there would be no fear of
rejection or contempt. Jon wouldn't care that
sexually she was frigid—wasn't that the word—she
goaded herself. Wasn't frigid the description of
herself she was always shying away from, fighting
against facing, but the truth nonetheless?

'I . . . er, thought we might be married by special
licence. Perhaps next weekend?'

Special licence. Sophy came out of her daze to
stare at him. 'In such a rush. Is that necessary?'

Jon looked apologetic. 'Well, it would save me
having to find a new nanny. You can't stay on
here, living here while I'm living here too if we're
going to get married, Sophy,' he told her with
surprising firmness.

She wanted to laugh. She *was* going to laugh, Sophy thought, on a rising wave of hysteria.

Catching back her nervous giggles she expostulated, 'Jon, this is the nineteen-eighties. You're talking like someone out of the Victorian era.'

'Your mother wouldn't think so.'

His shrewdness left her lost for words for a moment. He was quite right. Her mother would most definitely not approve of her living beneath Jon's roof once she knew they were getting married. Neither, she realised hollowly, would her mother be at all pleased by the fact that they *were* getting married. She closed her eyes, imagining the scenes and recriminations. Jon was not her mother's idea of what she wanted for a son-in-law. She would also want a large wedding with Sophy in traditional white, a June wedding with a marquee and . . .

Groaning slightly she opened her eyes and said faintly, 'Yes, you're right. A special licence would be best and then we needn't tell anyone until afterwards.'

There was a strange gleam in Jon's eyes and this time she was almost sure it wasn't the sunset, reflecting off his glasses, that caused it.

'I'll, er . . , make all the arrangements then. Do you want to tell the kids or . . .?'

'I'll tell them tomorrow when you're gone,' she suggested. 'They're always a bit down after you leave, it will cheer them up a bit.'

Although outwardly well adjusted and cheerful children, Sophy knew that neither of them could have gone through the experience of losing their parents without some scars. They were both

passionately attached to Jon and she had thought
him equally devoted to them. It had shocked her
immensely to hear him talk of sending them away
. . . it didn't equate with what she knew of his
character somehow.

'I, er . . . think I'll have an early night,' she
heard him saying. 'My flight's at nine and I'll have
to be at the airport for eight.'

'Do you want me to drive you?' Jon did not
possess a car; he could neither drive nor, it seemed,
had any desire to do so, although he had hired a
small car for Louise's use.

'No. I've ordered a taxi. Don't bother to get up
to see me off.'

Picking up their coffee cups, Sophy grimaced
slightly to herself. She always saw him off on his
journeys because she lived in perpetual dread that
if she did not he would lose or forget something of
vital importance. She made a mental note to tell
the cab driver to check the taxi before Jon got out
of it and then, bidding him goodnight, carried
their cups to the kitchen.

She was tired herself. It had, after all, been an
eventful day. On her way to the room she always
had when she stayed over at the house and which
was next to the children's room, she had to walk
past Jon's room. As she did so, she hesitated, still
amazed to think that Louise had actually gone
into that room fully intent on making love to its
occupant. That earlier and extraordinarily disturbing mental vision she had had of their bodies
sensuously entwined she had somehow managed to
forget.

CHAPTER TWO

SHE was awake at half-past-seven, showering quickly in the bathroom off her bedroom. The room which she occupied was what the estate agent had euphemistically described as 'a guest suite'. Certainly her bedroom was large enough to house much more than the heavy Victorian furniture it did and it did have its own bathroom but after all that it fell rather short of the luxury conjured up by the description bestowed on it.

She dressed quickly in her jeans and a clean T-shirt. Her body, once gawky and ungainly, had filled out when she reached her twenties and now she had a figure she knew many women might have envied; full breasted, narrow waisted, with long, long legs, outwardly perhaps, as her friend had once teased, 'sexy', but inwardly . . . She was like a cake that was all tempting icing on the outside with nothing but stodge on the inside, she thought wryly, pulling a brush through her hair and grimacing at the crackle of static from it.

There wasn't time to pin it up and she left it curling wildly on to her shoulders, her face completely devoid of make-up and surprisingly young-looking in the hazy sunshine of the summer morning.

As she went past Jon's door she heard the hum of his razor and knew that he was up. Downstairs she checked that the cases she had packed for him the previous night were there in the hall. In the kitchen she ground beans and started making coffee. Jon was not an early morning person, preferring to rise late and work, if necessary, all through the night and despite the fact that she knew he would do no more than gulp down a cup of stingingly hot black coffee, she found and poured orange juice and started to make some toast.

He didn't look surprised to find her in the kitchen, and she knew from his engrossed expression that he was totally absorbed in whatever problem was taking him to Brussels.

Jon was the computer industry's equivalent of the oil world's 'trouble shooter'. She had once heard one of his colleagues saying admiringly that there was nothing Jon did not know about a computer. Although she knew that Jon himself would have been mildly amused by her lack of logic, she herself would have described his skill as something approaching a deep empathy with the machines he worked on.

As far as she was concerned the computer world was a total mystery but she was a good organiser, an excellent secretary and Jon found her flair for languages very useful. He himself seemed to rely entirely on the odd word, nearly always excruciatingly mispronounced from what Sophy could discover. But then, who needed words to communicate with a computer? Logic was what was needed there . . . and Jon had plenty of that, she thought wryly as she poured and passed his coffee. Only a man of supreme logic would propose to a woman on the strength of needing her to look after his wards and run his home. And also to keep other women out of his bed, Sophy reminded herself.

She didn't ask him if he wanted toast, simply pushing the buttered golden triangles in front of him. He picked one up, absently bit into it and then, frowning, put it down.

'You know I don't eat breakfast.'

'Then you should,' she reproved him. 'It's no wonder you're so thin.' But he wasn't, she remembered . . . recollecting that brief, unexpected glimpse of hard muscles.

She heard the sound of a car approaching over the gravel. So did Jon. He stood up, swallowing the last of his coffee.

'I'll ring you on Wednesday to let you know what time I get back. If anything urgent crops up in the meantime——'

'I know where to get in touch with you,' she assured him. She would have to drive into Cambridge later and leave a message on the office answering service asking callers to ring her here at the house. Her mind raced ahead, busily engaged in sorting out the host of minor problems her being here instead of in Cambridge would cause.

She walked with Jon to the taxi . . . sighing in faint exasperation as he forgot to pick up his briefcase, handing it to him through the open door and then turning to speak to the driver.

'Ticket . . .' she intoned automatically, turning back to Jon. 'Passport, money . . .'

He patted the pocket of his ancient tweed jacket, a faintly harassed look crossing his face.

Registering and interpreting it correctly Sophy instructed. 'Stay there, I'll go and get them.'

She found them in a folder beside his bed, and sighed wryly. She remembered quite distinctly handing them to him yesterday and telling him to put them in his jacket pocket.

She ran downstairs and handed the documents to him, catching the driver's eye as she did so. He was looking faintly impatient.

'I'll see you late Wednesday or early Thursday.' She closed the taxi door and waited until it had turned out of the drive.

Back in the kitchen she munched absently at Jon's toast and drank her coffee. She and Jon were to be married. It was incredible, ridiculous ... only strangely it didn't seem that way. Already she felt an oddly comfortable pleasure in the thought, as though some burden of pressure had been released. She *wanted* to marry him, she realised with a start of surprise ... or at least ... she wanted what marriage to him would give her. She frowned. Didn't that mean that in her way she was just as selfishly grasping as Louise? But, unlike Louise, she did care about Jon. As a person she liked him very much indeed. As a man he was so totally unthreatening to her that she found his company relaxing. Marriage to Jon would be like slipping into a pair of comfortable slippers ... But on Saturday? She comforted herself with the thought that it was hardly likely that Jon would be able to organise a special licence so quickly. In fact she doubted he would even remember about it once he got on the plane. No doubt the task of sorting out all the arrangements would fall to her once he came back but she would still prefer not to tell her parents until after the ceremony.

Coward, she mocked herself, hearing sounds from upstairs that meant David and Alex were up and about.

She told them about Jon's proposal after breakfast. All three of them were outside, sitting on the lawn. Their open delight and excitement made tears sting her eyes. David flung his arms round her embracing her exuberantly, Alex hanging on to her arm.

'I'm glad he's marrying you and not that nasty old Louise,' she told Sophy. 'We didn't like her, did we, David?'

'No, and neither did Uncle Jon . . . otherwise he would have let her sleep in his bed.' A thought seemed to strike him. 'Does that mean you'll be sleeping in his bed, Sophy?'

A strange paralysis seemed to have gripped her. She wasn't sure how much the children knew about adult behaviour. They must have learned something from school but their parents had been dead for three years and she could hardly see Jon satisfactorily explaining the so-called facts of life to them. On the other hand, it was pointless telling them a lie.

'No, I won't, David,' she said at last.

She watched him frown and saw that for some reason her answer had not pleased him.

'That's because both of you are so big, I expect,' intervened Alex, ever practical. 'You wouldn't both get in one bed.'

'They would in Uncle Jon's,' David told her gruffly. 'It's huge.'

It was . . . king size and Jon normally slept diagonally across it. She knew because she occasionally had to wake him up in the morning when he had an early business appointment and he had been up late the previous night working. She had never needed to do much more than lightly touch his duvet mummy-wrapped body though.

'If you're going to get married, why won't you be sleeping in his bed?' he persisted doggedly.

'Married people don't always share the same bed, David,' she told him, giving him what she hoped was a reassuring smile. 'You know what your uncle's like. He often works very late and I like to go to bed early. He would wake me up and then I wouldn't be able to get back to sleep.'

He looked far from convinced, muttering, 'Ladies always sleep with their husbands,' and betraying a innate chauvinism that made Sophy smile. Already at ten he was very, very sure in his masculinity and of its supremacy which was surely something he didn't get from Jon. He was also, as she had often observed, very protective of his sister . . . and too, of her. She bent forward and ruffled his dark hair.

'Perhaps Uncle Jon doesn't want her to sleep with him, David,' Alex offered, smiling at him. 'He didn't want Louise to.'

The little girl was more right than she knew, Sophy thought grimly, glad of the distraction of the telephone ringing.

As she had half suspected it was her mother, eager to tell her all about the previous evening's dinner party.

'Chris came too,' she told Sophy, oblivious to her daughter's lack of enthusiasm, 'and he brought his wife. Such a lovely girl . . . tiny with masses of blonde curls and so obviously in love with him. She's expecting their first baby. He asked after you, and didn't seem at all surprised to hear you weren't married.' There was a hint of reproof in her mother's voice. 'He even laughed about it.'

Sophy realised as she replaced the receiver that she was actually grinding her teeth. So he had laughed, had he? Well, he would soon stop laughing when he heard that she *was* married! She stood motionless by the telephone staring blindly out of the study window for a few seconds picturing the ordeal the dinner party would have been for her had she been there ... that future dinner parties would have been if it hadn't been for Jon's extraordinary proposal. Without being aware of it he had saved her from the most galling humiliation and pain. Now she needn't even see Chris, never mind endure his mocking taunts on her unmarried state.

Over the next couple of days, cautiously at first and then with growing confidence, like someone blessedly discovering the cessation of toothache and then cautiously exploring the previously tormented area and finding it blissfully whole again, Sophy allowed herself to acknowledge the totally unexpected happiness unfurling inside her.

The children were a constant, sometimes funny, sometimes exasperating joy and one she had never thought to know. For some women the physical act of giving birth was acutely necessary to motherhood but she, it seemed, was not one of them. She could not take the place of the children's dead mother and did not seek to but it gave her a special delight to know that she would have the joy of mothering them. It was this, probably more than anything else, that convinced her that her decision to marry Jon was the right one. She still didn't know how he could even have thought of relinquishing his responsibility for them

but then his mind was so wrapped up in his
work, that everything else was obviously secon-
dary to it.

On Tuesday evening it rained and they spent the
evening going through some old photograph
albums David had found in a bureau drawer.

Once she and Jon were married she would ask
him if she was to be allowed a free hand with the
house, Sophy mused, glancing round the shabby
sitting room, and mentally transforming it with
new furnishings. At the present moment in time it
wasn't even particularly comfortable. Both the
sofa and the chairs had loose springs which dug
into vulnerable flesh if sat upon.

'Look Sophy, there's Daddy and Uncle Jon
when they were little.'

Sophy glanced down at the open page of the
album, her eyes widening fractionally as she
studied the photograph Alex was pointing out.

Two lanky adolescent boys stood side by side,
one topping the other by a couple of inches. Both
of them had identical shocks of near black hair—
both of them had the same regular features,
hinting at formidably good looks in adulthood.

'Uncle Jon looks really like Daddy there,
doesn't he?' Alex commented, wrinkling her nose.
'He doesn't look anything like Daddy did now
though, does he, David?'

Thus applied to, her brother studied the
photograph briefly and then said gruffly. 'Yes he
does . . . underneath.'

It was an odd remark for the little boy to make
and one, Sophy sensed, made in defence of his
uncle against his sister's comment.

'Uncle Jon would look much better without his

glasses,' Alex continued cheerfully. 'He should wear contact lenses like our teacher at school.'

'He can't,' David told her loftily. 'They don't suit his eyes, and besides, he doesn't need to wear his glasses all the time anyway.'

This was news to Sophy. She had never seen him without them, apart from one occasion she recalled, remembering watching him remove them here in this very room. Then she had been struck by the very male attractiveness of his profile, she remembered and then shrugged mentally. What did it matter what Jon looked like? It was the kind of man he *was* that was important. She already knew all about the pitfalls encountered in getting involved with handsome men. Chris was good looking.

On the Wednesday morning after she had dropped the children off at school she got back just in time to hear the 'phone ringing noisily.

Thinking it might be Jon, she rushed inside and picked up the receiver, speaking slightly breathlessly into it, barely registering her sudden spearing disappointment at discovering it wasn't him as she listened to the crisp American tones of the man on the other end of the line.

She explained to him that Jon was due back that day, and slowly read back to him the message he had given her, frowning slightly as she did so.

She knew, of course, that Jon often did work for various governments, but that call had been from the Space Center in Nassau, where apparently they were urgently in need of Jon's expertise.

Would that mean he had to fly straight out to Nassau, before they could get married? She shrugged slightly. It didn't really matter when the ceremony took place, surely?

The next time the 'phone rang it was Jon, ringing her from the airport in Brussels, to tell her the time of his flight.

'I managed to get through a little earlier than planned,' he told her, adding, 'any messages?'

Quickly Sophy told him about the call from Nassau, giving him the number and asking hesitantly, 'Will that mean that you'll have to fly straight out there?'

There was a pause so long that she thought at one point their connection had been cut and then Jon said slowly, 'I'm not sure.' Having re-checked with him the number of his flight, Sophy said goodbye and replaced the receiver.

She would have to ring Heathrow now and check what time it was due to arrive ... her mind ran on, mentally ticking off all that would have to be done. The children would have to be collected from school, fed ... Yet all the time at the back of her mind was that same ridiculous sense of apprehension.

Suppose Jon had changed his mind about wanting to marry her? How long would he need to be in Nassau? What if he ...?

Stop it! she urged herself firmly, reminding herself that less than a week ago there had been no thought in her mind of marriage to anyone, let alone her boss and now here she was in a mild flurry of panic in case they did not marry.

Since the time needed to get to Heathrow and back to meet Jon's flight interfered with the children's school leaving time, and because she knew of no one she could ask to meet them in her place, Sophy rang the school and asked to speak with the headmistress, quickly explaining the situation and getting permission to collect David and Alex on her way to Heathrow just after lunch.

Neither of them stopped chattering during the drive. Oddly enough, this would be the first time either of them had been to the airport and since Sophy always believed in having a little time in hand once they had parked the car she was able to take them to the viewing gallery to watch the flights taking off and landing.

'Will we see Uncle Jon's plane from up here?' David demanded at one point.

Sophy glanced at her watch. Jon's flight was due in in five minutes.

'Yes,' she told him. 'We'll watch it land and then we'll go down to the arrivals lounge to wait for him.

The flight was on time and the plane landed perfectly, so there was no reason for her to feel that odd choking sensation of fear clutch at her throat, Sophy chided herself, especially when she had already watched half a dozen or so planes come and go without the slightest trace of apprehension.

'Look! Look, Sophy ... they're putting the stairs up,' Alex told her excitedly, tugging on her hand. 'Can we wait and see Uncle Jon get off?'

Sophy knew from past experience that Jon was likely to be the last to leave the plane but in the face of the little girl's excitement she could hardly refuse. It would be a bit of a rush down to the arrivals lounge ... and she always liked to be on hand just in case Jon ran into any problems. There had been that time he had left his passport on the plane and another when he had lost the keys for

his briefcase, and the strange buzzing sound
emanating from it had drawn frowns and stern
looks from the security authorities. In the end it
had simply been the alarm he had forgotten to
switch off but . . .

'All right,' she agreed, 'but then we'll have to
rush back down.'

'Look . . . they're getting off now,' David called
out, 'but I can't see Uncle Jon.'

As Sophy had guessed, Jon was the last off the
plane, a clutch of dark suited business men in
front of him, the whole party impeded by the slow
progress of an old lady who was having difficulty
walking.

One of them, obviously growing impatient,
pushed past her. His companions followed suit,
and Sophy felt an impotent cry of warning rise
in her throat as she saw the old lady lose her
balance.

What happened next was so out of character
that for a moment or two she actually doubted the
evidence of her own eyes.

Jon who never seemed to be aware of what was
going on around him . . . Jon who could often be
so clumsy and awkward, moved forward so
quickly that Sophy blinked. He caught the old
lady before she could fall, supporting her with one
arm while he held on to his briefcase with the
other. She had never seen anyone move so quickly,
Sophy reflected, nor move with such controlled
reflexes, unless it was on the sports field.

'Gosh, did you see the way Uncle Jon saved that
lady?' Alex asked, round-eyed. 'It was really fast,
wasn't it?'

'That's because of playing rugger,' David

informed her loftily. 'He used to play when he was at Cambridge.'

'And he did rowing as well,' Alex chipped in, as Sophy drew them away from the viewing windows and towards the arrivals lounge.

She had known about the rugby but it had never occurred to her to think of Jon as an athletic man. Chris who prided himself on his physical fitness spent at least three evenings per week in the gym, jogged and played amateur football but, as far as she knew, Jon did none of these things. There were of course those totally unexpected muscles shaping his shoulders and chest though. Irritated with herself without knowing why, Sophy tried to re-direct her thoughts.

For once, Jon managed to negotiate the hazards of passport control and baggage checks without any mishaps.

As he came through the gate Alex slipped her hand from Sophy's and ran towards him. Watching him field her as easily as any rugby ball and transfer his baggage to his other hand, Sophy was forced to admit that there were obviously still some aspects of her future husband that she was not familiar with. The knowledge was a little unsettling. Up until now she had thought she knew Jon very well indeed and had been quite content with the slightly exasperated toleration which was the normal feeling he aroused within her. Indeed she liked feeling faintly motherly and superior to him, she realised. Thoroughly startled by this sudden discovery about herself, she was the last of the trio to step forward and greet him.

'That was really good how you saved that old lady from falling, Uncle Jon,' David was saying.

'We watched you from the gallery, didn't we, Sophy?'

Over David's head the navy blue eyes fixed rather myopically and vaguely on her own.

Alex piped up, 'Yes, Sophy was so surprised that her mouth was open—like this.' She demonstrated Sophy's stunned surprise far too well, the latter thought uncomfortably, feeling the slow crawl of embarrassed colour seeping up under her skin as Jon continued to look at her.

Her embarrassment heightened when David asked suddenly, 'Aren't you going to kiss Sophy, Uncle Jon? You can do now that you're going to get married.'

'I don't think I will right now, old son, if you don't mind.' Watching Jon ruffle David's hair and listening to the mild, even tone of his voice as he side-tracked his nephew away from such a potentially embarrassing subject, Sophy knew she should be grateful to Jon for what he had done but for some strange reason, what she was really feeling, if she was honest, was a sense of genuine pique. Jon couldn't have made it more plain that the thought of kissing her held absolutely no appeal for him, she thought irrationally. Was she really so unattractive to him that . . .? She stopped abruptly, stunned by the train of her own thoughts. Of course Jon did not want to kiss her— her or anyone else . . . indeed that was the reason she had felt able to agree to marry him. So why . . .?

It must be something to do with all the re-united couples and families freely embracing around them that had aroused that momentary and totally unnecessary fit of pique inside her. Feeling much better now that she had found a logical explanation for her irrational feelings, Sophy hurried to catch up with the others and led the way to where she had parked the car.

CHAPTER THREE

IT was gone ten o'clock, the silence in the study as they both worked a companionable one and then Jon got up and walked over to the window, his back to her as he stared out into the garden. His hair had grown slightly while he was away, Sophy noticed absently and it looked better, even curling faintly into his nape.

'Will you have to fly out to Nassau immediately?' she asked him suddenly, uneasy with the silence she had found so relaxing only seconds before.

He turned round and smiled mildly. 'No, not straight away. Not until Sunday.'

'So . . .' All at once her throat was dry. 'So you'll still be here for the wedding, then?' Fool, idiot, she derided herself mentally; without him there wouldn't *be* a wedding and she had made him sound like one of the guests.

'Oh, yes . . . I've made all the arrangements. Got the special licence organised through someone I know in Brussels.'

'You're not having second thoughts, then?'

Good heavens, what was the matter with her? What was she asking him for? She was behaving like a total fool.

'No. Are you?'

It was unusual for Jon to ask such a direct question and in such a crisp tone. She shook her head without looking at him, suddenly too restless to stay in her seat. She got up and paced a few steps.

'There is one thing though.' She tensed. 'When we were discussing the ... er ... style of our marriage I neglected to mention one point.'

'Yes?' Her mouth felt frozen and stiff, so much so that it was difficult to shape the word.

'We have discussed my reasons for our marriage, Sophy but I don't think we've fully discussed yours. I know you care deeply for the children,' he went on before she could speak, 'but—and please correct me if I am wrong—you could always have children of your own. No, please,' he stopped her when she would have spoken. 'You are, in addition, a very attractive woman.' He saw her expression and his mouth twisted slightly. 'I assure you, Sophy, that even my shortsightedness is not sufficient to blind me to that fact. A woman whom I am sure very many members of my sex would be only too pleased to marry. Men who would want to share with you a far more intimate relationship than the one I am offering.'

It was ridiculous to feel embarrassed but she was.

'I don't want that kind of relationship,' she managed to say thickly, turning away from him.

'I see. This is, I presume, because of the romantic involvement you once had with someone else. You did tell me some such thing the first time we met,' he reminded her.

Her face flamed. She had had so much to drink that night she could not remember what she had told him, but it embarrassed her now to think that she had probably poured out to him all her

maudlin misery over what had once been her love
for Chris.

'I take it there is no question of this, er . . .
relationship——'

'None at all,' Sophy managed to interrupt
huskily.

'I see. Having suffered the pangs of love once
and been hurt by it you have no wish to risk
yourself with such an emotion again, is that it?'

It wasn't because she was frightened of *loving*
that she was marrying him, Sophy reflected, but it
was much simpler and easier to let him believe that
than to tell him the truth.

She lifted her head and looked at him, forcing a
cool smile. 'Yes, Jon, that is it. The relationship
you are offering me, the chance to take over the
role of mother to the children, is exactly what I
want.'

'Very well . . . but I must tell you, Sophy, that,
er . . . that there can be no question of me
tolerating a sexual relationship which you might
form outside our marriage.'

'You mean you wouldn't want me to take a
lover?'

'Yes, that is exactly what I mean.'

It was getting dark and in the dusk she could
barely see across the room.

The aura that Jon projected when she was not
able to see him clearly was unnervingly at odds
with the man she knew him to be. Even his voice
seemed to have changed, become slightly silky and
somehow subtly menacing.

'You have my word that there will be no
question of that, Jon,' she told him quietly and
truthfully. Not wanting him to ask any more

questions she gave a small shrug and added lightly, 'Perhaps, like yourself, I am one of those humans whose sex drive is so low as to be almost non-existent.'

She thought for a moment he seemed to tense, as though about to say something and wondered uncertainly if she had perhaps hurt or offended him by being so frank. No man would enjoy hearing himself described as virtually sexless, she thought guiltily.

'And this man . . . the one you loved, Sophy?'

'He's married now. It would never have worked. He didn't . . .' she swallowed and told what was in effect merely a half lie. 'He didn't care in the way that I did.'

Suddenly and inexplicably she felt quite exhausted. 'It's been a long day, Jon,' she told him quietly. 'If you don't mind, I think I'll go to bed.'

She knew it would be a long time before Jon came upstairs and, although he smiled vaguely at her as she went out of the room, she sensed that his mind was already on other things.

It had never occurred to her that he might question her motives in agreeing to marry him and was relieved that he had assumed that it was her non-existent love for Chris that had motivated her. It rather surprised her that he should remember her wine-induced confidences on the night of the party when they first met. She had been feeling particularly down at the time otherwise she would never have said a word.

'So are you really and truly married now?'

Sophy nodded her head, and smiled at Alex. She

was still quite amazed that Jon had managed to arrange the details without any hitch.

She had also been a little surprised at his insistence on a religious ceremony but had said nothing. In all honesty she had to admit there had been something comforting and right about the familiar Church service that had soothed away a lot of her last minute doubts. Now it was too late. They were married, Jon looking exceedingly uncomfortable in a suit he must surely have had since he came down from university and so heavy that it was totally unsuitable for a hot July day, she thought exasperatedly.

'I'm going to have to do something about your clothes,' she told him wryly. 'They're atrocious.'

'Are they?' He stared vaguely at her, frowningly perplexed, and yet as he turned his head slightly to answer a question David had asked him, Sophy was sure she saw his mouth curl faintly in amusement. What had she said to amuse him? Nothing, surely?

There was no question of a honeymoon of course. Jon was flying to Nassau in the morning and following the early morning wedding ceremony Sophy intended to spend the afternoon checking that everything was in order for his trip. 'I'll have to give my mother a ring and tell her the news,' she murmured, blenching a little at the thought of that ordeal.

'Er, no. I think it would be better if we drove over there now and I told her.'

She stared at Jon unable to believe her ears. Jon was terrified of her mother.

'Jon, there's really no need,' she began.

'I think there's every need.' The cool firmness in

his voice silenced her protests and even David and
Alex stopped what they were doing to look at him.
Probably because they were so unused to hearing
their uncle speak in such decisive tones.

'But you don't have time. Your flight——'

'Is all perfectly organised, thanks to my wife.
And we have plenty of time. We'll have a quick
snack lunch and leave straight away. All of us.'

And so it was that at three o'clock in the
afternoon Sophy found herself drawing up outside
her parents' front door. Once she had stopped the
car Jon clambered out, knocking his head as he
did so. The front passenger seat of her car was far
too small for him. It was easy to overlook how big
a man he really was, Sophy reflected, watching
him help the children out.

'You're going to need a larger car.'

'Only when you're travelling in it,' Sophy told
him wryly, leading the way through the garden to
the back of her house, knowing that on such a
lovely day her parents would be in the garden.

They were, but they weren't alone and Sophy
came to an abrupt halt as the ring of her high-
heeled sandals on the crazy paving path caused the
tall blonde man lazing in a deckchair to turn his
head and look at her.

'Sophy . . . good heavens.'

He hadn't changed, Sophy thought, registering
the lazy insolence in his voice, the mockery with
which his glance slid over her body, as though
reminding her that he knew how lacking in
femininity it really was.

'Sophy?' Her mother suddenly appeared through
the french windows, carrying a tray of tea things,
her mouth rounding in astonishment. 'You didn't

say you were coming over this afternoon.' There
was just a touch of reproof in her mother's light
voice, and Sophy suppressed a faint sigh. Her
mother liked everything done by the book,
arrangements properly made ... She should have
thought about that.

'It's my fault, I'm afraid, Mrs Marley.'

For the first time since seeing Chris she became
conscious of Jon standing beside her.

'Your ... Oh!' There was no mistaking the
displeasure in her mother's voice and Sophy felt
her guilt turn into quiet despair.

'Where's Father?' she asked, scanning the garden.

'He's showing Felicity, my wife, the new rose
arbour he's building,' Chris answered easily. 'I
rather think I shall have to watch my wife, Mrs
Marley,' he added charmingly to Sophy's mother,
'I do believe she's falling rather hard for your
husband.'

Listening to her mother's girlish trill of laughter,
Sophy was overwhelmed by a familiar feeling of
alienation. She didn't fit in here in this neat over-
tidy garden ... in this peaceful English family
scene. Chris was more at home here than she was,
she thought bitterly, and her mother more pleased
by his company than she ever was by hers.

'Nonsense, you foolish boy,' she chided Chris.
'Anyone can see that Felicity only has eyes for
you. She's so much in love with you.'

She could almost see Chris preening himself
under her mother's flattery and suddenly Sophy
felt the most acute dislike for him. She had fallen
out of love with him a long time ago but this
dislike was a new and gloriously freeing thing,
giving her the courage to say calmly, 'Mother,

there's something I——'

'I think I should be the one to break our news to your parents, Sophy.'

The deep and commanding tones of Jon's voice broke through her own, silencing her. She blinked and turned round to study him, wondering at this sudden assumption of masculine authority, half expecting to see someone else standing behind her. But no, it was still Jon, looking thoroughly hot and uncomfortable in his baggy cords and thick woollen shirt, his glasses catching the sunlight and obscuring his eyes from her.

Their voices had obviously carried down the garden, and Sophy watched her father walking towards them accompanied by Chris's wife. She was every bit as pretty as her mother had said but Sophy felt no envy for her, only a certain wry sympathy. Unless he had changed dramatically, Chris did not have it in him to be loyal and loving to one woman, even one as lovely as this. Her pregnancy barely showed, her light summer dress showing off her summer tan.

'Darling, let me introduce you to an old friend of mine.' Irritatingly it was Chris who took charge of the proceedings, drawing his wife towards him.

'Oh, not another old flame, darling . . . .' The fluttery voice was unexpectedly hard, and instantly Sophy revised her opinion. Chris's wife was not the delicate little flower she looked. On the contrary, she was every bit as hard as Chris himself, she thought inwardly, taking the hand the other girl extended.

'Heavens, aren't you tall!' Innocent blue eyes slid upwards over Sophy's body. 'You must be almost six foot.'

'Five-ten actually.' From somewhere Sophy managed to summon a cool smile. Six foot made her sound like a giantess—a freak almost.

'And this,' Chris was looking past Sophy now to Jon and the children. His mouth curled in a dazzling smile, laughter lighting his eyes as he looked at Jon. 'You can only be Sophy's boss!' His glance swept derisively over Jon's appearance, and Sophy could almost see him comparing it with his own. The immaculate white cotton jeans, the cotton knit jumper in blues and greens banded with white . . . the elegantly cool casualness of his appearance in comparison to Jon's.

Chris's rudeness did not surprise her, but the blindingly fierce stab of mingled anger and protectiveness she felt, did. She reached out instinctively to take Jon's hand in her own, unaware of the deeply gold glitter in her eyes as she said firmly, 'And my husband. That's what we came to tell you . . . Jon and I were married this morning.'

'Married!' Her mother looked shocked and disbelieving, and Sophy was furious with her when she cried out, 'Oh, Sophy . . . no . . . how could you do this to us?' her eyes dropping immediately to her daughter's tautly flat stomach.

Fury kicked sharply beneath her heart as Sophy realised what her mother was thinking.

'Sophy is not pregnant, Mrs Marley.' She was still holding Jon's hand and the firmness with which he squeezed her fingers was intensely reassuring. She was beginning to feel as though she had strayed into a bad dream. She had known her parents would not be pleased . . . but that her mother should actually think she was pregnant.

She was burning with embarrassment on her parents' behalf. Neither of them had made the slightest attempt to put Jon at ease or to make him feel welcome.

'Then why such a rush?' her mother complained. 'Why didn't you say anything the last time you were here?' She looked suspiciously from her daughter's flushed face to the one of the man behind her. 'I know what it is,' she said shrilly. 'You've married her so that you'll have someone to look after those children. I told you he was making use of you.'

Sophy couldn't endure it. She turned blindly towards Jon saying huskily, 'I think we'd better leave,' but the hard pressure of his hand holding hers held her back.

'You do your daughter a severe injustice, Mrs Marley,' he said very gently. 'I married Sophy quite simply because I love her.'

Even her mother fell silent at that, rallying enough to add huffily, 'Well, I still think you should have told us, Sophy. I can't understand why you should have got married in such a hole-and-corner fashion at all . . . and in such a rush!'

'Because I want to be with Jon and the children, Mother,' she managed evenly. 'That was why.'

'Well you can't expect your father and me not to be shocked. Not even to tell us about the wedding——'

'I had the most wonderful wedding,' Felicity cut in cattily. 'Five hundred guests and a marquee on the lawn at home. Mummy said it was her dream come true for me.'

'Good old Sophy! Married, eh?' Chris was eyeing her with open mockery. 'I never thought I'd

see the day. You know, old boy, I once actually
bet Sophy that she'd never find a man to marry her.'

'Well, you see, you were wrong.'

Was she imagining the faint rasp beneath Jon's
mild tone? She must be, Sophy thought, her skin
suddenly burning with furious anger as she heard
Chris saying quite distinctly to his wife, 'Not as
wrong as all that.' He turned to Jon and taunted
smilingly, 'She told you about our little bet, then,
did she?'

'She may have mentioned it.' Jon looked totally
vague and disinterested. 'But it was a very long
time ago, wasn't it?' He said it so mildly that there
seemed to be no outward reason why Chris should
colour so hotly until Jon added equally mildly,
'Really I'm surprised you even remember it. Sophy
can't have been more than nineteen or so at the
time.'

The children were pressing quietly against her
side, and Sophy turned to her mother pinning a
smile on her face.

'I think we'd better leave now, Mother. Jon has
to fly to Nassau in the morning.'

'*Jon* has to . . .' Chris's eyebrows rose. 'Dear me,
how very unromantic but then no doubt as you're
both living in the same house you've already had
ample opportunity to——'

'Become lovers?' Jon seemed totally oblivious to
Chris's malice. 'Oh, about the same opportunity as
any other couple of our age and situation in life,'
he agreed cheerfully.

'Mummy would never have agreed with me
living with Chris before we were married,' Felicity
chipped in dulcetly, earning an approving glance
from *her* mother, Sophy noted.

'No?' Really, it was quite incredible how Jon's face changed when he removed his glasses. He had been in the act of polishing them when Felicity spoke and there was quite definitely something almost satanic about the way his eyebrow rose and his mouth curled as he looked across at the other girl.

'And we were engaged for twelve months.'

'A wildly passionate romance.'

Sophy couldn't believe her ears. Chris was red to the tips of his ears and an unbecoming tightness had formed round Felicity's bowlike mouth. Sophy was quite sure that Felicity and Chris had been lovers well before the date of their marriage; how could it be otherwise when Chris was such a highly sexed man. She had no doubt that the little act Felicity was putting on was purely for her parents' benefit.

'I think we'd better leave.'

Neither of her parents made any attempt to stop them going but Sophy didn't realise that Jon had misinterpreted the reason for her tiny sigh of relief, as they got in the car and he said in an unusually clipped tone. 'Don't let it bother you, Sophy. The loss is theirs, not yours. Good heavens,' he muttered in a much more Jon-like tone, 'can't they see that you're worth a dozen of that stupid, vain little butterfly?'

Wryly she smiled across at him, and said huskily. 'Thanks ... for everything.' She was remembering how he had claimed that he loved her, protecting her from Chris's malice.

All four of them were subdued on the way back, although it wasn't until the children were in bed

and they were alone that Jon again raised the
subject of her parents.

'I hope you weren't too hurt by what happened
today, Sophy,' he began uncertainly. 'If I had
known . . .'

'I stopped being hurt by the fact that I'm not the
daughter my parents wanted, a long time ago,' she
said calmly. 'But I was angry, Jon . . . angry and
embarrassed that they should show such a lack of
welcome and politeness to you.'

He shrugged and looked slightly uncomfortable
as though the emotion in her voice embarrassed
him.

'I don't suppose we'll see that much of them,' he
rumbled clearing his throat. 'Er . . . Benson, I
suppose he's the one.'

'Yes,' Sophy agreed tightly. 'Yes, he's the one
. . . but it's all over now, Jon. My life and loyalty
lie with you and the children now.'

'Yes . . .'

Why should she feel that there was a certain wry
irony in the way he was looking at her?

Sophy spent the fortnight Jon was away in Nassau
organising her new life. From now on Jon would
work mainly from home when he was in England,
so she moved some of the files from the office in
town to his study. She managed to do some fence
building in her relationship with her parents but
admitted to herself that it could never be the warm
one she had once wanted. As she had firmly told
her mother, Jon was now her husband and he and
the children came first. Grudgingly this had been
accepted, but Sophy doubted that there would be
much contact between them in future.

She also spent time planning how she was going to refurbish the house. Jon had given her permission to do exactly what she wanted and had also told her she need not stint on cost. She had been a little surprised to discover that he had also organised a new bank account for her and had placed into it what seemed to be an impossibly large sum of money.

She had always known that he was a reasonably wealthy man but she had not realised, until now, exactly how wealthy. Perhaps because Jon himself never looked like an even remotely prosperous man, never mind a rich one.

That was something else she would have to do something about, she decided on the Wednesday before he was due back. She would go through his wardrobe, discover what size he was and start re-stocking it. She still burned with resentment when she thought about the way Chris had looked at him.

If ever she had worried about falling for Chris again she did so no longer. Indeed it amazed her that she could ever have found him the slightest bit attractive. The wounds he had inflicted still hurt but she found the man himself contemptible.

Sophy was familiar enough with the clothes Jon wore not to be too surprised by the collection of hairy suits and worn tweed jackets she discovered in his wardrobe. Rather wryly she wondered what on earth it was about the colour of mud that attracted him so much but other than that, her search was briskly impersonal and she stopped only to check on sizes before closing the wardrobe door and leaving the bedroom. Its furniture, like that in the rest of the house, was of no particular

style or beauty. Jon had told her that he had
bought it with the house. She planned to get rid of
the majority of it, but not until she had decided
what was to take its place.

Her decision made, she didn't waste any time.
After picking the children up from school she
drove briskly towards Cambridge.

'You're going the wrong way,' Alex told her.

Sophy shook her head. 'No I'm not. I want to
do some shopping. Your uncle needs some new
clothes.'

The silence from the pair in the back seat
confirmed Sophy's view that she was far from the
only one to note the lack of appeal about Jon's
attire.

He must be boiled alive in those heavy cords he
favoured and those woollen shirts, especially
during the heatwave they were having at the
moment.

She wondered wryly how on earth he was
getting on in Nassau. When she had remarked that
he was going to be hot he had told her that the
temperature in computer operational rooms was
always maintained at a set point, no matter what
the climate.

It didn't take long to park the car and Sophy
knew Cambridge well enough to head straight for
a small street which housed half a dozen or so
exclusive shops catering for both men and women.

She stopped outside the window of one of them
surveying the grey blouson jacket with its royal
blue lining and the matching, pleated trousers, also
trimmed in blue.

'I don't think Uncle Jon would like that,' David
informed her doubtfully.

Sophy grinned. She could just picture Jon's face if she produced something as radically modern as that. No, what she had in mind was something rather more conservative.

'Then we won't go in,' she told David equably, herding the pair instead to a shop two doors down which stocked a range of Jaeger clothes for men.

It took her over an hour to make her final choice, which included two shirts, one in silk and one in cotton in a shade of blue which Alex had informed her was exactly the same as Jon's eyes.

Having chosen those it had proved fairly easy to pick out the basis of a new wardrobe for him based almost entirely on blue and cream— including a softly blue herringbone tweed jacket which she was pleased to see bore no resemblance whatsoever to the ones already in his wardrobe.

Having paid the bill and escorted the children outside she remembered that both of them seemed short of casual T-shirts and that she could do with some inexpensive casual wear herself. The heatwave which had begun in the early part of the month was still persisting with no let-up forecast and her wardrobe was not really geared to such hot weather.

It only took them a few minutes to walk to Marks & Spencer, where she gave in to Alex's entirely feminine whim to be kitted out in a range of separates in pretty pinks. Even David allowed himself to be persuaded into a pair of brushed denim jeans in a soft olive colour to which Sophy added several T-shirts and thin cotton jumpers.

'Look over there. Uncle Jon would like nice in that, Sophy,' Alex informed her, having by now thoroughly entered into the spirit of things.

On the display she had indicated, Sophy could see a range of men's casual separates in a soft, pale sand colour.

She went over to inspect them, trying in her mind's eye to imagine Jon dressed in the well-cut brushed denim jeans and matching bush shirt, the toning grey and sand jumper draped casually over the model's shoulders adorning Jon's, and failed miserably. Even so . . . he *was* short of jeans, and she could always bring them back. Recklessly she bought a full outfit, adding socks and the shoes that the assistant pointed out to her, only remembering on the way out that she hadn't got anything for herself.

A rack of pale green cotton shorts with matching patterned short sleeved shirts and plain T-shirts caught her eye, and while she was studying them Alex tugged away from her hand, coming back several seconds later proudly clutching a mint and white bikini plus a pair of matching shorts.

'Look at these, Sophy,' she demanded. 'They would look great with those shorts and things. You could sunbathe in the garden in them.'

It was years since she had worn a bikini—four at least. That was how long it had been since she had last been abroad. She no longer felt so ashamed of her body that she could not bring herself to reveal more of it than actually necessary, but even so . . . a bikini?

'I don't . . .' she began and then seeing how Alex's face fell, amended her remark quickly, 'I don't see why not! Come on, let's go and pay for all these things, and then as a special treat . . .'

'Fish and chips?' they both begged together.

Laughing, she gave way.

'Uncle Jon hardly ever lets us have chips,' David complained on the way home. 'He says they aren't good for you.'

'He's quite right,' Sophy agreed, firmly squashing any hopes David might have that she would not. There was a rather neglected vegetable plot in the garden and she had already tentatively wondered about planting it next year. There was obviously some of her father in her after all, she thought wryly. She must make a mental note to get the ground cleared and dug over in the winter, not by the arthritic James who normally did the gardening but by someone younger and stronger. Instead, James could supervise the planting next year.

'I wish we had a swimming pool,' Alex sighed when they reached home. 'A lovely, cool swimming pool.'

'Try a cold shower instead,' Sophy suggested wryly, laughing when both children groaned.

This evening the heat was almost oppressive, but there was no sign of any impending storm.

'What are you going to do with Uncle Jon's new clothes?' Alex asked after supper. 'Keep them as a surprise?'

'No, I think I'll just hang them up in his wardrobe ready for him.'

'But what about his old ones?' Alex demanded. 'Are you going to throw them away?' She posed the question with a certain amount of delighted relish.

'Er . . . no, I . . .'

'You could send them all to the cleaners,' David offered practically and knowingly. 'That way he

would have to wear the new ones but he wouldn't
be able to shout because you'd thrown the others
away.'

Slightly startled, Sophy glanced at David's
downbent head. She hadn't even thought he was
listening to their conversation, but he was
obviously far more astute and mature than she had
known.

'Uncle Jon never shouts,' Alex protested loyally.

'No, but he does get angry,' David told her
calmly, 'Not many people know about it, though,
because he just speaks very quietly.'

He was right, Sophy reflected. Jon did go very
quiet when he was angry, and somehow that
controlled softness in his voice was even more
alarming than if he had bellowed at full volume.

'I'm glad Uncle Jon married you and not
Louise,' Alex confided happily to Sophy, leaning
her head affectionately against the latter's knee.

'Don't be silly,' David told his sister scornfully.
'Uncle Jon would never have married Louise.'

'No, he was frightened of her,' Alex confided
naïvely. 'He always used to go ... er ... er ... a
lot more when she was there.'

If it was possible David looked even more
scornful. 'That wasn't because he was frightened
of her, silly,' he told Alex. 'It was because . . .' He
went bright red and closed his mouth, an
expression crossing his face that somehow
reminded Sophy of Jon.

'Because what, David?' she pressed, as confused
herself as Alex plainly was.

He wouldn't look at her, scuffing the toe of his
shoe against the worn carpet, eventually muttering,
'Oh, nothing . . .'

Wise enough not to press him, Sophy was nevertheless still bewildered. As she got them ready for bed she told herself that it could be nothing more than a little boy's natural desire to protect those closest to him, and David adored his uncle, there was no doubt about that.

CHAPTER FOUR

ON Friday morning, after dropping the children off at school, Sophy made her way to Cambridge to do the weekly food shopping. Exhausted by the heat and press of people in the shops she was only too pleased to get back inside her car. The air inside was stifling, and winding down the windows, she drove home.

She was expecting that Jon would ring sometime during the course of the day to tell her what flight he would be on. She had bought smoked salmon for dinner tomorrow because she knew he liked it, and there was a ham in the fridge which she had baked especially the day before. When she got back she would make up his bed . . . and perhaps pick some flowers for the sitting room.

Abruptly she shook her head. Their marriage was a business relationship, she reminded herself severely. Jon would be understandably embarrassed if he came home to find she had made a lot of special arrangements to welcome him. But even while she acknowledged the sense of her thinking there was a niggling sense of disappointment as though she had been denied some small pleasure she had been anticipating.

Although it was only eleven o'clock, the heat when she stopped the car on the drive, was enervating. Listlessly she ferried the shopping into the kitchen and put it all away. The cotton T-shirt she was wearing was sticking uncomfortably to her skin, and there were grubby marks on her matching cotton denim skirt where she had touched it with her hands. The pretty, pale blue outfit, so crisp and neat when she went out, now looked tired and limp. She had rolled her hair up into a knot to keep it out of the way and the back of her neck ached from the weight of it and the shopping.

Tiredly she made her way upstairs, going first to the airing cupboard and collecting fresh bedding for Jon's room.

The door was slightly open and with her arms full she had to lean against it to open it wider to get in.

'What . . .?'

She heard the startled exclamation as she stepped into the room and shocked by the total unexpectedness of it she stood stock still, her eyes flying wide open as she clutched the bedding to her.

'Jon?' Her voice sounded rusty and thick, totally unfamiliar . . . as unfamiliar to her as the figure standing beside the bed, she thought wildly, swallowing the lump of tension which seemed to have invaded her throat, totally unable to withdraw her stunned gaze from the body of the man standing in front of her, completely naked apart from the brief white towel wrapped round his hips.

Perhaps it was the whiteness of the towel that made Jon's skin look so brown, she thought hazily, silently observing the healthy sheen on skin that adhered firmly to male muscles. His hair was wet, which must explain why in its damp tousled state and the way it clung to his scalp it should so suddenly make her aware of the faintly arrogant masculinity of Jon's features. The blue eyes were narrowed and watchful but curiously brilliant and sharp for someone who needed such strong glasses, the dark hair clinging to his head mirrored in colour and texture by that which ran diagonally and vertically along the male planes of his body.

The most curious sensation was washing over her. She felt so weak that her legs barely seemed able to support her. With a small moan she tottered to the bed, sinking down on to it still clutching the bedding.

'Sophy! Are you all right?'

So it was Jon! No mistaking that pleasantly mild voice.

'No. Yes ... it's the heat,' she managed disjointedly, suddenly uncomfortably aware that the heat of which she spoke came from inside her body and not from outside. Anxiously she clutched the linen even closer to her chest, shamingly aware of the sudden tension in her nipples. For goodness' sake, she chided herself mentally, pull yourself together. She had seen men without their shirts on before—without even as much as Jon was wearing. At least, she had seen Chris ... But his body had been nothing like Jon's, she realised weakly. Nothing like as tautly masculine. She had never for instance possessed the slightest desire to reach out and touch Chris, to see if his skin felt as silkily warm as it looked.

'What are you doing here?' Her voice sounded breathless and too high. She could see Jon frowning as she managed to drag her bemused gaze from his body to his face. Thank God he was short-sighted, she thought wryly, feeling her face flame for what she might have betrayed to him if he hadn't been.

'I . . . er . . . got an earlier flight than I intended. Sorry if I shocked you.'

Shocked her? There was nothing but mild vagueness in his voice; nothing to make her feel that he didn't just mean his apology in the sense of having shocked her by his unexpected arrival, and yet . . . She glanced at him covertly and told herself she was imagining things in thinking that he was ascribing her shock as being due to his semi-nude state.

'Here, let me take those from you.' He stepped towards her and instantly she was aware of the clean, soapy smell of his body. Instinctively she shrank back, still clutching the bedding, all too uncomfortably aware that her body was still betrayingly aroused by the sight of him but he was already reaching for the linen in her arms and somehow Sophy found herself relinquishing it. As he moved back, his hand brushed against the curve of her breast and immediately Sophy jumped.

'Sorry about that . . . I can hardly see a damn thing without my glasses.' The words were muffled as he turned away from her.

His back was as brown and well-muscled as his chest, Sophy thought, admiring it and his legs, long and roughened by dark hairs. As she stood up and caught sight of her own reflection in the mirror she decided it was just as well Jon was short-sighted. Where her T-shirt clung to the contours of her breasts it clearly revealed their aroused contours and the firm peaks of her nipples.

'I'll, er . . . I'll come back and make the bed later,' she managed to say as she hurried out of the room and into the protection of her own.

It was only later when she had managed to restore a little of her normal calm, with a cool shower and a change of clothes that she realised she had said nothing to Jon about the changes she had made in his wardrobe.

She found him downstairs making some coffee, and what was more he was wearing the sand coloured stone washed denims she had bought for him in Marks & Spencer.

'Something seems to have happened to my clothes,' he remarked equably when she walked in. 'I don't suppose you happen to know anything about it.'

'Er . . . they're at the cleaners. I thought . . . that is we thought . . . well, with the heatwave continuing, I had to get the children some lighter things and . . .' Her voice petered out uncomfortably as she realised just exactly what she had done.

'You were thoughtful enough to get some for me at the same time,' Jon concluded gently. 'That was very wifely of you.'

'Well if you don't like them, you don't have to . . . that is . . .' Realising that she was gabbling, Sophy forced herself to stop. What was happening to her? Anyone would think she was frightened of Jon when in actual fact he was the mildest and gentlest man alive.

'I thought those awful hairy suits and ancient cords were too heavy for this weather,' she told him simply, 'but if you don't like what I got for you they can easily be changed.'

'You're not trying to change me into a male model, by any chance?'

A smile lurked at the corner of his mouth and

taking heart from it, Sophy shook her head, adding impishly, 'Some hope, you're far too big and muscular.'

She wasn't sure which of them looked the more surprised. A deep mortifying burn of colour spread over her skin but fortunately Jon seemed to be oblivious to it. He had turned away from her to watch the coffee filtering. He was probably as embarrassed as she was herself, she thought wryly, and wondered why she should find that thought so dismal. What did she want? For Jon to do something macho like take her in his arms and let her see how well her description matched reality? Jon wasn't like that. He wasn't interested in her, or any other woman, sexually. She knew that.

'I'm tired . . . I think I must be suffering from jet lag. I think I'll go out and have a sleep in the garden.'

Did he want to sleep or was he simply wanting to escape from her company? Sophy wondered, watching him wander outside. Well at least now she could go up and make his bed but when she got upstairs she found that he had made it for himself. She shrugged dismissively. Of course Jon was used to looking after himself . . . or was this a polite way of informing her that he did not expect to find her in his room again?

Moved by some impulse she wasn't ready to define Sophy went into her own room and changed into the bikini Alex had picked out for her. She had already worn it once earlier in the week and that exposure to the sun had turned her skin the colour of clotted cream.

When she got outside Jon was lying sleeping in a deck chair, oblivious to her presence. She tried to settle down; first by stretching her body out on the towel she had brought downstairs with her and then by going back inside to dig out a paperback book to read. It was all useless. A restless nervous energy seemed to possess her body, making it impossible for her to simply lie down and relax. When Jon had been asleep for just over a hour she got up and started on some desultory weeding. The activity helped to soothe her a little but her heartbeat seemed to be much faster than usual, her skin damp with a heat that wasn't entirely due to the sun.

At two o'clock she abandoned her self-imposed task and went back inside, getting out the blender to make lemonade, her hands moving deftly as she did so. Leaving it to cool she used what was left from the jug she had made the previous day to fill two glasses, putting them on a tray and then defiantly carrying it outside to where Jon still slept.

The sun had moved slightly and now slanted across his face, revealing the taut bone structure. The hair flopping on to his forehead looked disarmingly soft and silky. Would it feel like Alex's?

Suddenly aware of what she was doing Sophy snatched back the hand she had extended towards his face and instead placed it firmly on his shoulder, shaking him.

He was awake immediately blinking his eyes slowly as they focused on her. 'I've brought you some lemonade. If you sleep too much now, you won't be able to tonight.' How cross and ungracious she sounded, Sophy thought. What was the matter with her?

Jon reached for his glasses which he had discarded several feet away on the lawn and Sophy bent to retrieve them for him at the same time. It was a small task she had performed more times than she could count but this time, as she handed them to him and watched him put them on, for some reason her body felt as though it were in the grip of a deadly paralysis.

It was impossible for her to move away even when his slightly stunned glance slid over her, taking in the brevity of her bikini. She could almost see him cringing away from her, she thought bitterly, immediately stepping back and retreating to her own towel. Why on earth hadn't she put on something more discreet, covered herself up a little more? If she carried on like this much longer he might begin to think that she was . . . what? Trying to seduce him?

Prickles of heat ran across her skin, her body tense. What a ridiculous thought . . . of course she didn't want that. After all, one of the main reasons she had married him had been to escape from any sort of sexual involvement.

Confused and alarmed by both her thoughts and her feelings Sophy got up and rolled up her towel.

'Had enough?' Jon asked mildly, watching her.

'It's almost time to pick up the children.' It was true, after all. 'I've left all your post on your desk if you want to go through it.'

There, that made her feel better—restored their relationship to its proper footing—reminded her that there was nothing between them other than a business relationship and a certain amount of cool friendship, and that was the way she wanted it, she told herself firmly. She had the children to share her love with . . .

Love! She froze, staring blindly into space. How on earth had that crept into her thoughts?

The sudden touch of Jon's fingers on her bare arm made her jump visibly and swing round. He was standing right behind her, holding his empty lemonade glass, watching her rather uneasily.

'Sorry if I shocked you. I just wanted to say I'll come with you to get the kids.'

'Very well. It won't take me long to shower and get changed.'

For the first time it hit her that she was behaving far from naturally with Jon. She no longer felt completely at ease in his company . . . far from it.

She was as good as her promise, arriving back downstairs again within half an hour, dressed comfortably in a soft, mint green cotton skirt and a pastel-toned, patterned shirt.

Jon had his usual battle clambering into the car. 'Next week we get a new car,' he told her wryly as she drove off, adding, 'Is there any make in particular that appeals to you?'

Sophy shook her head.

'I'm told BMW make a good vehicle,' Jon offered. 'How about them?'

'They're very expensive,' Sophy warned him.

Beside her, Jon shrugged. 'That doesn't matter . . . safety and comfort do.'

'You managed to sort everything out in Nassau, then?' Sophy asked when the silence began pressing painfully on her screaming nerves.

'Yes. Oh, that reminds me . . . Harry Silver, my contact over there, will be coming to stay in

Cambridge soon for a week or so. He and I used to be at university together. I'd like to invite him and his wife over for dinner one night.'

He might just as well be an employer giving his housekeeper her instructions, Sophy thought bitterly, immediately chiding herself for the thought. *She* was the one at fault, she was reacting in a totally unfamiliar and unreasonable way and had been ever since she walked into Jon's room and found him there.

That must be it, she decided, relieved to have hit upon an explanation for her behaviour. It was the shock. The shock of seeing him, a mocking inner voice demanded, or the shock of *how* she had seen him?

'Is anything wrong?'

Sophy bit her lip. So even Jon had noticed her tension. 'No . . . I think it's just this heat,' she gave him a brief smile. 'Sometimes I find it a bit wearing. Unlike you.'

A strange silence followed her last two words, and for some reason Sophy felt constrained to explain them. 'That is . . . you've got such a good tan you must enjoy sunbathing.'

'There were times when I had to wait for them to run certain tests. Lillian was kind enough to take pity on me and let me have the use of her patio and pool whilst I was doing so.'

'Lillian?' Sophy asked sharply, taking her eyes off the road for a second to look at him.

'Harry's assistant,' Jon responded vaguely. 'She had a condominium near the Centre, with a communal pool. It was much more convenient to stay there whilst I was waiting for the results of the tests rather than to go back to my hotel.'

A sensation unlike any other Sophy had experienced in her life was boiling through her; a mixture of anger, resentment and . . . jealousy . . . she recognised dully. She was jealous of this unknown Lillian, Jon spoke about so easily. Was that why he didn't want *her* in his room because . . .? Abruptly she brought her careering thoughts to a halt. Why should Jon have reacted any differently to this Lillian than he did to any other woman? What on earth was the matter with her? She was behaving like a jealous wife suspecting her husband of having an affair.

Fortunately they had reached the school and in the excitement of the children greeting Jon she was able to bring herself under some sort of control.

Tea was a light-hearted meal, although she herself took a back-seat in the conversation.

'Uncle Jon looks nice in his new clothes, Sophy,' Alex announced approvingly. 'We got you some in blue because that's the same colour as your eyes,' Alex informed her uncle, dimpling a smile at him, 'and Sophy has sent all your old things to the cleaners.'

The weekend was as hot as the rest of the week had been and they spent most of it in the garden. Sophy was having trouble sleeping. Each day seemed to drain a little more out of her, and yet she was so tensely wound up that she just could not relax. Her whole body was gripped by a peculiar and unfamiliar tension which left her nerves on edge and made her muscles ache. But at least no one else seemed to be aware that anything was wrong with her.

Even worse than her growing inner tension was the compulsion she seemed to have developed to be with Jon, and yet when she was with him, she felt acutely tense, unable to so much as sit down for more than five minutes at a time.

The trouble was, she thought exhaustedly on Sunday afternoon, that while she had suddenly become aware of him as a man, Jon simply did not see her as a woman at all. He would be deeply embarrassed if he knew the reason for the way she occasionally found herself looking at his body. She was embarrassed herself. Embarrassed and annoyed. What was the matter with her? Even with Chris, when she had been deeply in love with him, she had felt no stirring of desire within her to know him as a man.

Perhaps it was simply the fact that Jon was so elusive ... so completely disinterested and unaffected by her that was making her behave like this, she decided, turning over on to her stomach and trying to relax. She could feel the heat of the sun seeping into her skin as she tried to come to terms with the reality of such contrary behaviour. Was that it? Subconsciously did she see Jon as a challenge? Was that what was making her behave so oddly? A desire to arouse within him a male reaction to her as a woman? But why? That was totally against everything she had felt when she first married him.

At last, worn out by her thoughts, she fell into a light sleep.

Someone was touching her skin with the lightest of movements, strong fingers moving against her spine. She moved languorously beneath them,

enjoying the slow sweet wave of sensuality rippling
through her.

Jon . . . Jon was touching her . . . caressing her
as . . .

'That's it, Uncle Jon, you've got him now.'

The breathy whisper close to her ear made her
tense and wake up properly, quickly rolling over.

Alex was squatting beside her, Jon bending over
her holding one palm cupped.

'You were being explored by a caterpillar,' he
told Sophy with a smile. 'We were trying to
remove him without disturbing you.'

A caterpillar! It was because of a caterpillar that
Jon had touched her? Indignation and disappointment merged sharply within her. For some reason
she almost wanted to cry.

'Hey, come on, it's nothing to be frightened of.
In fact he's very handsome, look.' Jon extended
his cupped palm towards her so that she could
admire the furry creature and dutifully she
managed to summon a thin grimace, her colour
changing suddenly as she remembered how her
body had slowly arched beneath what she had
thought was his caress. Had he realised? She
darted a quick glance at his face but it was mildly
unreadable, nothing in the blue eyes to tell her
what he might or might not have thought, and for
the first time she realised how very, very good Jon
was at concealing his thoughts and feelings.

After that it became ever harder for her. For
one thing it was no longer possible for her to deny
to herself that sexually she was attracted to Jon.
That more than that she wanted to touch him and
be touched by him in return. She tried to tell
herself that she was having these odd fantasies

simply because she knew they were impossible and that in that way they allowed her to imagine she was sexually responsive without running the risk of Jon discovering she was not, since he would never be her lover.

What made it worse was that she seemed forever to be bumping into Jon in a semi-nude state. He was working at the house and either he was just coming out of the bathroom clad in nothing more than a brief towel, or he was in the garden, sunbathing in a pair of faded denim shorts that fitted him so snugly they might almost be indecent.

And that was not all. Sophy knew she was challenging his sexuality. Knew it and despised herself for it, and yet seemed unable to do anything about it. She wanted him to react to her as a woman. But why? If he did she knew what the outcome would be. As far as she was concerned sex was something that was painful and humiliating. She was thoroughly confused by herself and what she was doing. Thoroughly and completely.

CHAPTER FIVE

'I'VE got to go into Cambridge today—I don't know when I'll be back, probably later this afternoon.'

They were all having breakfast and Sophy inclined her head in acknowledgement of Jon's remarks. From today she was going to start behaving differently, she told herself. It was pointless trying to attract the attention of a man who had told her that he had no interest in her sex. She had been acting very irresponsibly, and she was lucky that Jon was so completely oblivious to what she had been trying to do, otherwise he would have been very embarrassed.

Jon's taxi was due to arrive while she was taking the children to school, and driving them there she found herself fretting over the fact that she was not at home to see Jon off. That such a small thing should have such a tremendous effect on her, was worrying. She tried to rationalise her behaviour by telling herself she was naturally worried because she knew that Jon was bound to forget some all important something but deep down inside she knew it was not that. She wanted to be there physically, to be with him, she realised on a sudden start of disquiet, not liking the conclusions that went with the realisation.

When she got back, the house felt empty. She performed her normal household chores automatically and then went into the study to check through

the morning's post. There was nothing that was
particularly urgent but there was a letter with an
airmail stamp from Nassau addressed to Jon and
marked 'Private and Confidential'. Was it from his
friend? Or was it from the woman who had
allowed him to use her apartment and pool? She
didn't like the sensations stirring deep inside her.
She had no right to be jealous of any friendships
Jon might form outside their marriage and besides,
what was there to be jealous of? She had known
when she married Jon what their marriage would
be and she had been happy with that knowledge.
She had also believed that Jon was as immune
from sexual desire as she felt herself to be. And so
he was, she told herself firmly, but somehow she
couldn't stop herself from thinking that maybe in
Nassau he had discovered a woman who could
break through his barrier of indifference. The
thought made the unpleasant sensations lodged
beneath her breastbone, increase. Tension held her
body in a vice-like grip, jealousy tormenting her
mind with mental pictures of Jon's tanned body
entwined with that of some unknown but lithely
desirable woman whose face she could not see.

Telling herself that it was the heat that was
making her so on edge and prickly, Sophy went
upstairs, stripping off her clothes and standing
beneath the shower, letting the cool water slide off
her over-heated skin.

Only when it was starting to raise goosebumps
did she emerge from the water, towelling herself
dry briskly. It was too hot to work indoors, and
she was too restless to concentrate on anything.
She might as well spend what was left of the
morning sunbathing, she thought wryly, hunting

through her drawer for her bikini. As she stood up
she caught a glimpse of her nude body in the
mirror. The sun had turned her skin a soft, golden
colour banded by cool white where her bikini had
concealed it from the hot rays. The colour suited
her, she recognised, her attention caught and held
by her own reflection. It was years since she had
looked at her body—really looked at it that was,
perhaps not even since that débâcle with Chris.
Now she studied what she saw, with careful eyes,
noting the slender strength of her shoulders, the
fullness of her breasts tipped with deep coral, the
flatness of her ribcage and the slight swell of her
stomach. She had a woman's body now, not a
girl's, curved and feminine but those curves and
the warm glow of her skin offered a promise the
woman inside could not fulfill. She might look
entirely female and desirable, but she was not, she
reminded herself bitterly, and the desire she felt to
reach out and touch Jon and to be touched by him
in return must surely spring from some con-
tradictory impulse inside her which knew quite
well that it was safe to torment her in this fashion
since there was no question of that desire ever
being fulfilled. No doubt if Jon did make any
attempt to touch her she would recoil from him as
she had done from all the others, fearing his
discovery of the truth about her; that she was just
an empty sham of femininity.

She was supposed to be sunbathing, not
standing here letting herself get morose, she
reminded herself, hurriedly tugging on her bikini
and going downstairs.

The garden was slumbrous with heat, bees
droning drunkenly from flower to flower, heavy

with pollen. Above her the sky was a hot blue arc, the grass beneath her feet was drying out in patches where the sun had burned it. She really ought to do some weeding, she thought, wryly glancing at the untidy beds, but she was too tired. Since Jon came back she hadn't been sleeping very well, something she had refused to admit to herself until now.

She lay on her stomach, pillowing her head in a cushion, and then remembering the small white bank of flesh across her back, reached behind herself and unfastened the ties of her bikini. It was completely private in the garden and she was unlikely to be disturbed.

In her sleep she moved, turning on to her side, and curling her body inwards slightly into a position that was automatically defensive.

Someone was touching her, stroking her skin. Jon! A wave of pleasure shivered through her and she stretched beneath his touch like a cat asking to be stroked, opening her eyes and saying his name with sleepy delight.

Only it wasn't Jon, it was Chris, the expression on his face frighteningly resentful as his fingers tightened round her unprotected breast, squeezing painfully . . . hurting her.

She was instantly and icily cold, shrinking instinctively from him, any thought she had entertained that she might be turning into a sex-starved female ready to welcome any man's caresses dying instantly and completely. The only sensation Chris's touch aroused was one of intense revulsion. Angrily she reached out to push him away, but he was too strong for her, burying his fingers in her hair, and tugging painfully on it as he pushed her back on to the ground.

Somewhere she could hear the sound of a car and struggled harder but all her struggles seemed to do was to inflame him further. She could feel the hot urgency of his breath against her skin, his voice thick and angry as he muttered, 'You bitch . . . you deserve this!' His mouth was on hers, his teeth savaging her tightly closed lips. She could hear footsteps coming towards them, shaking the sun-baked ground so that she could feel the movements against her ear. She tried to push Chris away thankful that they were about to be interrupted but was unprepared for the suddenness with which he released her and stood up. She turned her head, but the sunlight dazzled her for a moment.

'I think you'd better tidy yourself up a bit, darling, your husband's here.'

What an actor Chris was, pretending that she had welcomed his touch when . . . Jon . . . Jon was back! She sat up quickly, struggling with the ties of her bikini.

'Why not let me do that for you?' Chris was actually daring to reach out and touch her.

'Get away from me!' She stood up shakingly, securing the strings, and looked at Jon. He seemed to be studying the progress of a particularly heavy bee.

'Thank heavens you're back. Chris forced himself on me, Jon,' she told him thickly. 'I was asleep and . . .'

'Oh come on, darling, surely you can do better than that?' Chris was jeering now, but she could see the very real hatred in his eyes, and wondered at the cause of it. Why was Chris doing this to her? And then instinctively she knew. He had never forgiven her for her frigidity and now he wanted to punish her for daring to find sexual happiness with someone else.

'I'm sure your husband is nowhere near as stupid as he looks.' He looked tauntingly at Jon, who returned the look with mild curiosity. Grinning at her, Chris walked away from them. Sophy watched him go in complete silence. Hadn't Jon understood what she was telling him?

She heard a car engine fire and then slowly purr down the drive and bitter resentment flooded through her body. It was wrong and unfair that Chris should be able to walk away like that after physically molesting her and humiliating Jon. She took a deep breath and found that she was shaking . . . tense with an anger that had to find an outlet.

'Do you realise that if you hadn't come back when you did he would probably have tried to rape me?' he cried emotionally. 'And you let him just walk away. You . . . for God's sake, Jon, what kind of husband are you?' she demanded thickly.

Had he even heard what she was saying? He appeared to be studying one of the flowers but at last he lifted his head and looked at her in that rather abstracted way of his, glancing away to remove a piece of fluff from his shirt-sleeve before replying.

'The kind who feels that when he discovers his wife in the arms of an old lover, discretion might possibly be the better part of valour,' he told her calmly. 'You must admit that I had no way of knowing whether his embrace was welcome or not, Sophy.'

'But I'm married to *you*,' she pointed out despairingly. God, didn't he even care the smallest bit? Wasn't he the slightest bit jealous or resentful? If she had been the one to walk into that scene . . . if she had discovered him . . .

'Our marriage does not give me the right to assume physical chastity on your part.'

'But you said——' She broke off. What was the use? Jon plainly did not care one way or the other, despite his statement before they were married that he would not expect her to take lovers.

'Always logical and calm, that's you, isn't it, Jon?' she demanded bitterly. 'You're just like one of those damned computers you're so fond of— incapable of any human emotional reaction.'

She pushed past him and ran into the house, going straight up to her room, and flinging herself face down on the bed. She badly wanted to cry, in a way she couldn't remember doing in years. Chris's attack had frightened her, her body ached with the tension that fear had brought, and her breast throbbed where he had hurt her but what hurt far more, was Jon's calm indifference. He had stood there and let Chris insult him and her, and he had said nothing—not even when she had told him that Chris had attacked her. He had looked at her with his face wiped clean of all expression— totally emotionless.

She was his *wife* for heaven's sake. She had a right to expect his protection . . . his . . . his championship. Chris had hurt and frightened her . . . and primitive though it was, she acknowledged that she would have liked to have seen Jon hurt and frighten him in return. Had he believed what Chris had said to him? She swallowed suddenly turning over and staring unseeingly up at the ceiling. Surely not? She had been so caught up in her own feelings, in the shock of listening to Chris's lies, that it had never occurred to her that Jon might believe them, that he might take what had happened at face value.

Did he really think she was that sort of woman? The sort who would break the solemn vows of marriage ... who would allow herself to be involved with a man who was already married, who had once treated her with such contempt? Didn't Jon know her at all?

Tiredly she got up, but instead of going downstairs and apologising to Jon for her outburst and talking to him about what had happened as she knew she should, she showered again, and dressed slowly, too heart-sick to face him. Her apology would have to wait until she was in a calmer frame of mind. As she went downstairs, she heard sounds from the study and guessed that he was working. Well, that gave her an excuse not to interrupt him.

He was still working when she went to fetch the children back from school. For once their energy and chatter gave her no pleasure. She felt drained and deeply unhappy. This was the time when she needed a mother or a sister to talk to, she thought wearily, someone who would understand what she was feeling.

When they got back, an unfamiliar brand new car was parked outside the house. Mentally admiring the sleek lines of the very expensive BMW, Sophy shepherded the children inside the house. The car probably belonged to one of Jon's clients, many of whom were extremely wealthy men and she paused outside the now silent study, reluctant to disturb a business meeting.

The children it seemed had no such qualms and burst in before she could stop them, Alex shouting out, 'We're back, Uncle Jon!'

Reluctantly she followed them to find that Jon was alone in the study. She glanced round it and then looked at him. 'I thought you had someone with you,' she told him. 'There's a car outside.'

'Yes.' For once he looked neither vague nor embarrassed. 'It's yours . . . I bought it for you this morning.'

She had to sit down to get over the shock. Jon had bought that car for her! 'But it's so expensive! Jon. . . .'

'You said we needed a larger car and from what I can discover, this one seems to combine all our requirements. Of course, if you would prefer something else?'

She shook her head. 'No . . . no, of course not.'

'It's ours?' David was wide-eyed with excitement. 'Come on, Alex,' he instructed his sister, 'let's go and have a look at it.'

In the end all four of them went back outside, the children enthusing over the car whilst Sophy admired it in stunned silence. She was pleased to see that it was fitted with rear seat-belts for the children. When she got inside she found it both luxurious and well equipped. At David's insistence they went for a short drive although she was not familiar enough with the car's automatic gears and power steering system to take them very far.

'Jon, it's . . . it's very generous of you,' she said haltingly when they got back. The words seemed to stick in her throat, her earlier accusations lying painfully on her conscience. She wanted desperately to call back those earlier ugly words, but found she could not do so in front of the children, and it still tormented her that Jon might actually have believed Chris's lies.

Supper was an uncomfortable, silent meal; even the children, it seemed, were aware of the tension existing between the two adults. Afterwards, when Sophy was supervising their baths, she was shocked when Alex asked her hesitantly, 'Have you and Uncle Jon quarrelled?'

'No, of course not,' she assured the little girl swiftly. 'Whatever gave you that idea?'

'I'm not sure.' She screwed her eyes up and then said slowly, 'P'haps because at teatime it just felt like you had quarrelled ... all stiff and sharp somehow.'

'Well I promise you we haven't,' Sophy reassured her kissing the curly head, feeling guilty because she was the one responsible for the atmosphere Alex had so accurately described.

She had to apologise to Jon, she acknowledged mentally as she tucked both children up in bed, and kissed them good night. She had been wrong to say the things she had to him and then to flounce off in a huff. After all why should she expect him to ... to behave like a real husband?

She pressed her fingers to her temples which were throbbing with tension and pain. What had she been hoping for when she ran inside like that? That Jon might follow her ... that he might ... What?

Telling herself that there was nothing to be achieved by putting off the evil moment she went back downstairs. Jon was in the study. She

knocked briefly and then went in, her eyes
immediately going to the letter in front of him,
recognising it as the one which had arrived from
Nassau that morning.

'This is from Harry Silver,' he told her.
'Confirming his visit. He'll be bringing his wife
with him. I thought we might have them here to
dinner.'

'Jon, I must talk to you.' How stiff and
unnatural her voice sounded. She could see Jon
frowning and her heartbeat suddenly increased,
thudding nervously into her chest wall. 'I'm sorry,'
she said miserably, 'and I owe you an apology . . .
I shouldn't have spoken to you the way I did . . . I
was wrong.'

'Yes, you were,' he agreed evenly, standing up
and coming round the front of the desk. There was
a look in his eyes she found hard to recognise, but
instinctively she took a step backwards, only to
find that Jon was right in front of her. 'Very
wrong,' he murmured softly reaching out and
pulling her into his arms. 'I'm not a computer,
Sophy . . . and I *am* capable of feelings. These
feelings.'

His mouth moved on hers with unerring
instinct, caressing, arousing . . . seducing her own,
she recognised in stunned bewilderment as it
parted eagerly responding to the warm exploration
of his lips like the thirsty earth soaking up rain.
The bruises Chris had inflicted were forgotten, her
whole body felt hollow and light, empty of
everything but the sensation of Jon's mouth on her
own. He was kissing her in a way she had always
dreamed of being kissed, she acknowledged hazily,
with an expertise and knowledge she had never

imagined he would own. Immediately she tensed
but Jon wouldn't let her go.

'Oh, no,' he whispered, transferring his mouth
from her lips to her ear. 'You don't get out of this
so easily, Sophy.' One hand left her body to cup
her face, firmly but without the pain Chris had
inflicted on her.

He had removed his glasses and this close to, his
eyes were unbelievably blue ... not sapphire and
not navy but something in between, she thought
hazily, unable to tear her own away from them.
Jon was still speaking and it took several seconds
for her to register the words.

'After all,' he said silkily, 'wasn't it this you
wanted when you lashed out at me earlier?'

Instantly she felt sick and shaken. Did he
honestly believe that of her; that she had
deliberately tried to incite him to ... to this?

She shook her head, the bitter denial bursting
from her throat before she could silence it.

For a second he said nothing, then she felt his
hold slacken slightly, his eyes shuttered as he
released her and stepped slightly away. Immediately she shivered, feeling bereft ... aching
for the warmth of his arms around her once more.

'Forgive me.' His voice was harsher than she
had ever known it. 'I obviously mistook anger for
frustration.'

Frustration? Slowly his meaning dawned and a
scarlet wave of anger scalded its way over her skin.
Did he actually think she had deliberately tried to
incite him to ... to make love to her ... because
she was suffering from frustration because he had
interrupted her with Chris? That she wanted *him*
to finish what Chris had started? The thought

made her feel acutely sick and for the second time that day she was bitterly angry with him.

Tears stung her eyes but she refused to let them fall.

'You couldn't be more wrong,' she told him thickly. 'I wasn't lying to you when I said Chris attacked me, and as for thinking I wanted you to ... to finish what he had started....' She swallowed hard on the nausea clutching her stomach. 'You're doing both of us an injustice. I can't think why you married me, Jon, if that's the sort of woman you think I am. I'm tired, Jon,' she told him listlessly as the surge of anger drained away, leaving her feeling exhausted both emotionally and physically. 'I think it must be this hot weather that's making everyone so on edge. I'm going to bed.'

She hesitated by the door, consumed by a totally crazy desire to turn round and go back, to beg him to take her back in his arms and kiss her again but somehow she found the strength to resist it.

Upstairs she was too tired even to start undressing. She caught a glimpse of her reflection in her mirror and stared at her swollen mouth touching it tentatively with her fingertips. When Jon had kissed her she had experienced sensations so totally alien and yet so totally known that she was still shocked by them. But not as shocked as she had been by Jon's assured experience. When she had thought about him kissing her she had imagined his touch would be hesitant, unsure and perhaps rather clumsy but his mouth had moved on hers with wholly masculine authority, subtly demanding, revealing a wealth of experience she had never expected him to have. For a man who

openly expressed a lack of interest in sex Jon had
revealed a totally unexpected degree of expertise.
And she wasn't sure she liked it. Where and with
whom had he gained that expertise? Had he once
perhaps been deeply in love? So deeply in love that
it had made him eschew all further emotional or
physical involvement? She shivered slightly, faintly
disturbed by the discovery than Jon was not what
she had thought him to be ... that there was
obviously much of himself that he kept hidden.
But why had he kissed her?

That was a question to which she could not find
an answer other than perhaps out of male pride
because she had verbally challenged his sexuality.

Yes ... she decided finally, that must be it. Yet
didn't that explanation too, indicate that Jon was
not the totally non-sexual, mild man she had
always believed him to be? Had she simply
deceived herself or had he deliberately deceived her
and if so, why? Why present an image to her that
was, at least partially, false? That was something
she was too tired to even try and analyse.
Tomorrow, she told herself sleepily, as she
prepared for bed, she would try to unravel these
mysteries tomorrow.

In the morning Sophy overslept slightly and, much
to the children's disappointment, opted not to use
the new car to take them to school. After
explaining that she needed to drive it by herself to
get used to it first, she managed to placate them.

She had promised to drive Jon into Cambridge
when she had dropped the children off and had
decided to combine it with a shopping trip.

'We could meet for lunch.' Jon suggested, as she

was parking. 'Unless of course you won't have time.'

Sophy had been dreading being alone with him after what had happened the previous evening but he was his normal mild, calm self, and she had even been able to persuade herself that most of last night's heart searchings had been prompted by nothing more than her own imagination. After all, it was not perhaps surprising that she should enjoy his kiss. She had wanted him to touch her for long enough.

'Er ... no. Lunch would be lovely,' she stammered, realising that Jon was waiting for her response.

'Good.'

The smile he gave her made her heart lurch drunkenly and, for some stupid reason, she simply sat in the car and watched him walk away, unable to take her eyes off his lean, lithe body. He was wearing his new clothes as though he had always worn them and watching the way more than one woman turned to observe his long legged progress down the street, Sophy found herself wishing she had left him to his baggy cords and shapeless shirts. She didn't want other women looking at him, she realised with a sharp pang. She didn't want them admiring the masculine lines of his body, the breadth of his shoulders beneath the fine cotton of his shirt ...

Like someone moving slowly in a dream, she shook her head, trying to disperse it, forcing herself to get out of the car and lock it.

Her shopping didn't take her long, and she was finished in plenty of time to get to the office where she had arranged to meet Jon. So much time in fact that when she found herself studying an attractive lemon sundress in a shop window, she gave in to the temptation to go inside and try it on.

It fitted her perfectly, enhancing the golden gleam of her skin and bringing out the red highlights in her hair. Tiny shoe-string straps tied on her shoulders in provocative bows, a broad, stiffened belt emphasising the narrowness of her waist, before the skirt flared out over a slightly stiffened underskirt.

'It might have been made for you,' the assistant said, truthfully.

'I'll take it . . .' Sophy took a deep breath, 'and I'll keep it on. . . .'

The other girl's eyes twinkled. 'Mmm . . . well I certainly think he'll appreciate it, whoever he is.'

'My husband.' The admission was made almost before she was aware of it and angry colour flooded her skin. Of course she wasn't buying this dress for Jon's benefit! She was buying it because it was cool and she was hot . . . and besides it was time she had some pretty things and . . .

Impatiently she waited for the girl to take her cheque and put her things into a bag, regretting now her impulsive decision to wear the dress but too embarrassed to do anything about it.

She found Jon waiting for her when she got to the office. He opened the door for her and, as the strong midday sunlight fell on his face, she realised he looked tired. Lines of strain harshened the shape of his mouth and for some reason he looked almost unfamiliar; harder, more male. As though she were seeing him properly for the first time Sophy stared at him, confused. He in turn was studying her, looking at her with such an air of open appraisal that the sundress, so pretty and cool in the shop, now seemed somehow provocative and dangerous.

'It's such a hot day I thought we'd eat at the Mill.'

The restaurant he named was on the river and very popular. Sophy doubted that they would be able to get a table but she was anxious to escape the tense atmosphere of the small office. It seemed to be stifling her. It must be the heat, she thought dizzily as they went outside but even in the fresh air the tension remained.

In the narrow streets the heat was like a thick blanket, clogging her throat when she tried to breath. Far too acutely conscious of Jon at her side, she started to walk faster, arriving at the car hot and out of breath. In contrast Jon looked cool and lazily at ease. But was he? Some sixth sense made her study him more closely. A tiny pulse flickered unevenly under his skin. This constraint between them was a new thing, and one she did not know how to handle. Almost overnight Jon had turned from a kind, unthreatening man whom she liked very much and was fond of in a sisterly fashion, into a stranger, for whom her feelings were anything but sisterly.

Her face burned as she remembered his laconic accusation the previous evening. She had goaded him deliberately, she recognised that now. She wanted him to react physically to her comments but not because of Chris. All the feelings she had been fighting so hard to suppress flooded through her as she started the car. Why did she have to discover them now, when it was too late? Why had

she not realised before their marriage that she was
vulnerable to Jon's attraction? Was it because they
were married that she was seeing him in this new
light?

The questions buzzed in her tired brain like
swarming wasps, making her stall the car and have
to restart it, whilst Jon sat silently at her side.

To her surprise he had booked a table for them
at the Mill. Not outside where everyone else
seemed to be eating but in the dim coolness of the
mill itself. Once a working flour mill, the building
had been enterprisingly converted into a restaurant
some years ago. Recently it had been taken over by
a young couple with an enthusiasm for wholesome
natural food, which was attractively presented.

Sophy ordered unenthusiastically, knowing that
she was far too wrought up to enjoy her meal. Her
throat seemed to have closed to an aching
tightness, her whole body in the grip of an
unfamiliar tension. She wanted to be with Jon and
yet she didn't. Being alone with him made her feel
nervous and on edge. Something she had never
experienced in his company before, but a feeling
she was familiar with nevertheless. She had
experienced it every time she had dated a man she
liked and whom she had thought might help her to
overcome the stigma that Chris had labelled her
with. It was the utmost stupidity to want Jon
physically, she told herself despairingly, and it was
not even as though he wanted her.

She managed no more than a few bites of both
her first and main courses, refusing a sweet, and
playing with her cup of coffee whilst Jon buttered
biscuits and helped himself to the Stilton.

Why had she ever thought him clumsy? she

wondered absently, watching the neat methodical movement of his hands. In moments she was totally absorbed in watching him, in wondering what it would be like to feel those long fingers against her skin . . .

'Sophy.'

She looked up, confused by the sudden curling ache in the pit of her stomach, her breath catching suddenly, trapped deep in her lungs as she saw the way he was looking at her.

'Jon?'

'Some boxes are better never opened, Pandora,' he said quietly in answer to her unspoken question, 'but it's too late for going back now.'

Sophy moistened dry lips with the tip of her tongue, dreading what he might be going to say. She had seen in that look they had just exchanged a recognition of the desire he had stirred within her and was ashamed of her own betrayal.

'What do you mean?' She was playing for time, hoping to stall whatever was to come but Jon did not want to play. She could tell that from the way his jaw tensed, his eyes narrowing faintly as he studied her face.

'Isn't it obvious what I mean?' he asked quietly, carefully pushing aside his plate and looking at her. She wanted to look away but it was impossible, some power beyond her own puny strength refused to allow her to drag her gaze away from his. 'I want you dammit, Sophy,' she heard him saying rawly, the words falling around her, splintering through her self-control and shattering it completely, shocking her with their intensity, stunning her into silence with their totally unexpectedness. 'I want you as a man wants a woman, in my arms . . . in my bed. Oh, it's all right, I'm not going to force myself on you. I simply brought you here so that we could discuss this sensibly.'

From somewhere she managed to find her voice, the sound of it raw and husky in her own ears as she stammered helplessly, 'But you don't . . . you aren't like that.'

His mouth twisted with unfamiliar cynicism, his voice very soft and faintly metallic as he told her, 'You're wrong, Sophy, I do . . . and I most certainly am, much as it pains me to admit it. Poor Sophy,' his voice mocked her in its irony, 'how shocked you look, and no wonder . . . but did you really think me so sexless? Oh, I know you don't find me physically appealing but unfortunately a human being's ability to experience desire is not in direct ratio to physical attractiveness. Or is that another truth you find hard to digest? Poor Sophy indeed. How disconcerting all this must be for you. . . . You preferred to see me as more machine than man, I'm afraid but you really only have yourself to blame,' he told her harshly. 'I'm not blind despite these . . .' he touched his glasses, his eyes and mouth hard. 'Whether you're willing to admit it or not, you've been deliberately provoking me recently. Why? Because of Benson?'

Unable to listen to any more, Sophy reacted wholly instinctively and did something she'd never done before in her life. She got up and fled from the room, rushing out to the car before Jon could stop her, quickly starting it and driving off.

It wasn't until she reached home that the full enormity of what she had done actually dawned on her. She had left Jon stranded at the Mill. All because she didn't have the courage to be as open with him as he had been with her and tell him that her recent provocative behaviour had sprung from a mingling of pique and curiosity and had had nothing to do with Chris at all. No, not just pique and curiosity . . . there was desire as well; the same desire that was curling through her body now as she remembered what he had said to her about wanting her.

Suddenly galvanised into action she ran to the 'phone and looked up the number of the Mill, quickly dialling it. It seemed an age before anyone answered. Impatiently she asked for Jon and, after what seemed like an endless wait, was told that he had left.

He must have got a taxi, she reflected guiltily. Why had she reacted like that . . . like a gauche and embarrassed teenager? What on earth could she say to him when he came home?

CHAPTER SIX

ONLY he didn't come home. At least not immediately, and he wasn't back when she returned from collecting the children from school either. She had dialled the office several times without getting a reply and was now beginning to get seriously alarmed ... he had every right to be angry with her but to do this. Where was he?

She had to fib to David and Alex, telling them that he had gone out on business. Fortunately they were too accustomed to his sudden departures and arrivals to question her more closely, because she was sure her anxious expression would not have deceived them for very long if they had.

Supper-time came and went and there was still no sign of him. Sophy stayed up until gone midnight, her mind in total panic. Had he walked out on her? Was he so angry with her that he could not bear to come back? Or had he perhaps taken her sudden flight as an indication that she found his revelations totally repellent ... that she found *him* totally repellent? Biting her lip anxiously she paced the floor, tension seizing her body as she heard a car coming up the drive.

The taxi driver greeted her appearance with a relieved grimace. 'Passed out cold I think he has,' he informed her bluntly.

At first when she looked into the taxi she thought he was right but Jon was conscious, although undeniably drunk. Between them she and the driver managed to get him into the house where he collapsed on to the settee.

The smell of whisky clung to his skin and his breath.

'At least he's not a violent drunk,' the taxi driver comforted her when she went out to pay him. 'Real gentlemanly he was until he passed out.'

Slowly Sophy went back inside. Jon never drank more than the odd glass of spirits or wine; she had never ever seen him like this, nor thought that she would. Had he done this to himself because he wanted her? She ached to tell him the truth . . . that she wanted him too, and wished more than ever that she had not rushed off in that silly fashion at lunch time, but she had been shocked and, yes, angry too that he could be so blind about her. It was insulting that he should believe that she could not see beyond his public façade to what lay behind but until very recently she could not, she reminded herself . . . until she had married him, until David had made that innocent remark about Louise—in fact, she had never considered him as a sexual human being at all . . . so perhaps it was no wonder he had spoken the way he had.

He moaned and she went across to the sofa, reflecting grimly that in the morning he would have an outsize hangover and a stiff neck if she left him where he was . . . but how could she move him? She tried and found it impossible and instead made him as comfortable as she could, relief invading her now that he was actually back.

'Why is Uncle Jon sleeping in the sitting-room?'

Alex asked the question innocently at breakfast time.

It was David who replied, eyeing his sister faintly scornfully, as he said. 'It's because he's been drinking. He smells just like Daddy did when he and Mummy had been to a party.'

'Yes but why does that make him sleep downstairs?' Alex persisted, breaking off as the subject of her question came into the kitchen. The blue eyes looked slightly bloodshot, the brown skin faintly sallow.

'Coffee?' Sophy asked quietly.

Jon nodded and then closed his eyes, moaning faintly as he did so. 'What happened?' he demanded wryly, sitting down beside Alex and taking the coffee Sophy poured for him.

'I don't really know. A taxi driver brought you back.'

'Oh, God, yes . . . I bumped into some friends I was at Cambridge with. Which reminds me . . . I think I accepted an invitation to a party for both of us tonight.' He fished in his pocket and produced a scrap of paper with an address scribbled down on it. 'Yes, there it is . . .'

'You haven't had enough partying?' Sophy asked him drily, taking the paper and smoothing it out.

'Mmm . . . but we ought to go. It's someone who's just setting up on his own and he needs my help. If you don't fancy it, I could always go alone.'

Instantly Sophy recognised that she did not want that at all. She wanted to be with him . . . accepted by his friends as his wife.

'No . . . no. It will be a pleasant change.' She

would have to arrange a baby-sitter, but that should not be too difficult. Helen Saunders at the Post Office had a teenage daughter who was trying to save up to buy her first car. Susan was a pleasant, responsible girl, who Sophy knew she could trust with the children.

'Why don't you go upstairs and go back to sleep?' she suggested to Jon, noting his bleary eyes and haggard appearance.

'Mmm . . . sounds like a good idea.'

She watched him go, conscious of an urge to rush after him and go with him to fuss over him as though he were genuinely her husband.

'Poor Uncle Jon, he looks really poorly,' Alex commented sympathetically, finishing her breakfast.

Susan Saunders proved willing to baby-sit, and having arranged to pick her up at eight Sophy went upstairs to study the contents of her wardrobe. She had attended several business cocktail parties with Jon before and knew what to expect. As his secretary she had always worn something business-like and formal but now she was his wife. In the end she selected a simple cream silk shift style dress which had been an impulse buy in London and which had been so hideously expensive she had been too guilty to wear it.

Holding it up against herself she saw how the cream silk emphasised her tan and the silky richness of her hair. The demure front was offset by the deep vee back; the dress would be pleasantly cool on what she suspected was going to be an oppressively hot evening.

Her mind made up, she went back downstairs, not giving in to the temptation to walk into Jon's room and see if he was awake. Sooner or later they were going to have to talk; she was going to have to explain to him that the reason she had fled so abruptly had not been because she was shocked by his disclosures or found them distasteful. Even now she found it hard to grasp that he had made them, that he had told her that he wanted her.

He came downstairs just after lunch, looking worn and tired. 'God, I feel dreadful,' he told her wryly. 'It's a long, long time since I've been in the state I was in last night.' He sat down at the kitchen table and leaned his head back. 'I have the most God-awful headache.'

Silently Sophy produced some Alka Seltzer, watching the face he pulled as he drank it. 'Filthy stuff,' was his only comment before he closed his eyes again.

'Jon, about yesterday.' It had to be said before she lost her courage but the look in his eyes as he opened them immediately silenced her.

'Not now, Sophy,' he said wearily. 'Just leave it, will you? I think I'd better get some fresh air . . .'

He didn't want her to go with him, Sophy could tell that. Was he regretting saying to her what he had? Idly her eyes registered his progress to the door, her senses wondering how she could ever have been ignorant of his masculine appeal; how she could ever have been blind enough to think of him as sexless . . .? A quiver of heat darted through her as her glance rested briefly on the taut outline of his buttocks and then slithered down the length of his legs. Suddenly it hurt to even breathe; she was terrified he would turn round and see what

was in her eyes. She reached clumsily for her mug
of coffee, her whole body shaking. So this was
desire, this fierce, hot need that pushed aside
everything that stood in its path; that demanded
and aroused. Jon wanted her, he had said so and it
ought to be the simplest thing in the world simply
to go to him and tell him that she wanted him too,
only it wasn't.

'Come and show me when you've got your dress
on.' Alex was in the sitting room with Susan and
David, and Sophy smiled and nodded. Jon was
already upstairs getting ready but she had only just
arrived back with Susan. According to Jon they
were supposed to be at his friend's for nine
o'clock. She had showered and put on her make-
up before going for Susan but she had not changed
into her silk dress.

She had decided to drive the BMW tonight—the
first time she had taken it out with a passenger,
although Jon was the most uncritical of men when
it came to being driven.

She almost collided with him at the top of the
stairs, his hands coming out to steady her, touching
her briefly, making heat sheet through her body.

How on earth had she ever considered him
unattractive, she wondered achingly. His hair was
still slightly damp and curled into his neck, the
white silk shirt he was wearing clinging to his skin.
The black pants weren't ones she could ever
remember seeing before and then she realised it
was part of a dinner suit and that he was carrying
the jacket—a new dinner suit, she was sure. He
was even wearing a bow tie, and as he moved past
her she caught an elusive hint of some masculine

cologne, faintly old fashioned and citrusy.

'I shan't be long,' she told him. 'I've only got to put on my dress and do my hair.'

Once it was on she wasn't sure if the cream silk had been a good idea. She had forgotten that the back was so low that it was impossible to wear a bra under it and the silk, almost perfectly decorous, seemed to hint at the shape of her breasts in a way she found unfamiliar. Her hair she left loose, sliding her feet into cream high-heeled sandals that made her taller than ever. For the first time in her life she was not ashamed or embarrassed by her height. Even in these heels she was nowhere near as tall as Jon. She picked up her bag and went downstairs.

'Wow ... you both look smashing!' Alex told her, her admiring eyes going from Jon to Sophy in excited wonder. Susan grinned at her and then blushed bright red as she looked at Jon. A sharp knifing feeling that Sophy recognised as jealousy tore through her. She was jealous! Jealous of an eighteen-year-old ... just because that eighteen-year-old had recognised instantly what she herself had been blind to for so long. Jon was an extremely attractive and desirable man!

'We shan't be back late.' Instead of being reassuring her voice sounded slighly brittle. She saw Jon frown as they went outside.

'Are you all right?' he asked her quietly. 'You seem on edge.'

'It's the heat.' It was partially true after all. Surely he knew the reason she was so on edge? He touched her arm as he opened the car door for her and she flinched, red hot darts of sensation destroying her composure.

'For God's sake, Sophy.' His voice was harsh against her ear. 'What the hell do you think I'm going to do? Give in to my animal passions and take you here in full view of the kids?'

He had managed to subdue the harshness to a laconic drawl which infused the words with a certain dry mockery, but they still made her shake with reaction. 'I'm sorry that you find the knowledge that I'm a fully functioning sexual being so distressing, but as I've already told you . . . you have nothing to fear.'

'I know that.'

'You do?' His mouth twisted in a way she was coming to know. 'Then you've a pretty odd way of showing it.'

He walked round to the passenger door of the car, which she unlocked for him, and got in beside her.

She had lost count of the thousands of times she must have driven him and yet tonight his presence beside her in the close confines of the car disturbed her. She was acutely conscious of the lean sprawl of his legs . . . of the rise and fall of his chest, and the cool scent of his cologne mingling with a different, more basic scent which her senses responded to on a deeper, primitive level.

She wanted him, she realised despairingly, and she would give anything not to be going to this party tonight but to be alone with him so that they could talk. Instead she forced herself to concentrate on her driving, absently noting the easy way in which the big car responded to her touch. It was a pleasure to drive, but right now she was hardly in a mood to appreciate that fact.

It was ten-past-nine when she pulled up in the

drive to Jon's friend's house. A mock Tudor building in an avenue of similar houses, it was an easily recognisable symbol of success.

She walked with Jon to the front door.

A small brunette opened it to them, smiling ravishingly at Jon, and exclaiming, 'Darling, you made it!' She giggled. 'After last night we weren't sure if you'd remember.' She took her time before looking at Sophy.

'So this is your wife? Please come in. You can't know how thrilled we were to bump into Jon last night in Cambridge.' She chattered on as she led them through the house to a long terrace at the back where the rich aromas of barbecued meat mingled with the heat of the evening. 'It's simply ages since we last saw him. Roy, my husband, was so pleased ... he's having trouble with this new computer of his and if anyone can help him it will be Jon. How long have you been married?'

She was still talking to Sophy but it was Jon who answered, his expression unreadable as he drawled, 'Not very long ... not long enough, in fact.'

Sophy could feel the brown eyes darting speculatively from Jon's face to her own. In time she might quite get to like this petite brunette but at the moment she was too uncomfortably aware of her speculation and her interest in Jon. My God, she thought despairingly, what was she turning into? A woman who was jealous of every mere look her husband received from other women? She must be going mad, suffering from some sort of sickness brought on by the heat. Or perhaps that frustration Jon had accused her of not so very long ago?

'There's an old friend here of yours that you

simply must meet, darling.' Their hostess was talking to Jon now, holding on to his arm in a way that made Sophy's fingers curl into tiny talons.

'Roy, over here a minute, darling,' she called to her husband, and Sophy watched the burly fair-haired man detach himself from a small group.

He looked older than Jon although Sophy recognised that they must be around the same age, clever hazel eyes studying her gravely as he shook her hand.

'So you are Jon's wife? You're a lucky man, Jon, she's lovely.'

'Hey enough of that,' Andrea threatened lightly, punching him on the arm. 'Just remember you are married to me . . .'

'Ah, you're jealous.' They were simply playing a game . . . but Jon could have said the same words to her and they would have been all too true.

'I think you'll find you know most of the people here,' Roy was saying to Jon. 'What can I get you to drink?'

'Get him a drink later, love,' Andrea interrupted. 'Jon, there's a very special friend of yours here tonight. An old flame,' she added, winking at Sophy, as though to show it was still a game but Sophy could feel herself tense. Jon had tensed too, his jaw hardening fractionally, his eyes closing slightly, such minor changes, that she suspected only she was aware of what they portended.

'Oh . . .?' He wasn't giving anything away in his voice either, Sophy recognised, watching him frown in the hesitant mild manner she had once thought typified the man himself and which she was now coming to know was simply a form of camouflage. What was Jon protecting himself from? Her mouth felt dry, her body tensing almost to the point of pain.

'Yes . . . Lorraine. You must remember her, Jon. Heavens, you and she were an item for a couple of terms at least. She used to be absolutely crazy about you.'

'But Jon managed to resist all her wiles, didn't you, my friend?' Roy was chuckling, ignoring his wife's frown. 'Just as well too, otherwise Lorraine would have had you neatly trapped in matrimony and then I would never have been able to meet this lovely lady.' He kissed Sophy's fingers gallantly as he spoke.

'We were all a little in love with Jon when he was at university,' Andrea told Sophy with a small smile. 'He was so different from the other under-grads, far more sophisticated and just that little bit withdrawn. It made him seem very exciting and out of reach . . . challengingly so, I'm afraid. We used to chase after him quite unfairly. All you wanted to do was to be left alone to get on with your work, didn't you, darling?' she added to Jon.

Roy laughed. 'Says you,' he teased his wife. 'How do you think he got that jaded, world-weary air you found so tantalising in the first place? It certainly wasn't by sitting up burning the midnight oil over his books!'

Jon looked distinctly uncomfortable. He tugged at his bow tie as though it were strangling him, but this time Sophy was not deceived. He was not really embarrassed. He was simply pretending he was. If she looked at his eyes, they were cool and faintly aloof, not embarrassed at all.

'Well you must come and say hello to Lorraine

or she'll never forgive me,' Andrea insisted, drawing Jon away from Roy and Sophy.

Silently, Sophy watched them go.

'You mustn't mind my wife.' Roy sounded kind and faintly uncomfortable. 'She's right when she said that most of the girls in our crowd had a thing about Jon. Poor guy, he was forced to live like a hermit in the end, just to get rid of them. In those days girls had just discovered sex,' he told Sophy with a grin. 'It was a difficult time for us men, being the pursued instead of the pursuers.'

'I'm sure,' Sophy agreed copying his bantering mood. 'It must have been hell.'

Roy was easy to talk to but that didn't stop her glance following Jon's dark head, watching it bend towards the blonde woman he had stopped beside. Andrea drifted off and left them, Roy was still talking and she must have been making the right responses but inside she was tormented by jealousy. What were they saying? Was this perhaps the one love of Jon's life? She ached to be with them; to hear what was being said, and was given her chance when someone else came up to talk to Roy. She walked unsteadily away, moving towards Jon. He turned as she reached him, surprise and something else—anger perhaps—flickering across his face.

'Lorraine, this is my wife, Sophy.'

There was no mistaking the expression in the other woman's eyes, it was vitriolic. So much so that Sophy found herself taking a step backwards.

'I think I see Peter Lewis over there. I'd like to introduce you to him, Sophy.' Skilfully Jon drew her away from Lorraine, leaving Sophy wondering if what they had been saying before she arrived was something for their own ears alone.

At eleven she began to feel tired. Jon was locked in conversation with Roy in the latter's study, so Andrea had told her. Although everyone seemed friendly, Sophy was disinclined to talk. She wanted to go home. She wanted to be alone with Jon.

'Deserted you already, has he?'

She recognised Lorraine's metallic voice instantly, turning to face the older woman.

'So Jon has finally married! My dear, how on earth did you manage it?' She laughed when she saw Sophy's face tighten. 'Oh come on. I know him, Jon may look like an extraordinarily attractive member of the male species but looks are all there is. Sexually he's a disaster area—I should know, I spent months trying to get him into bed with me when we were at university together and when I did ... God, what a non-event!'

Why was Lorraine telling her all this? Sophy wondered, listening to her.

The glossy red lips curled in open mockery. 'Oh, come on ... you must know it's true. I know quite well that Jon's been living like a monk since he left Cambridge. He always did have a hang-up about sex, and you *must* be aware of it, unless, of course, you haven't actually been lovers.'

Sophy felt acutely sick. She knew what Lorraine was doing now. The woman hated Jon, Sophy could see that hatred shining in her eyes but she couldn't know the truth, Sophy told herself, she was simply probing, looking for a weak spot in Jon's armour, trying to find a way to humiliate him, as perhaps, Jon had once humiliated her. Illuminatingly she wondered if she had possibly hit on the truth. Could Lorraine, like Louise, have been one of those women who had thought to seduce Jon and found the task impossible? She looked at the blonde, noting the hard eyes and arrogant pose. Lorraine was attractive, there was no denying that. At twenty-one or two she would have been beautiful ... and probably even more arrogant, certainly arrogant enough to swear vengeance against any man foolish enough to reject her.

She managed a slight frown. 'I'm sorry,' she began apologetically, 'but——'

'Oh, come on, my dear,' Lorraine interrupted her impatiently. 'Don't give me that, I know Jon hasn't changed. He was sexless at twenty-two and he's sexless now.'

'I'm afraid you're quite wrong.' Suddenly, soaringly she felt gloriously strong, glad to do something for Jon ... to protect him from this woman's malice. She even managed to smile freely for the first time that evening. 'I can't speak for Jon's past, of course,' she shrugged delicately, 'but I can certainly tell you that as his wife I have no complaints.'

'But then maybe, darling, you aren't his wife ... at least not in the way that really counts.'

Heavens, Lorraine was persistent—and thick skinned—Sophy thought wryly, but she was not going to let her get the better of their exchange.

'You mean you don't think we've made love?' Sophy raised her eyebrows and laughed openly. 'Oh, but we have.' She allowed her voice to become soft and dreamy, watching Lorraine's mouth harden and the colour leave her skin.

'I don't believe you.' Her voice was harsh, and for a moment Sophy felt sorry for her but then she remembered what Lorraine was trying to do to Jon.

'Then I shall have to make you,' she said quietly. 'What is it you want to hear, Lorraine? How Jon makes me feel when he touches me? How I feel when I touch him? Those are very intimate details to discuss with a stranger but what I can tell you is that in his arms I feel more of a woman than I've ever felt before in my life. Under his touch my body burns and aches for his possession. I would have gone willingly to his bed, marriage or no marriage. When his body possesses mine . . .' She caught the faintly strangled gasp the other woman made as she stepped back, raising her hands as though Sophy's words were blows, retreating to the other side of the patio to glare at her with patent venom.

'Sophy . . .'

She swing round, going pale as she found Jon standing behind her. How long had he been there? Had he heard? She swallowed tensely and looked at him but he was looking the other way.

'If you don't mind I'd like to leave. This headache . . .'

Relief flooded through her. Of course he hadn't overheard! Hot colour scorched her skin as she remembered what she'd said. Now that it was over she felt weak and trembly. There was nothing she wanted more than to leave, and she went mutely with Jon as he sought out their host and hostess.

They drove back in silence, Sophy leaving Jon to go upstairs whilst she took Susan home.

Once she got back she didn't linger downstairs herself. She too was tired, drained of all emotion. She paused outside Jon's room, without knowing why, listening to the floorboard creak beneath her foot.

The door was open and she heard him call her name. She went to the door and stood just inside it. He was sitting on the bed, his head in his hands.

'Why did you do it?'

His voice was a faint thread but she still heard it, the blood freezing down her spine as apprehension gripped her.

'Do what?'

She heard him sigh. 'Come on, Sophy, you know quite well what I mean . . . that little scene with Lorraine. I heard it all but both of you were too engrossed in each other to realise I was there. It certainly was a very talented performance on your part,' he added tiredly. '*How* did you do it? By calling up memories of how it was with Benson?'

Sophy could feel the blood draining out of her skin.

'No.' She practically choked on the denial. 'No . . .' she added more quietly, 'I simply used my imagination.'

He wasn't looking at her, but she could feel the tension gripping him. 'What exactly do you mean?'

Suddenly she was tired of fencing . . . of pretending. 'You're the logician, Jon,' she told him wryly, 'Surely you can analyse what I've said and draw your own conclusions. I didn't enjoy Chris's lovemaking, as a matter of fact. In fact I found it a total turn-off. It was painful . . . and empty. I can assure you that he found me less than satisfactory as well.'

'Really? So why is he still pursuing you?'

'Because he resents the fact that I appear to be enjoying with another man what I did not enjoy with him,' she told him bluntly, 'and he likes causing trouble.'

'You can say that again.' He looked directly at her for the first time, reaching one hand behind his neck to rub away the tension.

'Headache still bad?'

'Mmm . . .'

'I'll massage your neck for you if you like.'

Now why on earth had she said that? Tensely waiting for his repudiation she was stunned when he turned and stretched out on the bed, muttering, 'Thanks, that would be great.'

He had already removed his jacket, but his shirt was still on. Even so, Sophy dared not suggest that he remove it. Instead she leaned down towards him, flexing her fingers. She had learned the basics of massage after a bad fall in her teens when she had injured her leg and had found relief from the pain of it by massaging the tense muscles and it seemed it was a skill that once learned was never lost, although there was a world of difference in having Jon's hot flesh beneath her hands rather than her own.

Almost by instinct she found the hard lumps of acidic matter that denoted tension and started massaging them. She felt Jon tense slightly and then relax, although he said nothing. Time ceased to exist as she concentrated on her task. Jon was breathing slowly now . . . so slowly that she felt sure he must be asleep. She eased gently away, flexing her own body.

'Don't stop.' The slurred words stopped her in mid-movement, her eyes widening as Jon sat up, his fingers tearing impatiently at his shirt buttons until he had them all free. Shrugging out of his shirt he threw it on the floor, flopping back down on the bed. 'That feels good, Sophy,' he told her thickly. 'Do it some more.'

She obeyed him mindlessly, smoothing the sleek skin beneath her fingertips, enveloped in the musky male scent of his body as she bent closer to him, trying to tell herself that what she was doing was something she would have done for anyone.

Only he wasn't anyone. He was Jon . . . and she loved him . . . *loved him?* She tensed, staring blindly into space, waiting for her heart to catch up on its missed beat. Of course she didn't love him. She wanted him, desired him, yes . . . but love? She fought hard but it was no use, she *did* love him.

The knowledge was appalling. How long had she hidden it from herself? How long had she loved him? Days, weeks, months . . . before they were married, even? She shook her head, trying to clear her thoughts, and knowing it was impossible. The shock was too great.

'What's wrong?'

She withdrew as Jon sat up, backing away from him. He wasn't wearing his glasses but he was looking at her as though he could read every expression on her face.

'I want you.' He said it softly, reaching for her before she could move, fastening his fingers round her wrists and tugging her towards him until her progress was impeded by the edge of the bed. 'Was it true what you told me about Benson?'

'That he was the first man to discover that I was frigid, do you mean?' She was glad that he had reminded her of reality because it gave her something to fight with.

'Is that what you are?' He tugged on her wrists again, not very gently this time, laughing at her as she overbalanced and fell on the bed in an ungainly heap. She tried to roll away from him, her angry protest smothered by the heat of his mouth as it imprisoned her own.

Heat, searing and intense, beat through her in fierce waves, a heat that had nothing to do with the hot summer night outside. This heat was generated within herself, a blazing conflagration that threatened to totally destroy her. She had never, ever felt like this before. It frightened her that she should now.

Every instinct she had told her she must escape before Jon discovered for himself the humiliating truth but although his grip on her, now was only light somehow it was impossible to drag her mouth from his, to give up the aching pleasure of the way his mouth moved on hers aroused. His tongue touched her lips and they parted, admitting him to the moist sweetness beyond, the breath catching in her throat as the intimacy of his kiss engulfed her and she clung helplessly to his shoulders, aware of the hot sleekness of his skin beneath her fingers; aware of the frantic thudding of her heart against her ribs ... of the slow ache coiling through her lower body, the moist heat between her thighs.

Suddenly it was impossible to resist. Her tongue touched his, tentatively at first and then more daringly, her body melting with heat as she heard his fiercely indrawn breath and felt the muscles of his chest compress.

Her whole body was aching with desire for him and he had only kissed her. Only kissed her, that was all. Her lips clung despairingly to his as she felt their pressure ease and she thought she felt him smile as his mouth moved slowly over her skin, exploring the shape of her face, his breath warm against her ear.

'Let me take this off.'

She felt his fingers touch the single fastening that held her dress on and reacted instinctively, her body tensing, as she begged, 'Please don't do this, Jon.'

But it was too late and anyway he wasn't listening to her. His eyes were fastened on the twin peaks of her breasts, fully exposed to him now that their covering of silk had slithered away. Transfixed, she watched as his head bent slowly towards her breasts, remembering on a sudden wave of revulsion how Chris had bitten her tender flesh and how she had recoiled from him in pain and shock. Until now she had forgotten that . . . but she had not forgotten his anger and contempt.

She reached out protestingly, her fingers digging into Jon's shoulder. Her voice thick with anguish as she pleaded, 'Please . . .'

The downward movement of his head stilled and he looked at her. 'What is it?' he asked her softly.

Not even the familiar sound of his voice could calm her. 'I don't like it,' she heard herself whimpering. 'It hurts . . .'

She saw his eyes darken and tensed in expectation of the same angry contempt Chris had shown her but instead he said gratingly, 'Is that what he did, Sophy? Did he hurt you?'

She closed her eyes, not daring to reply in case she burst into tears. What was the matter with her? Not so very long ago she had lain awake at night tormented by her aching need for Jon to touch her but now that he was . . .

'Well, I promise you I won't.'

She could feel the tension in his body as his hands

cupped her breast. Despite herself she shivered slightly. He was looking at her, forcing her to meet his gaze, and then he bent his head and gently kissed each coral nipple with warm lips.

A shuddering sigh was wrenched from deep within her, the fear flooding out of her, pushed by the slow tide of desire coming in its wake. The sensation of Jon's mouth against her breast had been both reassuring and tormenting. She wanted more than the light brush of his lips against her skin, she realised achingly. Much, much more—but Jon was already moving away from her.

Reacting instinctively, she reached towards him curling her fingers into his hair, feeling the unmistakable hardening of her nipples beneath the heat of the sharp breath he expelled.

'Sophy.' He said her name roughly, warningly but she was past heeding him, her own voice taut with longing as she moaned softly. 'Jon, please . . .'

'Please what?' His voice was thick and slurred as though the words were unfamiliar to him, one hand cupping her breast, the other drawing her down against his mouth as he muttered against her skin, 'Please this?' and his mouth moved back to her breast.

For long, long moments, the only noise in the room was the tortured sound of her breathing and the moist movement of his mouth caressing her breast, his tongue moving roughly over the aroused peak of it until she was moaning in wild pleasure.

She ached when he released her but not because he had hurt her.

'Don't be afraid, I'm not going to do anything you don't want.'

She closed her eyes as she felt him move. Couldn't he see that what she was afraid of now was that she *would* want it . . . that in wanting him she would be vulnerable to him and that, like Chris, he would find her lacking and reject her? And that was something she could not endure.

She moved away from him and knew he had registered her withdrawal as he said her name sharply.

'It's late, Jon,' she told him huskily. 'I must go back to my own room.'

For a moment she thought he was going to stop her, and then she heard him sigh.

'Sophy, you know I want you,' he told her tiredly. 'I want you to want me in return, not to be frightened of me. Is it me you're frightened of, or sex in general?'

'A little of both,' she admitted huskily. 'I don't want you to look at me the way Chris looked at me, Jon,' she told him tormentedly. 'Believe me, it's better if I go now. If I stayed I promise you you'd only be disappointed.'

'Is that what he told you?' he asked her roughly. 'That all men would find you disappointing because he did?'

She managed a wry smile. 'I'm not a complete fool, Jon. There have been other men . . . oh, none of them were ever physically intimate with me because sooner or later our relationship always reached the point where it became obvious that I was disappointing them.'

'Are you sure you're not just saying all this because you find me a turn-off?'

'No!' Her denial rang with truth. She reached out and touched his face hesitantly, trying to smile at him. 'Believe it or not, Jon, I find you extremely desirable. But can't you see that just makes it so much harder? Because of that, I'm frightened of disappointing you.'

She got off the bed before he could say anything and picked up her dress, hurrying out into the corridor and into her own room.

CHAPTER SEVEN

SHE woke up during the night, not knowing what had disturbed her, conscious only of some sound alien to those she normally heard.

Her bedroom door opened inwards and she sat up in bed, her eyes widening as she saw Jon walk into her room.

He was wearing pyjama bottoms, dark silk ones, and she tensed as he came over to the bed, wanting him and yet afraid of what that wanting might lead to when he too discovered how useless she was as a woman.

As he reached for the bedclothes, she wriggled away, smothering a tiny gasp of surprise as he slid into bed beside her.

'Jon!'

Her protest was silenced by the warm brush of his fingers against her mouth. 'I can't sleep without you, Sophy,' she heard him saying huskily, as his arms went round her. 'I only want to sleep with you in my arms, that's all.'

Unbelievably he was already falling asleep as his arm drew her back against the warmth of his body. She knew she ought to wake him up and send him back to his own bed but it was good having him lie beside her, his body against her own. Instinctively she snuggled back against him, sighing faintly as his arm curved round her body just under her breasts.

They were married, after all, she reminded

herself as she fell asleep; and there was nothing immoral in them being here together like this. Apart, of course, from the fact that he did not love her, while she . . .

He wanted her though, she thought defiantly. He had told her so and there had been no reason for him to lie. What on earth was it that she had that Lorraine and Louise did not seem to possess? Perhaps he just wasn't keen on blondes, she thought wryly, suppressing a self-mocking smile as sleep stole over her.

She woke up early conscious that something was different, but not sure what it was until she felt the weight of Jon's arm across her body. It was just gone five in the morning. She really ought to wake him and send him back to his own bed. If Alex should wake early and come in for an early morning cuddle as she sometimes did . . .

She tried to wriggle out from under his arm so that she could shake him but instantly it tightened around her, threatening to crush her ribs. She heard him mutter something in his sleep and then move slightly taking her with him so that somehow her legs became tangled up in his.

She knew immediately that he had woken up, even before he murmured her name in husky surprise, the tone of his voice subtly changing as he repeated her name.

'Lovely Sophy,' he murmured against her ear. 'Who would ever have dreamed that I would wake up with you in my arms?' His hand skimmed the shape of her body and she felt him shake slightly as he asked, 'What on earth is this? It feels like something my grandmother might have worn.'

It was in fact a long cotton nightdress which was slightly Victorian in design. Normally she only wore it in winter but last night, for some reason, despite the heat, she had decided to put it on.

'Jon, you really ought to go back to your own bed.' She tried to turn round so that she could look at him, and found she wished she had not as she saw the lazy blue warmth in his eyes as he looked back at her. His jaw was dark and she touched it lightly, her eyes widening at the harsh rasp of his beard against her fingertips.

'You must have to shave twice a day.' Even as she spoke she was conscious of the banality of her comment.

Jon's mouth twitched slightly but his voice was quite grave as he whispered back, 'At least.' His fingers curled round her wrist, transferring hers from his jaw to his mouth. The sensation of his mouth moving against her fingertips was oddly erotic. She could feel herself starting to tremble, a low ache spreading through her stomach as he gently sucked her fingers into his mouth, his free hand stroking down her body to caress her breast.

'Jon . . .'

He released her fingers and pressed his own against her mouth. 'No, don't speak,' he told her softly. 'Don't say anything, Sophy. Not now.' And because suddenly she seemed to have been transported to a dream world where anything was possible and only Jon existed she found it easy to acquiesce, to simply let herself follow where he led and give herself over completely to the voluptuosity of his lovemaking.

She had discovered so much she had not known before about him already and here it seemed was something else she had not known, her body recognising instantly that his touch was that of a man who had once learned and never forgotten how to give the utmost pleasure.

Sighing beneath the seductive stroke of his fingers she let him remove her nightdress crying out softly when the heat of his body touched her own but not with pain, or fear, unless it was the pain of being so close to him and yet not part of him and the fear of losing this pleasure he was giving her almost before it was begun. His pyjamas followed her nightdress on to the floor, his hands drawing her against his body.

'I want you, Sophy.' He murmured the words into her throat, sliding his hands to her hips, holding her bones almost as though he might crush them. She shivered and reached out to touch him, tracing the hard slope of his shoulder, pressing her mouth to his warm skin, gently biting the satin firmness of it until she felt the husky groan move his chest. He had thrown off the duvet and it was light enough for her to see his body. Strong and fully aroused, making her shiver faintly with awareness and desire. It was not the sexual act of possession she feared but her own inability to respond to it; the crushing sense of anti-climax and rejection she knew must surely come when Jon discovered . . .

'What is it?' His voice was gentle, teasing her slightly as he murmured against her ear. 'Surely you have seen a naked man before?'

She hadn't really—at least not as openly as she was seeing him—but it wasn't that that held her spellbound in some sort of motionless trance. She swallowed and turned to meet his eyes. 'Never one as male as you, Jon,' she told him tremulously . . . and truthfully, watching his eyes darken and his mouth curl, as his finger traced the shape of her mouth.

'That was a highly inflammatory remark, wouldn't you say?'

She couldn't respond because his mouth was touching hers, caressing her lips with tormenting slowness, until she was forced to wind her arms round his neck and arch her body into his with an impatient moan of need.

She was aware of his fingers biting deeply into her upper arms as he held her against him, just as she was aware of the hard arousal of his body moving against her own but it was the fiercely draining pressure of his mouth she was aware of the most, the heated movement of his tongue as it sought her own. Desire, sharp and tormenting twisted in her stomach and she pulled her mouth free to whisper his name as she drew painful gasps of air into her lungs.

He was kissing her throat, her shoulders, nibbling at the tender flesh, trailing tormenting kisses down over the upper slopes of her breasts and then the valley between them. Her nipples were stiff, aching for the warmth of his mouth but he seemed determined to ignore them. Stifling a tormented moan, Sophy curled her fingers into his hair guiding his head to her breast, her body arching up to his mouth in open supplication.

She felt him shudder and for one agonising moment thought she had somehow disgusted him, but even as she tried to pull away his hand cupped her breast, his mouth hot against her skin as he muttered into the creamy flesh, 'Sophy . . . Sophy

. . . this time I can't be gentle.' And then his mouth was tugging urgently on the coral hardness of her nipple, unleashing a cramping, burning ache low down in her stomach, making her sob his name and drag her nails against his skin as she felt the tiny shudders of pleasure radiate through her body.

There was an odd ringing noise in her head . . . a distracting sound she did not want to hear, a tormented sound of denial dragged from her throat as Jon abruptly released her.

'The alarm's gone off,' he told her, sitting up slowly. He was breathing so hard she could see the rise and fall of his chest. Sweat clung to his skin. 'Sophy . . .?'

Sounds from the next room silenced him. 'Now obviously isn't the time to say all that I want to say to you,' he said wryly. 'I suspect that any minute now you're likely to be invaded.' He reached for his pyjama bottoms pulling them on, his body still openly aroused. 'As soon as we can we're going to have to talk.' He bent briefly and kissed her, just as the door opened and Alex came rushing in.

She stopped abruptly, staring round-eyed at them, demanding curiously, 'What are you doing in here, Uncle Jon?'

'I had a nightmare and your uncle spent the night with me,' Sophy fibbed lightly, giving the little girl a smile.

'Does that mean that you'll always be sleeping together now, like real Mummies and Daddies?' Alex enquired innocently.

Sophy dared not look at Jon. Would he want to sleep with her on a permanent basis . . . to make their relationship a physical as well as a legal one?'

'You're not wearing a nightie.' She had forgotten about that, and blushed guiltily. Jon, standing by the bedroom door was laughing and over Alex's head her eyes met his.

'Mummies don't need them when they sleep with Daddies,' he told Alex with a grin, sauntering out into the landing.

Of course it was too much to hope for that Alex would let the subject drop. She was full of it over breakfast, telling David all about it, and Sophy was conscious of a certain slightly adult awareness in David's expression as he looked at her. 'Married people should sleep together,' he told Alex firmly.

Luckily Sophy was able to change the subject before Alex could continue it, reminding the children that they would be having visitors at the weekend.

It was on Friday that Jon's friends arrived from Nassau, and on Saturday evening they were coming round for dinner. Sophy still wasn't sure what she was going to serve. She felt very nervous about meeting them although she told herself there was no reason why she should.

An emergency call from one of his clients meant that Jon had to go out immediately after breakfast. His client's offices were in London and he told Sophy before he left that he might not be back that night. She felt empty and very much alone when he had gone, almost as though a shadow had fallen across her day. If she had doubted that she loved him before, she didn't do so any longer. It took a considerable effort to rouse herself enough to take the children to school and once she had done she found herself reluctant to go back to the empty house. Instead she drove into Cambridge and spent what was left of the morning glancing through cookery books in the library and trying to plan her dinner party menu.

Something simple, she decided . . . and something cool. In the end she decided on salmon and cucumber mousse followed by chicken and avocado salad with a cheeseboard and homemade ice-cream to follow. She would have to consult Jon about the wine. Jon . . . it was ridiculous how even the inward sound of his name had the power to arouse and alarm her. Why should he want *her*? She had no way of knowing . . . she could only accept that he did and be thankful for it.

The dining and drawing rooms were not rooms that they normally used as a family, and Sophy grimaced faintly over their unappealing appearance. Jon had given her a completely free hand with the renovation of the house, but the weather had been so hot that she had not been motivated into making any changes. Now, with the dinner party imminent, she wished that she had. There was nothing wrong with the rooms themselves but they were furnished with clumsy, sale-room oddments and badly needed decorating. The only real improvement she could make was to fill them with freshly cut flowers and keep the lighting dim, she decided wryly when she had finished dusting and vacuuming both rooms on Friday morning.

There had been no 'phone call yet from Jon and while she was missing him dreadfully she was also apprehensive about his return. They needed to talk he had said to her but what did he intend to say? Now that she had admitted to herself that she loved him, it seemed impossible that she had not known the truth before; that fierce jealousy she had felt when Alex had innocently told her about Louise for instance . . . she ought to have known then. But she hadn't wanted to know. She had felt safer simply liking him; safer thinking of him as a non-sexual being. She had never even tried to look beyond the façade he presented to the world, because she had been quite content with that façade.

When he still hadn't returned by midnight on Friday evening Sophy went to bed. She knew where he was working and had she wanted to do so she could have put a call through to him at any time during the day but pride had stopped her. In the past it had always been Jon who rang her to tell her when he was due to return, and she was not going to cause either of them embarrassment by being the one to ring him now. She was painfully aware of what both Roy and Andrea had told her; that in the past Jon had been blatantly pursued by her sex and had apparently not liked it. She had enough intelligence to guess that Lorraine's virulent hatred was more likely to have sprung from Jon's rejection of her than from the lack of skill in bed which she had accused him of— after all hadn't she herself had proof positive that the latter simply was not true?

She shivered slightly beneath the duvet, her bed suddenly far too large and empty without Jon in it but she was not going to be like those others. She was not going to pursue and chase him. That was easy enough to say, she thought tiredly as she gave in to the urge to sleep, but it might be far harder than she envisaged to do.

'When's Uncle Jon coming back?'

They were having breakfast in the kitchen—a leisurely, late breakfast as it was Saturday morning, and once it was over Sophy intended to devote the rest of the morning to preparing for the evening's dinner party.

'I'm not sure.' She responded to Alex's question as calmly as she could. She had been awake since seven o'clock, her ears straining for the sound of the telephone, but so far there had been no call.

Almost as though she had conjured the sound up by wishful thinking, the kitchen 'phone suddenly shrilled.

'I'll get it.' Alex was out of her chair first, running to pick up the receiver.

'Uncle Jon . . . when are you coming back?' She paused and then held out the receiver to Sophy. 'He's leaving now but he wants to speak to you.'

Her hand was shaking slightly as she took the receiver from Alex.

'Hello, Jon.' She hoped her voice sounded calmer to him than it did to her.

'Sorry I couldn't make it back earlier.'

Was she imagining the constraint she thought she heard?

'That's okay. Was the problem more difficult to solve than you expected?'

There was an odd pause and then when Jon did speak his voice was slightly muffled. 'Yes . . . yes, you could say that. I should be back by mid-afternoon.'

After asking her if there had been any urgent

telephone calls he hung up. Now that he had rung she felt worse than she had done before. She felt as though a wall had suddenly sprung up between them, as though for some reason Jon was deliberately setting a distance between them.

The preparatory work for the dinner party kept her fingers busy but left her with not enough to occupy her mind and by the time the mousse was chilling in the fridge and the ice cream was in the freezer, she had managed to convince herself that Jon was bitterly regretting ever having touched her. Everything that Chris had said to her was true. Jon found her just as undesirable as Chris had . . .

She kept herself busy, polishing the old fashioned silver cutlery she found in one of the sideboard drawers, carefully washing china and crystal that she had also discovered tucked away in the sideboard cupboards.

She had bought an expensive white linen tablecloth, deeply trimmed with lace, and Alex who had volunteered to help her with the silver polishing and then with the table, stopped to admire the rich gleam of the green and gold banded dinner service and the sparkle of the heavily cut crystal.

Fresh flowers brightened up the heaviness of the room and decorated the centre of the table. All she really had to do now was to prepare the salads and the chicken.

Alex watched round-eyed while she made the mayonnaise leaving Sophy to reflect that she had after all gained something from her mother, for it was she who had taught Sophy to cook. She recognised now that she had absorbed a good deal of her mother's housewifely skill almost without being aware of it.

At three o'clock Sophy heard a car stop outside. Instantly an explosive mixture of fear and excitement gripped her stomach. Watching Alex's exuberant and totally natural pleasure, she wished for a moment that she too was free to welcome Jon back the way she wanted to but she had to be more circumspect, so she deliberately held back a little washing and then drying her hands, timing her arrival at the front door to coincide with Jon's.

Her first thought was that he looked tired—far more tired than she had seen him looking before, and instinctively she reached out to touch him, withdrawing her hand as though it had been stung as she realised what she was doing.

'You look tired.' The words left her lips before she could stop them.

'I could do with a shower . . . it's no pleasure travelling at the moment—especially in a taxi without air conditioning.' He bent down and picked up the overnight case he had put on the floor. 'I'll go up and get changed.'

'Would you like a drink or something to eat?'

Jon paused at the foot of the stairs and shook his head. 'No . . . I ate before I left.' He took off his glasses and rubbed his eyes. Something he normally only did either when he was tired or when something was bothering him. Her love for him tugged at Sophy's heart. She wanted to go up to him and wrap her arms round him but instinctively she was frightened of being rebuffed.

On Saturday afternoon Sophy made her weekly telephone call to her mother, something which was

more a duty than a pleasure, especially when her
mother still continued to make slightly disparaging
references to Jon. For once though, she seemed
uninterested in the subject of her son-in-law,
rushing to tell Sophy the moment they had
exchanged 'hellos'.

'The most shocking thing has happened—I can
hardly believe it. Felicity has left Chris. Poor boy,
he is absolutely devastated. He adored her, you
know . . . spoilt her really. Of course I've done my
best to comfort him. Girls do funny things when
they're in her condition but even so . . .'

Sophy listened while her mother poured out a
good deal more in the same vein, inwardly
thoroughly bored with the whole subject of Chris.

'He may come over and see you,' she told Sophy
just as she was hanging up. 'I told him you'd be
delighted to see him. After all it's a time like this
that he needs his friends.'

'Mother, I wish you hadn't.' Sophy was really
angry but there was nothing she could do other
than hope that Chris would have the sense to
know that her mother was wrong and that Sophy
was not likely to welcome him. She had sensed the
last time she saw him that he resented the thought
that she had found happiness with someone else
and she had no wish to play the sympathetic
listener to him. Shrugging in mild irritation she
went back to her preparations for the meal.

Jon was outside with the children. Soon it would
be time to call them in for their tea. She had got
them a Walt Disney video to watch while they
were having dinner and both of them had
promised to be on their best behaviour. Not that
they were ever particularly naughty, she thought

fondly. Once everything was done she could go upstairs and get ready. Nervous butterflies fluttered in her stomach. She was dreading meeting Jon's friends and being the object of their curiosity.

After all her apprehension about meeting Jon's friends, Sophy discovered that they were a very pleasant, down to earth couple with whom she instantly felt quite at home. Mary-Beth confided to her over the salmon and cucumber mousse that she sometimes felt she must be the world's worst cook and that even her ten-year-old daughter could make a better sponge cake than she did herself. 'And doesn't she just let me know it,' she groaned with a smile.

Their two children, she explained to Sophy, were staying with her parents in North Carolina.

'Harry has so many meetings organised for this trip that it just wasn't worth bringing the kids with us. I can quite happily waste a few days shopping in London but the kids would hate that.'

She followed Sophy out to the kitchen when she went to get the main course, commenting as she walked in, 'Jon says you haven't had much chance to get to grips with the house yet. Of course, you haven't been married very long.'

'No,' Sophy agreed with a grin. 'And if it hadn't been for the fact that the fault on the Nassau computer was relatively non-urgent, we'd have had to put the ceremony off completely.'

Mary-Beth's eyes widened and she protested. 'Oh, didn't Jon tell you—and I thought it was so romantic too but poor Harry was practically foaming at the mouth at the time—Jon refused to come out until after the wedding. He told Harry there was simply no question of him postponing it. Not even if it meant that Nassau would have to look for someone else. I must tell you that I was stunned. Jon's a devoted computer man and always has been as long as I've known him. I was, however, delighted to discover that his work means far less to him than you. Fancy him not telling you.'

'I suppose he didn't want to at the time because he knew it would upset me,' Sophy offered, trying to slow down the hurried racing of her heart-beat. Jon had done that. But why? Their wedding could have been put off . . . and why hadn't he told her?

'He's obviously crazy in love with you,' Mary-Beth continued. 'We could tell that from the way he talked about you when he came to Nassau. Mind you there are some people who can never see a thing.' She lowered her voice slightly. 'One of the women who works on the Nassau project was really smitten with Jon. I told her he was married but she's one of those super-intelligent females who always goes all out for what she wants. You're lucky Jon is the faithful type, I wouldn't be telling you any of this if he weren't,' Mary-Beth assured her frankly. 'To be honest, sometimes Lillian worries me. I don't know what it is . . . a sort of obsessiveness about her somehow, a facility to blot out everything bar what's important to her.

'Lillian.' Sophy repeated the name lightly. 'Jon mentioned her to me. He used her pool during his rest periods.'

'Yes . . . I know.' Mary-Beth pulled a wry grimace when she saw Sophy's expression. 'Look, you've got nothing to worry about . . . Jon's crazy about you. He couldn't wait to rush back home.'

Sophy smiled, sensing that the other woman was regretting ever bringing up the subject of Lillian. It was silly to be jealous of the other woman. After all Jon had married *her*; had told her that he desired her. But not that he loved her, she thought achingly . . . and that was what she wanted. She wanted Jon to love her in the same total and complete way she loved him. But despite everything that Mary-Beth had said to the contrary Sophy knew that he did not.

It was gone one o'clock when the Silvers left. Leaving Jon in the drawing room Sophy wandered tiredly into the kitchen and started to attack the washing-up.

'Leave that. I'll do it. You've done more than enough.'

Jon had walked into the kitchen so quietly that she hadn't heard him and now he made her jump, almost dropping the plate she was holding.

'You're exhausted, Sophy.' She caught his frown as he reached out and turned her round, taking the plate from her. 'Go on up . . . I'm still wide-awake. I'll get rid of this lot.'

She wanted to protest that she wanted to stay with him, that they could wash up together, go to bed together but she knew she could not. As she hesitated, still standing within the curve of his arm, she found herself wishing that he would at least kiss her, even if it was only one of the lightly affectionate kisses he gave the children. For a moment she even thought he might. His head bent and then lifted again, and then he was releasing her, gently pushing her in the direction of the door.

She wanted to ask him why he had lied to her

about the urgency of the work in Nassau, but she knew she could not.

Even though she tried to stay awake until she heard Jon come upstairs she fell asleep almost immediately she got into bed, not waking until the alarm went off in the morning.

On the following Tuesday Jon got a 'phone call whilst they were working together in the office. Never a particularly vociferous talker, the brief, monosyllabic curtness of his responses made her lift her head from the correspondence she was studying. It was unlike Jon to sound curt or to look as frowningly involved as he did now.

When he had hung up, she asked automatically, 'Problems?'

For a moment he seemed to hesitate and then he said bleakly, 'Yes . . .' He paused, and stared out of the window, and Sophy had the distinct impression that his mind was a long, long way away. They had never had that talk he had promised and in fact since the weekend she had been intensely conscious of a barrier between them.

'I'm afraid I've got to go to London again. I'll have to leave this afternoon.'

'Will you be gone long?'

He frowned again, and said curtly, 'I have no idea, Sophy.'

His tone chilled her, it was almost as though she had angered him in some way by asking. Could he sense how she felt about him. Was he already resenting the thought of the demands her love might lead her to make on him?

After that she was careful to keep all her

comments to him strictly related to business matters. As soon as they had gone through the post she excused herself, explaining that she wanted to go upstairs and pack for him.

It was strange how being in love with someone could invest even the most mundane of inanimate objects with a special poignancy because they were part of the beloved, Sophy thought, carefully packing Jon's shirts. He was normally very neat in his habits but the shirt he had discarded the previous night lay across a chair and she picked it up, instantly tensing. The scent of Jon's skin clung to the cotton fabric, and she had to fight against a crazy impulse to buy her face in it and absorb that tiny bit of him into herself.

She made them both a light lunch but scarcely touched her now. Jon was not particularly hungry either, she noticed, watching him push his salad round the plate. It struck her then that he had lost weight and even looked faintly gaunt. His expression withdrawn ... brooding almost, as though something—or someone—weighed heavily on his mind.

Had he guessed how she felt? Was he, because of that, regretting that he had married her? He wanted her he had said ... but that wanting had been a physical need not an emotional one. Perhaps that was what he wanted to talk to her about ... to warn her that he could not reciprocate her feelings.

She drove him to the station and waited there until he was on the train. He did not kiss her goodbye, nor did she let him see how much she had wanted him to.

For the children's sake she tried to behave

normally, but she missed him intensely and some
sixth sense told her that something was wrong ...
that there was something he was concealing from
her.

It was Thursday morning before she heard from
him. A brief telephone call merely to tell her what
train he would be returning on.

'I'll drive into Cambridge and pick you up,' she
offered, but he vetoed her offer, saying, 'No, don't
bother. I'll have no trouble getting a taxi.'

Hurt and rebuffed, Sophy said nothing, letting
him say 'goodbye' and hoping he wouldn't catch
the misery in her own voice as she responded to
him. At least he would soon be back ... and they
could talk. Or at least she hoped they could.

Neither David nor Alex would be home until
early evening, as both of them had been invited to
a schoolfriend's birthday party and another
mother had offered to give them a lift home since
she had to pass their house on the way to her own,
so if Jon did want to talk to her, today would be
an ideal opportunity.

Motivated by an impulse which she told herself
she would have been wiser to resist, Sophy spent
almost an hour getting ready for Jon's arrival. She
put on her yellow sundress and did her face, telling
herself as she did so, that all she was likely to
achieve was to make Jon feel even more
uncomfortable but it was impossible to resist the
age-old feminine instinct to make herself as
attractive as she could for the man she loved.

When she heard a car coming up the drive, she
dropped her mascara wand and brushed her hair
feverishly. It was only one o'clock ... and Jon had
specifically said that the train didn't reach

Cambridge until one. It was a half an hour drive from Cambridge to the house ... but then of course, it wouldn't be the first time he had got a timetable wrong.

Unable to hide the eagerness in her eyes she rushed downstairs and into the hall, flinging open the front door.

'Well, well, surprise, surprise ... so you *are* pleased to see me after all.'

In dumb dismay Sophy watched as Chris climbed out of the car on the drive and staggered towards her. He had been drinking, she realised nervously, and there was a look in his eyes that made her feel slightly apprehensive.

'I thought you were Jon.' The admission was made before she could check herself, and she cursed herself under her breath as she saw the triumph in his eyes.

'So, all alone, are you?'

She made to shut the front door, but it was too late. Chris was inside, breathing heavily as he glowered at her. 'It's all your fault,' he told her thickly, lurching towards her, and grabbing hold of her arm. 'All of it.'

'Chris ... you've had too much to drink,' Sophy protested. If only she could get him into the kitchen she might be able to sober him up and send him on his way. 'Look, let me make you some coffee.'

'Don't want coffee.' His voice was becoming slurred. 'Revenge ... that's what I want. Ruined my life, that's what you did. Bloody—!' He called her a name that made her wince. 'Frigid bitches like you ought to be destroyed ... because that's what you've done to me. It's your fault Felicity left

me. Christ, remembering what it's like touching
you is enough to make any man impotent . . .'

Sophy tried not to listen while he hurled further
insults at her. Surreptitiously she tried to free
herself from his grasp but he suddenly realised
what she was trying to do and grabbed hold of her
with both hands, shaking her until she thought her
neck would break.

'Are you cold in bed with him?' he demanded
thickly, suddenly, his eyes narrowing onto her
own, glittering with a hatred that suddenly turned
her blood to ice water. 'Are you, Sophy?'

She cried out as he shook her again and her
head hit the wall with a sickening thud. For a few
seconds she thought she was going to faint but
then the pain cleared. 'Let me go, Chris,' she
pleaded, regretting the words, the instant she saw
the satisfaction gleaming in his eyes. How on earth
had she ever imagined herself in love with him . . .
this apology for a man? He was so weak and
immature, so ready to blame others for his own
failings. Suddenly she was furiously angry with
him, her anger overcoming her earlier fear.

'No woman could be cold in bed with Jon,' she
told him truthfully, watching the fury twist his
face.

'You're lying to me.' He said it thickly, pushing
his face against her own so that she was forced to
inhale the sour whisky fumes that clung to his
breath. 'Don't make me angry, Sophy,' he warned
her. 'You won't like it when I get angry. Felicity
didn't,' he added, watching her.

Suddenly Sophy knew that he was threatening
her with physical violence and she felt acutely sick.
This was the man her mother had wanted her to

marry; had held up to her as perfect husband material ... this ... this creature who had just openly boasted to her that he had used violence on his wife.

Suddenly she was so angry that there was no room or fear. 'Is that what you like, Chris,' she sneered, 'hitting women?' She watched his face contort and was horrified by the violence in him but knew that to let him see her shock would be to add to his sense of power over her.

'I think it's time you left, Chris,' she told him coolly. She saw the indecision flicker in his eyes, and knew that her controlled manner had disconcerted him. She could even feel the grip of his hands relaxing slightly. Pressing home her advantage, she added, 'Jon will be home soon.'

She knew instantly that she had made a mistake, the very mention of Jon's name brought forth a torrent of invective and abuse so foul that she had to close her ears to it.

'You made a fool of me by marrying him,' he told her pushing her back against the wall, 'but he won't want you anymore when he sees what I've done to you ...'

He must be mentally deranged, Sophy thought as she tried to fight down her own panic, sensing that to show it would only be to inflame Chris even further. Even making allowances for the fact that he was drunk, his behaviour still hinted at an instability of temperament that shocked and frightened her, all the more so for being concealed so carefully in the past. And yet now she remembered that he had always had a streak of cruelty ... always enjoyed hurting people.

She was about to make one last plea to him to

set her free when she heard a car outside. Chris, still mouthing threats and insults at her, apparently had heard nothing, and Sophy prayed that Jon would find them before Chris did anything to hurt her. She didn't even dare move in case Chris realised . . . but then she heard a car door slam and saw Chris lift his head.

'Is that him?' he demanded, shaking her. 'Is it . . .?' He was starting to drag her towards the kitchen. She had a mental image of the dangerously sharp cooking knives hanging on the wall just by the door and her stomach clenched in mute protest. She mustn't let Chris get in there.

Panic shuddered through her and she reacted instinctively, screaming Jon's name . . . hoping her scream would penetrate through the thick front door.

For agonising seconds nothing happened . . . and she was terrified he hadn't heard her. Chris was still dragging her towards the kitchen and then blessedly she heard the kitchen door open, and Jon was calling her name. At the same time the front door opened and a burly taxi driver stood there. Jon had obviously heard her cry for help and had instructed the driver to take the front door whilst he took the back.

'In here, guv!'

She heard the driver call out and then the kitchen door burst open and Jon was standing there. She gave a tiny sob of relief and closed her eyes, only to open them again as Chris was thrust away from her.

'It was her fault,' she heard him telling Jon in a faintly whining tone. 'She asked me to come over here. She told me she wanted to see me . . . that she wanted me to take her to bed——'

'No! No . . . that isn't true!' She was sobbing the denial, unable to believe what Chris was saying. She saw Jon raise his fist and Chris cringe away and then the taxi driver was in between them. 'Best not do that, guv,' he told Jon warningly. 'Let the law handle it . . . it's always the best way.'

'From a legal point of view maybe, but not from an emotional one,' Jon responded rawly but nevertheless his fist unclenched and though he was not particularly gentle as he hauled Chris well away from her, Sophy saw that he had himself well under control.

It was the taxi driver who rang for the police.

After that Sophy lost touch with what was happening. All of them had to go down to the police station, where she had to give a statement. Jon wasn't allowed to stay with her but she knew she had nothing to hide and managed to keep control of herself long enough to answer the questions.

When at last she was reunited with Jon, she was glad of the protective arm he put round her. It was sheer bliss to simply relax against his chest . . . so solid and safe, after the terror Christ had inflicted upon her.

'Will you be wishing to press charges, sir?'

Jon replied immediately. 'Yes, we will.' He felt Sophy tense and looked down at her. 'I know it won't be very pleasant,' he told her quietly, 'but for the sake of his wife, and any other unfortunate woman who might come in contact with him, I think you should.'

Sophy knew that he was right but more important than that was the recognition that in speaking as he had, he was saying that he completely believed her version of what had happened. She had told him about it in the car on the way to the police station, and he had been so silent that there had been a moment when she had actually wondered if he thought that she was the one who was lying and Chris was telling the truth.

Neither of them spoke about what had happened on the drive back. When they got inside Jon detained her, by placing his hand on her arm.

'I think you ought to go upstairs and try to rest. You're probably still suffering from shock.'

'I can't rest,' she told him honestly, 'I'm far too wrought up. I was so frightened . . .' she said it under her breath. She shivered as he said roughly, 'If he had hurt you . . .'

She stopped him, shaking her head, putting her hand over his in an effort to soothe him. 'But thanks to you he didn't.' She shivered slightly. 'To think I never really realised what he was like.' She paused and then said huskily, dropping her head so that she wouldn't have to look at him. 'Thanks for . . . for believing me.'

She heard him swear under his breath, something he rarely did and her head jerked up. His mouth was white with strain, his eyes dark with anger. His hand cupped her jaw, his thumb stroking her mouth, the unexpected physical contact making her gulp in air, the raw ache inside her, suddenly mingling with a heady, delirious sense of release. If Chris had managed to deceive her so well about himself, perhaps he had deceived her in other ways as well. Perhaps she was not as sexually inadequate as she had always believed. After all, Chris had never ever made her feel the way Jon did. She had never ached for Chris the way she did for Jon, never melted at his lightest touch the way she did with Jon.

'Sophy . . .' The husky sound of his voice seemed to come to her from a great distance, almost as great as the distance that lay between them. With a small moan she moved, pressing herself against his body, feeling him tense in surprise and then unbelievably reach for her, taking her in his arms, his mouth hot and urgent on hers. He was kissing her as though he had never touched her before, as though he had starved for the taste and feel of her. She could feel his physical arousal and felt her own body stir in response.

'Sophy . . . Sophy.' Even when he had stopped kissing her, Jon didn't seem to be able to let her go or stop saying her name. It must be the release of tension which was causing such an intense reaction in him, she thought hazily, shuddering as his hand touched her body, longing suddenly to be free of the constrictions of her clothes.

Almost as though her desire had communicated itself to him he stepped back from her and then picked her up. She was no tiny little doll but he took the stairs almost effortlessly, shouldering open the door to his bedroom and then turning so that he could use his foot to kick it closed.

'No!' Her protest was an instinctive female denial of the desire she saw glittering in his eyes, but he misinterpreted it, thinking it was him she was denying, and contradicted thickly, 'Yes . . .' reiterating, 'yes, Sophy. Yes . . .' as he slowly slid her body back down to the floor, keeping her pressed hard against him, so that she was hopelessly aware of every male inch of him.

Never in a thousand lifetimes had she imaged Jon capable of such intensely sensual behaviour and every pulse in her body quickened in response to it. There was no room for fear that she might somehow disappoint him, that was forgotten in the thick clamouring of her blood.

CHAPTER EIGHT

SECONDS, or was it aeons, passed, Sophy wasn't aware of which . . . only of the heavy beat of Jon's body into her own, the timeless message of need and desire that passed from flesh to flesh and was returned.

She was dimly conscious of Jon reaching behind her to slide down the zip of her dress, just as she half heard the slithering sound the cotton made as it fell to the floor. All these were peripheral things, barely impinging on what really mattered, on the sensation of Jon's hot flesh pressed against her own as she tugged open his shirt and sighed her pleasure at being able to touch him as he was touching her.

Neither of them spoke. They were too busy touching . . . kissing. An urgent, aching impatience swept through her commanding her to actions at once both totally familiar and totally necessary so that nothing short of death could have stopped her from reaching down and fumbling impatiently with Jon's zip.

She felt his chest expand as he drew in his breath and for a moment teetered on the brink of her old insecurities but then his hand was on hers, helping her complete her task, his voice raw and thick with pleasure as she touched the maleness of him.

Then he was pushing her back against the door, muttering hoarse words of pleasure and arousal against her mouth, one hand sliding into her hair, the other curling round her waist as she melted into him . . . greedy for him.

His mouth left hers, long enough for him to groan. 'The bed . . . Sophy, we can't . . .' but he was moving away from her and that blotted out the meaning of his words, leaving behind only the sound and her fear that she was going to lose him, so she arched her body into his, winding her arms round him, grinding her hips into his in instinctive incitement.

'Sophy . . .' She could hear the grating protest in his voice, but could take no need of it. To lose him now would be to die. Her senses clamoured desperately for fulfilment, her body out of her control and obeying a far more primitive command than that of the mind. She wanted him . . . needed him. Not just against her but within her, deep inside her, at that place where her body pulsed and ached.

Moaning feverishly, she ran her hands over his torso, arching her back until her breasts were flattened against his chest, her hips writhing against him in a sensual rhythm they seemed to know by instinct.

'Dear God, Sophy . . .'

She felt the shudder run through him and saw the sweat cling to his skin. She could feel his heart racing and knew with a deep thrill of triumph that he had as little control over his response to her as she had of hers to him . . . less perhaps, she realised as he kissed her fiercely, his tongue eagerly invading her mouth. She could feel the frantic throbbing of his body against her, his weight pressing her back against the door and then suddenly he wrenched his mouth from hers, a harsh, inarticulate sound emerging from his throat. She knew, even without feeling him tug off her briefs that his need could not wait any longer.

She felt him lift her, balancing her weight against him and without having to be told automatically wrapped her legs around him, her hands clinging to his shoulders as she felt the first longed for movement of his body against her own.

Each driving thrust made her shudder with pleasure, her body eager to accommodate him, her muscles supplely responsive to the maleness of him.

Her spine arched her body taut as a bow in mute response to the driving force of him within her, the harsh oddly co-ordinated sound of their breathing an erotic stimulation she hadn't even realised existed.

It was over far too quickly, their bodies escaping the rationale of their minds, moving frantically together, meeting greedily as though they had starved for this frenetic physical union, Sophy thought, as her body trembled in the aftermath of the convulsive climax that had so recently racked her. She could still hear Jon's harsh breathing. She could feel the tension in his locked muscles as he slowly released her, letting her slide her feet back down to the floor. Neither of them spoke . . . She didn't honestly think either of them were capable of speaking. Jon arched his back, relieving her of his weight, his arms rigid, his hands against the door either side of her head. He leaned his forehead against his arm, and she could see that his hair at the front was soaked with sweat.

'I shouldn't have done that.' His voice was slow

as though he had difficulty in forming the words.
He raised his head and looked at her. 'Did I hurt
you?'

She ached, it was true . . . and there had been an
edge of violence in their lovemaking but it had
been a shared, wanted violence . . . a need in both
of them perhaps to work out physically the
tensions Chris had caused.

'Only in the nicest possible way,' she told him
honestly, checking as she felt him tense.

'You shouldn't say things like that to me. They
have a disastrous effect on my self-control . . .' He
picked her up, completely surprising her, and
carried her over to the bed.

'You lied to me,' he told her pleasantly,
watching her eyes.

'I . . .' She was confused and apprehensive, but
he didn't give her time to say anything.

'You told me I wouldn't enjoy possessing you
. . . that I would find you disappointing.'

Incredibly in the fierce urgency of their coming
together she had completely forgotten her old
fears, and now her mouth fell open slightly. All at
once she felt oddly light-headed—free, she realised
giddily—for the first time since she reached
womanhood, she was truly free of all fear and
inhibition.

They were both sitting on the bed, but Jon got
up and pulled off his shirt. While she was
completely nude he was still almost fully dressed
and she blushed to realise she had been so
impatient for him she hadn't even paused to
consider that fact before . . .

'What are you doing?'

He paused to smile at her as he pulled off his

trousers. 'I'm getting ready to make love to my wife,' he told her with a smile.

Sophy stared indignantly at him. 'I thought you just did . . .'

The humour died out of his eyes, and suddenly his mouth was grim. 'That wasn't so much making love as satisfying an intense physical need. This is making love.' He turned to her, touching her with gentle fingers, stroking the velvet smoothness of her skin, pushing her down onto the bed and lying beside her, kissing her slowly and thoroughly, until she sighed languorously her body awash with the most deliciously sensual awareness.

Now that the frantic need for haste was gone, she could touch him as she had been longing to do for so long. With her hands . . . and with her lips, delighting in his husky moans of pleasure as she discovered how best she could please him.

He had no need to make such discoveries. He already knew how to please her, she thought shiveringly, as his mouth caressed the hard peaks of her breasts, teasing and stimulating them until she cried out and arched against him.

It was only when his mouth touched the moist heart of her femininity that she tensed, trying desperately to wriggle away from him but his hands slid up under her, holding her hips, pinning her to the bed.

He raised his head and demanded rawly, 'Let me, Sophy. I want to pleasure you. I want to give you all that he never did. Trust me . . .'

She tried to relax, quivering under the slow assault of his tongue, gasping in shock at the sudden surge of pleasure invading her, her restraint completely swept away as Jon took advantage of her involuntary relaxation, his mouth moving delicately against the tender nub of flesh he had so unerringly found, ignoring her frantic protests to him to stop.

Then suddenly she was no longer capable of any form of protest; incapable of anything other than submitting to the waves of pleasure convulsing her body.

Some time later ... she wasn't capable of working out how much, she felt him move to take her in his arms and gently lick away her tears of pleasure. He took her hand and placed it on his body and under his guidance she felt the full male power of him.

It seemed impossible that her body should ache for him already but it did, as though simply by feeling his arousal she herself immediately shared it.

'See,' he murmured into her ear. 'That's what loving you does to me, Sophy.'

She shivered, immeasurably affected by the knowledge that he desired her; that she was capable of arousing such desire within him.

This time there was no urgency ... no haste ... and the slow, almost languorous way he filled her, made her sigh and murmur with delight, her body moving effortlessly to the rhythm he set.

She fell asleep in his arms, conscious of an overwhelming sense of well-being ... of inner peace and a joy so intense, she felt it must radiate from her in a physical aura. She loved him ... and she was already asleep before she remembered that he did not love her.

'Good, I'm glad you're awake. Uncle Jon said we

weren't to wake you.' Sophy opened her eyes slowly. What was she doing in Jon's bed? And then she remembered.

To cover her embarrassment she asked Alex, 'What time is it?'

'Supper-time,' David told her gloomily. 'I'm starving, and all Uncle Jon can cook is beans on toast.'

'That's a lie,' Alex retorted hotly, immediately defending her idol. 'He can do lots of things.'

'Such as?'

Sophy let them argue, closing her eyes and slowly trying to come to terms with what had happened. She and Jon had made love. She shivered lightly and felt tiny beads of sweat spring up on her skin as she remembered exactly how they had made love.

The children's quarrelling suddenly pierced her thoughts and she sat up, clinging to the duvet as she realised that she was still naked.

'Stop it, both of you,' she said firmly. 'I'll get up and come down and make your supper.'

'See what you've done now,' Alex accused her brother, 'Uncle Jon said——'

'What Uncle Jon said was that neither of you were to come in here and wake Sophy up,' that gentleman said drily from the doorway.

None of them had seen him come in. Sophy felt herself flush a brilliant scarlet as he looked at her. Alex, who was looking at her uncle rather guiltily, missed Sophy's reaction but David did not. A little to her surprise he got up off the bed, and taking hold of Alex's hand, said firmly to his sister. 'Come on . . . we're going downstairs.'

Sophy didn't want them to leave. She didn't

want to be alone with Jon ... She felt both
embarrassed and apprehensive. What must he
think of her? Had he guessed that she loved him?

'David, it seems, is growing up,' he murmured
lightly as he took the place his nephew had
vacated beside her on the bed, elucidating when
she looked puzzled. 'He obviously thought we
wanted to be alone.'

He bent his head, so that she couldn't see his
expression and said slowly, 'Sophy, we have to talk.'

He had said that before but this time the flare of
panic inside her was far greater. 'Not now, Jon.'
There was a note of pleading in her voice that
made him look at her. 'I feel so muzzy,' she told
him, fibbing a little. 'Chris, the shock ...'

'Of course.' His voice was completely even but
she was conscious of a sudden coolness in his
manner, a faint withdrawal from her which,
because she was so acutely aware of everything
about him, she recognised immediately and which
defeated her tenuous self-control. This afternoon
both of them had been acting out of character. She
couldn't blame him if now he was wishing none of
it had ever happened but at least nothing could
ever take from her her memories of him as her
lover ... and as her lover he had been both
demanding and tender. She had memories she
would cherish for the rest of her life. But memories
would not keep her warm at night when Jon was
not there ...

'We'll talk another time, then.' He was getting
up, and soon he would be gone.

She forced a brief smile.

'I'll be down shortly.' She saw that he was about
to protest and added, 'I won't sleep if I stay in bed

... and besides I'd have to go back to my own room.'

She held her breath as she waited for him to contradict her statement and tell her that she was sleeping with him from now on but he didn't and at last she had to expel it, and listen with an aching heart as he said mildly, 'As you wish.'

No doubt he was relieved that she was going back to her own room, she thought bitterly as she showered and then dressed. After all, by making that statement she had saved him the embarrassment of asking her to go back.

We must talk, Jon had said, but they didn't seem to get the opportunity to do so. It was now almost twenty-four hours since he had returned from London, and he had spent almost all of the morning shut in his study.

Sophy had gone in once with a cup of coffee. Jon had been on the 'phone, the conversation he was having abruptly cut short as she walked in, almost as though he did not want her to overhear what he was saying. After that she didn't go in again.

What had happened to that easy friendship that once had existed between them? Did love automatically kill friendship, or was it that friendship was quite simply no longer enough?

She was just about to make lunch when Jon walked into the kitchen and announced that he was going out.

'I'm meeting Harry in Cambridge,' he told her, 'I shan't be very long.'

She offered to drive him in, but he shook his head. 'It's okay, I've already booked a taxi.'

Sophy turned away, hoping he would not see the hurt pain she knew was in her eyes, and she thought she had succeeded until she heard him say raggedly, 'Sophy, I . . .' She turned round and saw the hand he had extended towards her as though he wanted to touch her, fall back to his side, his expression grimly unreadable, as he left his sentence unfinished.

There was such an air of constraint about him that even a complete stranger must have been aware of it, Sophy thought miserably as she watched his taxi drive away. What was causing it? Her? Their relationship?

She had some work to do for Jon—bills to send out and correspondence to attend to, but although her fingers moved deftly enough over the keys of her typewriter, her mind was not really on what she was doing.

When the doorbell rang she started up in surprise, her heart thudding nervously. She was not expecting anyone and after Chris's visit yesterday she felt acutely nervous, her mouth dry and her palms sticky. The bell rang again and she forced herself to get to her feet and walk to the front door.

Keeping the safety catch on, she opened it fractionally.

A tall, dark-haired woman stood there, her back to the door, one high-heeled, sandalled foot tapping imperiously, scarlet nails drumming impatiently against a cream leather shoulder bag.

Water-straight black hair fell to her shoulders in a satin sheet, her arms and legs were deeply tanned and the perfection of her slim body was provocatively revealed in a vibrant red cotton sheath dress that clung to her curves.

As Sophy opened the door, she turned her head, slanting faintly almond-shaped, brown eyes surveying Sophy with arrogant disdain. Her face was as beautifully tanned as her body, her mouth painted the same rich scarlet as her dress. The car she had arrived in was parked across the drive, as though it had been stopped in a hurry.

'You are Jon's wife?'

Sophy felt her heart sink as she caught the challenging ring in the American accented voice.

'Yes. Yes, I am.'

'Good. We have to talk.' She stepped closer to the door, and Sophy automatically released the chain, stepping back.

'I'm afraid I don't know you . . .' she began, fascinated as well as slightly repelled by the sneering curl of the full mouth as the other woman mocked.

'I cannot believe that. I'm sure Jon must have mentioned me to you. I am Lillian Banks. Jon and I are lovers.'

Sophy recognised the name immediately but distantly, all her powers of concentration focused on her visitor's final statement.

This was the woman whose pool Jon had used when he was in Nassau. The woman Mary-Beth had described to her as rather unbalanced . . . as almost obsessive about Jon.

'Lovers?' Her tongue felt thick and clumsy, making it difficult for her to form the words. 'I . . .'

'You are shocked I can see.' Slim shoulders shrugged. 'I knew how it would be but I told Jon it was better that you knew. He is a gentle man and would not wish to cause anyone pain.' She shrugged again. 'He has married you because of his responsibilities of course but from the moment we met both of us knew——'

'You're lying.'

The scarlet mouth smiled.

'Why don't we sit down comfortably and discuss this as adults?'

Sophy could not understand how Mary-Beth could ever have thought of this woman as being anything other than completely self-possessed and in control. Like a robot she found herself leading the way to the sitting-room, doing what she was instructed to do.

'I know this must be a shock to you but these things do happen. Jon and I knew the moment we met. We have so much in common. His work . . . our feelings about so many things. You may not believe this,' she looked sideways at Sophy and then smiled secretively, the almond eyes veiled by thick dark lashes as though she were gloating over something very special and private, 'but it was several days before Jon and I even went to bed together. We had so much to talk about.' She laughed, and then looked at Sophy again, adding softly, 'Of course when we did go to bed, I knew immediately how it would be.' She moistened her lips with her tongue, and Sophy felt acutely sick, imagining that full mouth clinging to Jon's, touching his body.

'But I love him.' She hadn't realised she had said the painful words out loud until she realised that Lillian was looking directly at her, the almond eyes narrowed and almost feral in their hatred.

'Maybe,' Lillian said flatly, 'but Jon does not love you. He loves me. Oh, yes, it is true,' she continued before Sophy could interrupt. 'Why else would he invite me to come to England? Why else would he meet my plane . . . book us both into the same hotel?' She smiled again, the cold cruelty in her smile making Sophy feel as though those scarlet nails had just been raked across her heart, inflicting wounds that would never heal.

'Oh, it is quite true,' Lillian said softly. 'You may check if you wish. We were booked into separate rooms of course. Here, I have the number of the hotel.' She opened her bag and gave Sophy a brochure.

'Well . . . are you going to ring them?'

What was the point? Sophy knew she couldn't be lying. Everything was so clear now. No wonder Jon had been so off-hand with her . . . so strained before he went to London. But he had come back. He had made love to her . . .

'Unfortunately we had a quarrel while we were there.' She shrugged again. 'Jon wanted me to come back here with him but I told him he must tell you about us first. We argued and he left. This morning though he telephoned me and we made up . . .'

Suddenly the reason Jon had made love to her was sickeningly clear to Sophy. He had quarrelled with Lillian and had made love to her out of nothing more than sheer physical frustration. She felt sick to her soul when she thought of how she had responded to him, how she had felt in his arms . . . but it had not been her he was loving, it had been this woman sitting so triumphantly opposite her, watching her now with hard, cold eyes.

'Why have you come here?' Sophy asked tonelessly.

'Surely that is obvious? To see Jon and to tell you that you no longer have any place in his life. You must understand that Jon and I love one another, that I am the one he wants at his side.'

'But *I* am the one he married,' Sophy persisted, not really knowing why she was fighting or what for; she had already lost it all.

'A piece of paper that means nothing ... Jon will divorce you.'

What could she say? Part of her could not believe that any of this was really happening. The Jon that Lillian was talking about was not the Jon she knew ... but then what did she really know about the man she had married? She had thought him sexless, remote, totally engrossed in his work and she had discovered for herself that none of those things were true.

'Of course you will be provided for financially.'

Sophy glanced up at that, her mouth hardening, but before she could speak her tormentor continued coolly. 'You will stay here in this house with the children. Jon will come back to Nassau with me.'

She would stay with the children? She blinked and stared at Lillian. 'The children are Jon's responsibility,' she said coldly. 'They are the son and daughter of his dead brother.'

For the first time since Lillian's arrival she felt she was the one with the advantage. Lillian blinked and frowned, her superb composure deserting her briefly, her mouth twisting petulantly.

'Jon does not want them,' she said positively at last. 'All he wants is me.'

Now it was Sophy's turn to frown. That did not

sound like the Jon she knew . . . or at least thought
she knew but then she remembered that before
they had married Jon had mentioned putting the
children in a home. He seemed to love them so
much, though. Just as he seemed to want you so
much, a bitter little voice mocked her, and look
how real that was.

Through the sitting-room window she saw a taxi
come down the drive and stop. Motionlessly she
watched Jon get out, and pause to pay the driver.
He looked tired, she noticed, immediately checking
the pain and anguish that welled up inside her.

From her chair Lillian could not see the
window. Smiling tightly at her Sophy got up.

'Please excuse me a second,' she muttered
moving to open the door. She really could not
endure any more, and certainly not the sight of
Jon being reunited with the woman he loved.

She reached the front door at the same time as
Jon, opening it for him. He started to smile at her,
the smile freezing suddenly, as he demanded,
'What's wrong?'

Sophy was shaking now with a mixture of anger
and agony. How could he stand there and pretend
a concern for her they both knew he could not
possibly feel?

In a voice tight with pain she told him. 'You've
got a visitor—in the sitting-room. Lillian Banks!'
She almost spat the name at him, half of her
knowing that she was reacting like someone in a
soap melodrama, the other half acknowledging
that like any other human being she was
conditioned to react to pain so instinctively that
her responses were bound to appear trite and
theatrical. 'She's just been telling me about your

plans for the future—plans which it seems don't include either me or the children ... Well, that's fine by me,' she rushed on bitterly. 'In fact it's probably the very best thing that could have happened.' It wasn't what she had intended to say at all, but hurt pride compelled her to make some attempt at self-defence; to at least try to hide from Jon the hurt he was causing her.

His hand shot out gripping her wrist, making her cry out sharply in physical pain.

She had never seen him look so hard or so angry before, and she could not understand why he was doing so now. 'Are you trying to tell me you want our marriage to end, Sophy?' he demanded harshly. 'Is that what you're saying?'

'Yes! Yes!' She practically screamed the word at him, tears flooding down her face as she tried desperately to pull away from him. The sitting-room door opened and Lillian exclaimed purringly, 'Jon, darling ...' Sophy felt the pressure round her wrist relax and instinctively made her escape, fleeing upstairs to the privacy and sanctuary of her own bedroom.

Once there, oddly enough, her tears stopped. The pain inside her was too intense for crying. Later she couldn't recall how long she stayed there ... how much time elapsed after Jon's arrival before he left again, this time with Lillian.

From her window Sophy saw them both get into Lillian's car. Lillian was smiling but she couldn't see Jon's face.

So this was how marriages ended, she thought emptily once they had gone. So this was what it felt like to be the victim of a broken marriage. Empty ... alone ... waiting for a pain so enormous and overwhelming that the very thought of it made her shiver in dread.

Somehow she managed to go downstairs and through the motions of making herself a cup of coffee. Somehow she remembered that the children had to be collected from school, that life had to go on as normal.

The 'phone rang. She hesitated before answering it, and then picked up the receiver.

'Sophy?'

She recognised Harry's American accent straight away.

'Is Jon there?' He sounded anxious and flustered.

'He's just left.' How toneless and light her own voice was. She replaced the receiver slowly. The 'phone started to ring again almost immediately, its summons imperative and sharp. She stared at it unblinkingly and then took it off the hook. She had the children to pick up, she must remember that.

Later Sophy realised that she had had no right to be driving at all that afternoon, never mind in such a potentially lethal, powerful car. All her actions were automatic and reflexive, directed by that tiny part of her brain which was not trying desperately to assimilate her pain.

She even managed to smile at David and Alex as they clambered into the car and started chattering to her, although she was conscious of David giving her one or two puzzled looks.

How could Jon not want them? A fierce wave of protective love for them surged over her. Well she would want them and she would fight for the right to love and care for them. Slowly different pieces

of information were filtering through her brain.
She stared at the house as she parked the car. How
could she afford to keep it on? How much of an
allowance would Jon give her? He was a
comparatively wealthy man but her heart rebelled
at the thought of taking so much as a penny from
him. If she wanted to keep the children though,
she would have to support them. She couldn't
work full-time and give them the love and
attention they were going to need. Didn't Jon care
what he was doing to them, even if he didn't care
about her? He owed it to them. She sighed and
tried to redirect her thoughts. She had seen this
same situation played out so often before . . . when
did adults ever really think about their children,
when they were gripped by the intensity of love?
People these days weren't brought up to put others
before themselves any longer and in many ways
that was a good thing. Too many people, mainly
of her own sex, had made themselves martyrs to
others' demands and needs too often in the past . . .
but the children. Stop thinking about it, she told
herself as she went into the house. She knew she
had to stop the tormenting thoughts swirling
round in her mind or go mad from the agony of
them. She tried to submerge them in physical
activity, busying herself making the milkshake the
children always had when they came back from
school.

'When will Uncle Jon be back?' David asked as
he and Alex sat down at the table. Instantly Sophy
stiffened. What should she tell them? For the first
time it struck her that Jon might not come back at
all, ever. The knowledge was like a physical blow,
so painful that she went white.

'Sophy, what's wrong?' There was anxiety and something else in David's voice. Fear?

Resolutely Sophy pulled herself together and tried to smile. Her facial muscles were so stiff she could barely move them.

'Nothing,' she said as reassuringly as she could. 'I'm not sure when he will be back.'

'Where's he gone?'

That was Alex, frowning slightly, picking up the atmosphere of tension that hung over the kitchen. 'Where is he?'

'He had to go out.' Careful, Sophy, she warned herself, any more of this and you'll be breaking down completely. Walking over to the sink so that she had her back to them, she said as carelessly as she could, 'You know what he's like when he's . . . working. I don't really know when he'll be back.'

It seemed to satisfy them, but for how long? Surely Jon wouldn't leave her to tell them alone? But no . . . he wasn't that sort of man. Was he?

CHAPTER NINE

THE 'phone rang at ten o'clock and she knew it was Jon even before she picked up the receiver. It was the call she had been dreading all evening, ever since she had put the receiver in its place after putting the children to bed.

'Sophy?' He said her name roughly, angrily almost and that hurt. By what right was he angry with her? She was the one who should feel that emotion but her pain was too great to allow her the relief of anger.

'Sophy, we need to talk.' Urgency laced the words closely together making his voice sharper, different. Already he was alien to her ... not the Jon she knew but a different Jon.

Jealousy tore at her, making it impossible for her to speak to him without breaking down completely, her 'No!' rough and unsteady.

'Sophy!' He said her name again, and the receiver shook in her damp hand. She knew she did not have the control to go through what had to be gone through right now. She couldn't even listen to the angry cadences of his voice without breaking apart inside, without remembering how he had said her name while they made love ... how the reverberations of it had passed from his body to her own.

'Jon, please. Lillian has told me everything.' She was speaking quickly, lightly as though not daring to linger over the words in case that made them too real. She heard him swear and flinched.

'Sophy . . . please . . .'

'No . . . no. I don't want to talk about it, Jon. Let's just go ahead and get a divorce. I'll stay here with the children.' Her voice petered out as she sensed his shock. 'Unless you want us to move out.' She thought she heard him draw in his breath harshly, a sound of painful anguish as though somehow she had hurt him. Or was it that hearing the words was making it real for him too . . . making him see what he would be doing to David and Alex. The children will stay with you, Lillian had said, we don't want them.

'No! Promise me you won't move out, Sophy. Promise me.'

'Very well . . .'

She heard him sigh as though her soft acquiescence was not enough and then he was saying thickly, 'Have you thought about what this is going to do to the kids, Sophy?'

Had *she* thought about it? All at once she was angry, so much so that she could not speak to him any more. She put down the receiver with a bang and then wiped her damp palm distastefully on her skirt.

The 'phone rang again almost immediately and she stared at it wanting to deny its imperative call, but somehow impelled to pick up the receiver.

'Sophy. No, don't hang up . . . listen to me. If you need to get in touch with me for anything, I'm staying with Harry and Mary-Beth in Cambridge.' As though something in her silence encouraged him he went on raggedly. 'We have to talk, Sophy. We . . .'

It was that 'we' that did it. There was no 'we' where they were concerned. They were not a single unit but two separate ones.

In a cold precise little voice she barely recognised as her own she asked slowly. 'And Lillian, Jon, is she staying with Harry and Mary-Beth too?'

She heard him swear, and then say curtly. 'Yes, she is, but Sophy——'

She cut him off before he could say any more, telling him quietly, 'Then I don't think we have anything to say to one another really, do you, Jon?'

This time, after she had replaced the receiver, the telephone did not ring again and she did not really expect it to.

Upstairs alone in bed, she tried to clear her mind so that she could force it to accept a truth it did not want to know. It hurt that Jon had not even told her himself about Lillian. She had known something was wrong but she had had no idea what that something was.

She laughed then, a high hysterical sound that shocked her own ears until she controlled it. How ironic that Jon should meet and fall in love with Lillian such a very short time after marrying her.

How doubly ironic when she remembered what Mary-Beth had said about Jon postponing the trip so that they could be married first. How he must have regretted not waiting. She turned uneasily in her bed wondering how long it would take their divorce to go through. She wasn't very well up in the legalities of these things. And then her mind drifted to David and Alex. Both of them adored Jon. How could she tell them what was happening in such a way that neither of them would ever know that their uncle had rejected them?

It was all so out of character somehow and yet wasn't she just telling herself that because she didn't want to believe the truth? She had to hand it to Lillian, coming to see her like that. In her place she doubted that she would have had the courage to do so. And yet Sophy knew that Lillian had enjoyed telling her, hurting her. The thought of Jon deliberately lying to her, so that he could be with Lillian, was so galling and painful that she could scarcely endure it. And then to come back and make love to her . . . to substitute her for Lillian, because that was surely what he had done.

He said he wanted you, an inner voice taunted her . . . perhaps he had, Sophy acknowledged. Man was a strange animal and could desire what he did not love . . . or perhaps that had simply been his way of trying to fight free of his love for Lillian. Perhaps he had felt honour bound to at least try to make a success of their marriage and maybe he had hoped that in making love to her he could forget the other woman. Obviously he had not done so.

By the time morning came, she was totally exhausted and had to drag herself downstairs to get the children's breakfast.

Both of them commented on her pale face.

'I haven't been feeling very well,' she fibbed to them and saw David's eyes widen as he asked her curiously, 'Does that mean you and Uncle Jon are going to have a baby? Ladies sometimes aren't very well when they do.'

A baby? She managed a tight smile and shook her head negatively. But what if she was wrong?

What if she was carrying Jon's child? It was, after all, perfectly possible.

She would just have to worry about that eventually if it actually happened, she told herself grimly.

Because it was a Saturday there was no need for her to take the children to school but both of them had made arrangements to see friends and by the time Sophy got back from ferrying them to their individual destinations it was gone eleven o'clock.

As she turned into the drive she realised that the day had become very overcast, the threat of thunder hanging sullenly on the too still air.

It was time the weather broke; they needed a storm to clear the air and rain for the over-parched garden. A tension headache gripped her forehead in a vice as she walked inside. She had always been petrified of storms. Not so much the thunder but the lightning—a childhood hang-up from a story someone had once told her about someone being struck by lightning and 'frizzled to death'. Knowing now that her fear was illogical still did not remove it and she shivered slightly as she made herself a cup of coffee, dreading the storm to come.

The house had never seemed more empty. She had loved it when she first came here as Jon's assistant, and what happy plans she had made for it when she had agreed to marry him. She had pictured it as a proper home ... Now she was alone with the reality that said a house no matter how pleasant was merely a shell. It was people who made that shell a home.

By one o'clock the sky was a sullen grey; and it was dark enough for her to need to switch the kitchen light on. The sudden ring on the front doorbell jarred her too sensitive nerves.

Jon! She whispered the name, trying to control the crazy leap of her pulses and to deny the sudden mental picture she had of the man. How could there ever have been a time when she had scathingly dismissed him as sexually unattractive? Being married to him had been like discovering a completely different person hidden away behind a protective disguise.

In his touch, in his kiss, was all the maleness any woman could ever want, she acknowledged weakly, knowing, even as she fought to subdue the traitorous leap of hope jerking her heart, that it would not be Jon outside. After all why would he ring the bell when he had a key and why would he come back at all, when he had already taken what he really wanted with him?

Nevertheless she went to open the door, her face losing all colour when she saw Mary-Beth standing outside.

'No. Sophy . . . please let me in,' the American woman pleaded, guessing from her expression that Sophy did not want to see her.

Good manners prevented Sophy from shutting the door in her face but her back was rigid with withdrawal as she stepped back into the hall.

'Sophy, Jon doesn't know I'm here,' Mary-Beth began, following her into the kitchen, watching as Sophy tensed as she caught the distant noise of thunder—so distant that Sophy had had to strain her ears to catch it. The storm was still a good way off. She tried to relax. She had no idea what Mary-Beth was doing here, but since she had come . . . She sighed, and asked her guest if she wanted a cup of coffee.

'What I want is for you to sit down and tell me why you've thrown Jon out,' Mary-Beth told her forthrightly. 'I thought you loved him.'

'I do.' The admission was wrung out of her before she could silence it, her face ashen as she realised her idiocy.

Her ears, tensely alert for the sound, caught the still distant dullness roll of fresh thunder.

'Do you find storms frightening?'

She gave Mary-Beth a tense grimace, and acknowledged shortly, 'Yes.' Another time she might have wondered at the faintly pleased gleam she saw in the other woman's eyes but not now.

Her defences completely destroyed by losing Jon, the threat of a thunder storm was just more than she could cope with.

'Sophy, come and sit down.' Very gently Mary-Beth touched her arm, picking up both mugs of coffee and gently shepherding Sophy into the sitting-room.

She waited until they were both sitting down before speaking again and then said quietly, 'I can understand why you feel hurt and angry with Jon for deceiving you but why won't you let him talk to you . . . explain?'

Sophy tried to appear calmer than she felt. 'What is there left to talk about?' she asked emotionlessly. 'I think Lillian has already said it all.' She shrugged and spread her hands, disturbed to see how much they shook. 'She and Jon are lovers . . . Jon wants to divorce me so that he can be with her. It is all quite plain really . . . I don't need telling twice.'

Her voice sharpened with anguish over the last words and she got up, pacing over to the window to stare at the yellow tinged greyness of the overcast sky.

'Lillian told you that she and Jon were *lovers*?'

Why was Mary-Beth sounding so shocked? Jon and Lillian were staying with her. She must be perfectly aware of the situation.

'She told me everything,' Sophy reiterated expressionlessly. 'About how Jon asked her to come to London ... how they stayed there together in an hotel.' Her mouth twisted bitterly. 'She even suggested I should ring the hotel and check.'

'Sophy?'

She swung round to look at Mary-Beth as she caught the anxiety in her voice but the frown on Mary-Beth's face suddenly lifted. 'Oh, it's all right. You will be staying here?'

'If Jon lets me. Lillian told me that they don't want the children and even if I didn't love both of them very much myself, I could hardly walk out and leave them.' She saw Mary-Beth look at her watch and then the American was saying hurriedly, 'Look I must run ... Are you doing anything during the rest of the day? Going out?'

She must be embarrassed, Sophy realised, and that was why she was having to take refuge in inane social chit-chat; even so she responded to the questions, shaking her head and explaining that both children were out with friends and would not be back until after supper.

Thunder rolled again, marginally nearer this time and Sophy winced.

'If I were you I'd go upstairs and bury your head under a pillow,' Mary-Beth suggested. 'That way you won't hear it.'

Sophy walked with her to the door and watched until her car had completely disappeared feeling that somehow she had just severed her final link with Jon. The ache in her temples had become a fully fledged pain; pain, in fact, seemed to invade her whole body. She went upstairs on dragging feet but instead of going into her own room she went into Jon's.

The room was clean and tidy just as she had left it after cleaning it yesterday morning and yet overwhelmingly it reminded her of him. One of his shirts half hung out of the laundry basket by the door and she went automatically to push it in, tensing as her fingers curled round the soft cotton and she was irresistibly aware of how the fabric had clung to his body. Like a sleepwalker she lifted the shirt from the empty basket, pressing its softness to her face. She wanted to cry but the tears had solidified in a lump in her chest—a lump that ached and hurt with every breath she tried to take. A scent that was exclusively Jon's filled her senses with an awareness of him and almost without realising what she was doing she stumbled over to his bed and flung herself down full length on it, still clutching his shirt. Outside the sky darkened, suddenly split by the first sizzling arc of lightning. Sophy cried out curling up into a tense ball, burying her face in Jon's pillow.

Her fear of the storm seemed to release the tight knot of pain inside her and suddenly she was crying, tearing, ugly sobs that shook her body and soaked the shirt and pillow she was still clinging to. Outside the storm drew nearer and her tears slowly gave way to terror. Logic told her that she

should get up and close the curtains but the fear
chaining her to the bed was too great.

An hour, maybe more, passed as she lay there
too terrified to move and yet oddly comforted by
the indefinable presence of Jon that still clung to
the room.

Suddenly it started to rain, almost torrentially
so, the sound of it drowning out everything else.

Downstairs a door banged and Sophy listened
to it, wondering if she had left a window open. If
so the floor beneath it would surely be soaked.

Closer now the thunder rolled, lightning arcing
brilliantly across the sky, illuminating the darkness
of the room. She moaned and covered her ears.

'Sophy.'

A hand touched her shoulder. Her eyes opened
in stunned disbelief to look into Jon's. He was
bending towards the bed. His shirt was soaked
through, clinging to his skin and he had brought in
with him the cool fresh smell of rain. He opened
his mouth to speak, the words drowned out by the
ferocity of the storm, the brilliance of the lightning
jagging across the sky making Sophy scream out in
terror and release her pillow to fling herself against
him, burying her face in his shoulder.

She felt him shake and for a moment thought he
was laughing at her but then she felt his hand on her
hair, his voice roughly concerned in her ear, as his
arms came round her, and his voice soothed her fear.

'I'll go and close the curtains.'

She didn't want to let him go but suddenly all
that had happened reminded her that she had no
right to be in his arms . . . no place within their
security and so she withdrew from him, and
watched him walk across the floor.

The curtains were thick, old-fashioned ones, and instantly blotted out the storm, together with what little daylight there was. In the gloom she could barely make out Jon's outline, until he switched on the bedside lamp.

'That's some storm out there,' he told her wryly. 'I'm soaked ... I'll have to take this off.' He stripped off his shirt, dropping it into the laundry basket, opening his wardrobe to get another; all simple automatic movements and yet ones that moved her to great joy and pain. He didn't put the shirt on though, pausing to turn and look across the room at her.

'Sophy, why wouldn't you let me talk to you?'

His voice was quiet, and if she hadn't known better she might have said it was quite definitely edged with pain.

She could feel the tight knot returning to her chest and couldn't speak, simply shaking her head. She knew he was coming towards her and that she should get off his bed and move away but something told her that her legs simply would not allow her to stand. As he reached her he stretched out his hand, and gently tugged away the shirt she had been clinging to.

A hot wave of colour flooded her skin as Sophy found herself unable to free herself from his gaze. He had taken off his glasses—to dry them, she supposed, and had not put them back, so that she could quite clearly see the wry amusement darkening his eyes to indigo blue.

'What's this?'

He said it softly, watching her like a hunter stalking his prey ... seeing far too much for someone who was supposed to be so short-sighted.

'I was cold.'

She saw his eyebrows lift with pardonable mockery, shock jolting through her body as he said softly. 'How disappointing . . . I was hoping it was a love-object substitute . . .' he sat down beside her and concluded silkily, 'and that that love-object was me.'

How could he do this to her? Her fingers curled into her palms, not even the dying sound of the storm having the power to frighten her now.

'Why are you saying these things to me?' she demanded huskily. 'Isn't Lillian enough for you?'

His prompt 'No,' stunned her. She could only stare silently up at him, her mouth slightly open. All humour had gone from his eyes now and in fact they were almost frightingly grim.

'I could shake you, Sophy, for being so stupid,' he told her bitingly. 'How on earth could you be so easily deceived?'

'Deceived?'

'I don't care what Lillian might have told you.' He reached out and cupped her face. 'Sophy, Lillian and I were never lovers. Oh, I know what she told you,' he continued before she could speak, 'but only because Mary-Beth told me. I had no idea that Lillian had——' He broke off, his mouth curling in bitter derision. 'That woman astounds me, astounds and frightens . . .'

'Jon . . .'

'No . . . listen to me. Let me tell you the full story,' he paused and when she made no move to speak he started softly, 'I told you that I met Lillian when I went to Nassau but what I didn't tell you was that she seemed to develop what, for lack of a better description, I can only describe as

some sort of fixation about me.' He grimaced
faintly. 'It got so bad that I was actually having to
find ways to avoid her. When she first invited me
to use her apartment and pool I had no idea. In
the end I had to appeal to Mary-Beth for help and
it was then that I discovered that Lillian has a
history of these almost violent fixations. It's a sad
story in a way. In many respects she's absolutely
brilliant ... perhaps almost too much so.
Apparently she had some sort of breakdown just
after she left university but she's very good at her
job and Harry, who's a bit of a softie in many
ways, took her on to his staff after he heard about
her history of mental problems from his pre-
decessor. Workwise he has no criticism of her at
all but emotionally, she doesn't seem to have any
conception of reality or self-control.

'When he told me all this I was glad that I was
leaving Nassau so soon—and not only for that
reason,' he added cryptically. 'I got the shock of
my life when I walked into that hotel in London
and found her waiting for me there in the foyer.
Apparently Harry had had to ring Nassau and he
had spoken to her on the telephone—about some
problems she was having with her work. She asked
him about me and without thinking he mentioned
that I was going to London to do some work for
Lexicons, which happens to be a company that
Nassau deal with.' He shrugged tiredly.

'Harry admits now that that was a mistake, but
as he says, it never even crossed his mind that
Lillian would ring Lexicons, pretending to be my
wife and find out from them which hotel they had
booked me into and when I could be expected
there.' He saw Sophy's expression and smiled

harshly, 'She was quite proud of what she did, believe me. For me it was like the start of a nightmare. Every time I tried to persuade her to go back to Nassau she started threatening to destroy herself. Finally I managed to persuade her to let me ring Harry and he came down to London straight away to talk to her.

'The plan was that Harry would see her safely on to a plane to go home and that she would be met at the other end but somehow it backfired and she managed to give Harry the slip.

'He rang me yesterday morning to warn me. That was why I went out to see him so that we could try and work out what on earth she was going to do. The last thing I expected was that she would turn up here.

'Lillian is an extremely mentally disturbed young woman, Sophy,' he said quietly. 'If I give you my word that she and I have never been lovers and that I would never want her as my lover, would you believe me?'

'Where is she now?' Her throat was dry with tension.

'With Harry and Mary-Beth. I managed to persuade her to drive me over there yesterday afternoon. I thought you were angry with me because I hadn't told you what was happening. I should have done but our own relationship seemed too tenuous ... so fragile that I felt I couldn't risk destroying it by burdening you with problems that weren't really yours. Especially after the shock of Chris's attack.'

'She said you loved her ...' Her voice was cracked and uneven. 'She said you wanted to divorce me.'

'She's a very sick person, Sophy, so totally out of touch with reality that I'm afraid she'll never be wholly sane again. Believe me, I did nothing ... nothing to encourage her in her fantasies.' He smiled rather grimly. 'There was only one woman on my mind whilst I was in Nassau and that was you. Do you believe me?'

'Yes.' She said it huskily and knew that it was true. Her heart somersaulted as he lifted her hand to his mouth and pressed his lips to her palm, caressing it softly with his tongue.

'How did you know what Lillian had said to me?'

'Mary-Beth told me. She also told me something else.' Sophy tensed and looked at him, remembering her own admission to Mary-Beth that she loved him.

'She said you were frightened of thunder storms,' Jon told her softly, 'and that she'd told you to bury your head under a pillow. I'm glad you chose my pillow, Sophy.'

She could feel the heat coming off his skin, and being in his arms was like coming home to safety having known great pain and fear. His mouth touched hers, lightly, questioningly and she clung to him, abandoning all pride as she was swamped by her own shattering response to him.

She could feel his heart thudding erratically against her, his mouth hot and urgent as it moved over her own. She wanted him to go on kissing her for ever, but already he was releasing her, putting a distance between them.

'I still haven't been entirely honest with you.'

She thought for a moment her heart-beat had stopped. He smiled gravely at her and said quietly,

'When I asked you to marry me I had no intention
of it ever being merely a convenient arrangement,
devoid of love and physical contact.'

'You hadn't?'

He shook his head, said 'No,' and then laughed
at her expression. 'I begin to think you're the one
who needs glasses, Mrs Philips,' he teased her
softly, 'otherwise you'd surely have seen that I'd
been lusting after you ever since you came to work
for me. From the very first time we met in fact.'

She stared at him in disbelief, stammering, 'But
. . . but I thought——'

'That I was a sexless, vague, confirmed
bachelor, more interested in computers, than
human beings,' he said wryly, 'Oh yes, I do realise
that and I had been cursing my far too effective
armour plating for quite some considerable time.
It was the look on your face when you heard
David saying that Louise had wanted to get into
bed with me that finally gave me hope.'

'What sort of look?' Sophy asked him suspiciously.

His smile was both innocent and tantalising.
'Oh, the sort that said you were looking at me as a
man instead of simply your lame dog boss.'

Sophy shook her head. 'But why pretend to be
something you weren't, Jon? Why pretend to be so
sexless and . . . dull?'

He hesitated for a moment and then said slowly,
'I know this will make me sound unattractively
vain but when I first went up to Cambridge, like
many another before me I wanted to have a good
time. My father was comfortably off . . . those
were the days when teenagers didn't have to worry
too much about getting a job . . . when, in fact,

our generation thought it was the hub of the whole world. It was my first real time away from home, I had a generous allowance and a small sports car my father had bought me when I passed my 'A' levels. I wasn't short of congenial feminine company. In short I lived a life of hedonistic pleasure rather than scholarly concentration. That all came to an abrupt end just after my third term. My tutors started complaining about the standard of my work . . . that sobered me up quite a bit, until then I'd never really had to work, you could say that it had all come too easily to me. Then a friend of mine was sent down—drug trafficking; a girl I'd gone out with died—all alone in a filthy squat with her arm all bloated out with septic poisoning from using a dirty needle—she was mainlining on heroin. I had to identify her. It all brought me down to reality.

'When term resumed after the Christmas recess I decided I was going to turn over a new leaf. I'd talked to my brother—Hugh was eight years older than me, already married then, but still enough in touch with his own youth to listen sympathetically to me—but it seemed that my friends or at least some of them didn't want me to change. Then I had to start wearing glasses. I discovered quite quickly that people who didn't know me reacted differently to me . . . and so gradually I evolved a form of disguise and somehow it stuck with me. There was nothing to make me want to abandon it, until I met you and even then it seemed I wasn't going to be able to reveal myself to you in my true colours, so to speak.'

Sophy looked questioningly at him and he said drolly,

'Ah well, you see I had observed how you reacted to me ... and how you reacted to any male who was even just slightly aggressively masculine and I didn't want to frighten you off. You felt safe with me, that much was obvious and because of that I could get closer to you. Some disguises are used for protection,' he told her, 'some for hunting ...' He laughed at her expression. 'Ah yes, my poor little love, I'm afraid you ...'

She didn't let him finish, flushing suddenly as she remembered his bland and extremely irritating indifference to her timid sexual overtures in the early days of their marriage ... an indifference which she had naïvely thought sprang from unawareness.

'You knew ...' she accused.

'Knew what?' He was smiling dulcetly at her.

She swallowed, and said huskily, 'That I wanted you.'

After the way you looked at me when I came back from Nassau I hoped you might,' he agreed tenderly, 'but I had to be sure it wasn't merely that I was a challenge to you, Sophy. I had gambled too heavily for that. You see,' he told her quietly, 'as I soon discovered well before I married you, what I once thought was merely lust turned out to be love and that love hasn't diminished for knowing you ... quite the contrary. *That* is what I have been trying to talk to you about, Sophy.' He touched her face lightly with his fingers and she trembled wildly, hardly daring to look at him. 'We have been lovers, and you have given yourself to me physically with a generosity that no one else has ever matched or ever could, but have you given yourself to me emotionally, Sophy? *Can* you give yourself to me emotionally or is it still Benson, despite all that he has done to you?'

'Chris?' Sophy stared at him. 'I never loved Chris. Not really, not like . . .'

'Not like?' His voice was placid, belying the expression in his eyes. It made her heart race and suspended her breath until she realised he was still waiting impatiently for her response.

'Not like I love you,' she told him.

He expelled his breath on a harsh sigh and said roughly, 'God, Sophy, you don't know how you've tormented me.'

She smiled at him, going willingly into his arms as he dragged her against him. 'Oh, I think I've a fair idea,' she told him demurely, 'after all you've done your own fair share of tormenting.'

From the shelter of his arms, she looked up at him, watching the way his eyebrows rose in query.

'All that parading around practically nude,' she elucidated for him, 'making me want you, making me love you . . .' She looked up at him again and smiled, 'and probably damn well making me pregnant into the bargain.'

'Have I done?' He looked smugly and irritatingly malely pleased at the prospect.

'I don't know,' she admitted, 'but, Jon . . .' she protested as he turned round with her still in his arms and rolled her onto the bed, following her there, and pinning her down with the superior weight of his body.

'Jon, what are you doing?' she demanded.

He was grinning at her and her heart turned over inside her as she read the purpose in his eyes and he told her softly, 'It would certainly be one

sure fire way of keeping you tied to me. Besides . . .'
He paused to kiss her, smothering her mumbled
protest until she was forced to give up and respond
to him.

'Besides . . . what?' she asked breathlessly when
at last he had released her.

'I love loving you so much,' he told her simply.
'No woman has ever meant to me what you do,
Sophy, or ever will. I could have wept when you
told me that you weren't fully a woman. I could
have killed Benson for what he had done to you.
You were too inexperienced to even realise what
he *had* done. How he had pushed his own
inadequacies off on to you.'

'*You* made me a woman, Jon,' she told him
huskily, feeling his body tense against her and
thrilling to the vibrant masculinity of it. Only one
thing still troubled her, creasing her forehead as
she said hesitantly, 'Jon, just now when I said I
might be pregnant you seemed pleased but you
threatened to put the children into care. You . . .'

'I gambled that their supposed plight would
push you into marrying me far faster than any
amount of reasoned argument,' he admitted wryly,
'but believe me I would never have done it.
They're my brother's children, Sophy, and I love
them very much, just as I shall love our own very
much . . . but never quite as much as I love you.'

Beneath him her body quivered and she reached
up to wrap her arms round him, her voice
breaking slightly as she murmured, 'Make love to
me please, Jon. Show me that this isn't all some
impossible dream.'

'No dream but reality,' he whispered against her
mouth. 'The reality of our love.'

SUBSTITUTE LOVER

BY
PENNY JORDAN

WORLDWIDE BOOKS
LONDON • SYDNEY • TORONTO

First published in Great Britain in 1987
Reprinted in Great Britain in 1993
by Worldwide Books, Eton House,
18-24 Paradise Road, Richmond, Surrey TW9 1SR

© Penny Jordan 1987

ISBN 0 373 58952 2

99-9305

Made and printed in Great Britain

CHAPTER ONE

AHEAD of her loomed the motorway exit sign for the village. Stephanie sighed faintly, the soft sound whispering past vulnerably curved lips. The late afternoon sunlight burnished her long hair into a shining copper cloak. Normally she wore it up in a neat chignon, but today she had left it loose.

Only the inward clenching of her stomach muscles betrayed her growing tension. She hated coming back so much. Fear and pain mingled inside her, making her fingers grip harder on the steering-wheel.

If it wasn't for Gray ... She shuddered visibly, aching to close her eyes and blot out the terrible images blocking out the gentle, rolling countryside and the wide span of the motorway.

Never, ever, no matter how long she lived, would she forget that terrible night when they had come to tell her that Paul was dead. The shock of it, coming so quickly on the heels of that last bitter quarrel, had produced a burden of guilt she carried with her still.

Even now, ten years later, she often woke in the night re-living that last fatal evening they had spent together. The quarrel had blown up over nothing—and it had not been the first time. After only three months of marriage Paul had become a stranger—a frighteningly violent stranger, too, at times—who called her frigid and sexless, and complained that he wished he had never married her.

He had stormed out of the cottage and she had let him, too confused and miserable to try and coax him back.

It had been a bad summer, with constant gales and dangerous seas. She had never dreamed that he intended to take out his boat, but he had. Who knew what thoughts had been in his mind in those last few hours of his life? The seas had been far too dangerous for a lone yachtsman, so the coastguard had told them, and Paul, reckless as always, had omitted to wear his buoyancy jacket and safety harness.

He had been swept overboard by one of the giant waves, or so the authorities surmised, because his body had been found on a beach by an early morning stroller.

His grief-stricken parents had demanded to know why she hadn't alerted the coastguard earlier, when he had not come home, and Stephanie had been forced to lie, unwilling to add to their pain by telling them that there had been other nights during their brief marriage when he hadn't come home, when she had slept alone in the wide double bed she had grown to hate. But John and Elise Chalmers had worshipped their only child, and she had not had the heart to destroy their image of him.

She knew that they blamed her for his death, and in her heart of hearts she felt equally guilty. If she had been a different type of woman ... if she had had the sexuality to keep Paul at her side, he would not have grown bored with her company ... would not have been driven by the relentless devil that possessed him, unleashing a streak of violence in him that she had never suspected existed.

They had married too young and on too short an acquaintance; she knew that now. Neither of them had really known the other, and by the time they realised how intrinsically different they were it was too late— they were married.

Tears stung her eyes briefly, her guilt momentarily overlaid by sorrow. Paul had been so alive . . . so good-looking and arrogantly male. She had stopped loving him within weeks of their marriage—the first time he had hit her he had destroyed her image of him and with it her almost childish adoration; but that did not stop her regretting his death and the waste of such a very young life.

Only Gray had stood up for her and said in that quiet, slow voice of his that she was not to blame for Paul's death. But Gray didn't know the truth. Even now he still didn't know the truth, but his defence of her, the way his arms had held her, comforting and protecting her in the shocking aftermath of the news, had formed a bond between them that nothing could ever break.

Automatically she turned off the motorway, taking the pretty country road that dipped between the gentle hills and then meandered through the New Forest down to the coast. Her bright yellow VW preferred the gentle pace of country driving, the engine almost purring as the motorway was completely lost from sight and they were swallowed up by golden fields, ripely heavy with their summer crop.

Her friends in London teased her about her devotion

to her little car. She earned a good living from her work as an illustration artist, and then additionally there was the income she derived from her share in the boat-yard that had been in Paul's family for several generations.

She always felt uncomfortable about that inheritance, but Gray had urged her not to dispose of it, and she had agreed. Now that Paul's parents were dead, she and Gray were joint owners of the yard.

Pauls and Gray's grandfather had started it, passing it on to his two sons.

Gray's parents had been killed in a sailing accident when he was fourteen years old, and he had virtually been brought up alongside his cousin. But Paul had never really liked Gray. She had known that from the first and had put the animosity between them down to the seven-year age-gap. As a teenager, newly arrived in the area, she had found Gray both distant and rather formidable.

It had been her father's interest in boats that had led to her introduction to Paul. The boat-yard was one of his accounts at the branch of the bank he had just been transferred to as manager, and he had taken Stephanie with him, on a visit to inspect the yard.

Paul had been working in the yard, a slim, golden-haired young god with a deep tan and a self-assured smile.

She had thought their love was mutual, but she realised now that to Paul she had only been a new challenge. He had a reputation locally as something of a playboy, but she hadn't known that then.

She had been a rather shy teenager, a product of an

all-girls' school, studious and not as knowledgeable about sex as most of her peers.

She had just left school, and had been looking forward to going to art school after the long summer break. And then she had met Paul.

Within days they were virtually inseparable. When Paul discovered her reservations about allowing him to make love to her, and the fact that she was still a virgin, he had announced that they would get married.

That had been typical of his impulsiveness and his determination to have his own way, Stephanie had recognised later, but at the time she had been too bemused to do anything but follow where he led. Of course they had encountered massive parental objections, from both families; but the more their parents urged them to wait, the more determined Paul became that they would not.

Even Gray had suggested that they get to know one another a little better before making such an important commitment, but Paul had laughed at him, she remembered, sneering that since Gray was not married himself he was not qualified to speak.

In the end their parents had given way, perhaps in the fear that if they did not, they might do something even more reckless . . . and who knew . . . perhaps they would have done. Paul had whispered on more than one occasion that if it was the only way, they could start a baby. 'Then they'll have to let us get married,' he had coaxed.

Whether or not she would have gone that far she didn't know. Certainly she had been bemused enough by her feelings for him to do almost anything he suggested. Her parents had tried to tell her that she was suffering from a classic case of infatuation but she hadn't wanted to know ... she hadn't wanted to believe them.

In the end, Paul had got his way. They had had a small family wedding, she had worn a white dress; and they had moved into a pretty cottage down near the harbour that Paul's parents had bought for them. Mr and Mrs Chalmers had a large house just outside the village, and Gray lived in what had been his grandfather's cottage quite close to the boat-yard.

Their honeymoon had been a bitter disappointment—for both of them. Paul did not have the patience or the experience to arouse her to the point where she could enjoy his lovemaking, and he had swiftly grown impatient and then angry with her for her lack of response.

The first time he had hit her had been after a quarrel, and she had been too shocked to do anything other than stare at him. Her father had never raised a hand to her in all her life, and the cruelty of Paul's blow hurt her emotions more than her flesh.

Of course, he had immediately been contrite; they had made up their quarrel and he had sworn never to touch her in anger again.

Within days he had broken that promise and, by the time their honeymoon was over, Stephanie had learned to fear her new husband's sudden surges of temper.

She returned to her new home and her new life sick at heart and cowed in spirit.

People noticed of course, especially her parents, but

she had too much pride to tell them the truth. Inwardly she felt, as Paul claimed, that she was to blame for his violence, that she invited it in some way, and deserved it for her inability to respond to him as a woman.

His violence towards her quickly escalated to the point where she cringed every time he came near her.

They stopped making love within days of returning to their new home, and quite soon after that Paul started staying out later and later at night, and then not coming home at all.

He had made no secret of the fact that there were other girls, but whenever she suggested that they end the marriage he had flown into one of his almost maniacal tempers, and she soon learned not to bring the subject up.

His death might have freed her from the physical violence of their marriage, but emotionally she was still trapped, both in her own guilt for failing him as a woman, and her fear that she was somehow not like other members of her sex—not capable of responding sexually to anyone's embrace.

Her memories of the unhappiness of the few short months of her marriage, and the guilt feelings that had come afterwards, were so strong, that she hated returning to the village.

Paul's parents no longer lived there—they had moved away shortly after his death, when Paul's father had sold out his share of the boat-yard to Gray. Now they were both dead, increasing her sense of guilt. They had both adored Paul, worshipped him almost, seeing no fault in him.

Stephanie's own pride had made it impossible for

her to discuss with anyone the cruelty of Paul's treatment of her, and so it remained locked inside her, a dark, unhappy secret that still had the power to destroy her sleep.

There had been no man in her life since Paul. What would have been the point? She would only have incited them to violence once they discovered her lack of sexuality. Gray was the only man in her life, and their relationship was a sexless, friendly one that could quite easily have existed between two members of the same sex.

The road crested a hill. To her left she could see the bright glitter of the river, slow and majestic in its steady progress towards the sea.

Soon she would be there. A quiver of apprehension ran through her, all her doubts and dreads about the wisdom of obeying Gray's request that she come down here betrayed in the cloudy darkness of her eyes.

Her body—too slim and fragile, perhaps, for a woman of twenty-eight—tensed, ready to absorb the shock of pain and guilt that waited for her with her first glimpse of the estuary and the sea.

It was a small place, the village, where everyone knew everyone else. They all knew about her loss; about Paul's death, but none of them knew about her deeper anguish. Perhaps fearing his parents' discovering the truth, Paul had gone into Southampton on those nights when he didn't return home, and had found there, or so he had told her, the sexual satisfaction he could not get from her, his wife.

Cold . . . frigid. The accusations, so well remembered, hammered against her skull, turning her skin pale with anguish.

If only Gray had come up to London to discuss the business of the boat-yard with her, as he had done in the past, but this time he had been insistent that she return here. He had even threatened to come and get her if she refused and, knowing he meant it, she had eventually, reluctantly, given way.

Perhaps in her shoes another woman might have tried to prove Paul's accusations wrong by taking one lover after another, but Stephanie couldn't do that. She was too afraid that Paul had been right. She had failed with him, and she would fail with anyone else.

Instead, she had locked herself away behind the barrier of her guilt, using Paul as an excuse for not forming any new relationships. No other man was going to get an opportunity to abuse her physically, or hurt and betray her because she couldn't satisfy him; no other man was going to turn from her to someone else, as Paul had done.

Not even Gray had known, as she wept in his arms, that she cried not just for Paul himself but for the betrayal of their love and her own failure to prove herself a woman. And he would never know it.

The village was in sight now, and she automatically tensed her muscles, glancing at her watch. Gone six o'clock, but Gray would probably still be at the boat-yard. She would go there first, rather than the cottage.

Gray lived there alone now and had done for several years. The shock of losing her son had led to Paul's mother's death, and Paul's father, Gray's uncle, had

died two years later from a heart attack. Now only
Gray was left.

The boat-yard was on the far side of the village,
right down on the bank of the estuary. It had been in
Gray's family for about a hundred years.

As she parked her VW and climbed out of it, Gray
emerged from his office and came towards her. Tall,
with forbiddingly broad shoulders and a shock of
night-black hair, he was a commandingly masculine
man. Densely blue eyes studied her and, shockingly,
Stephanie momentarily recognised in them the age-old
appraisal of a man looking at a woman.

Gray moved and the appraisal was gone, leaving her
to suspect that she must have imagined it.

The late afternoon breeze coming off the estuary
flattened the silky curve of her skirt against her hip and
the long line of her legs. She lifted a hand to push her
hair back off her face and heard Gray growl, 'You're
getting too thin. What have you been doing to
yourself?'

'I'm not thin, just fashionably slim!' she protested.

He was wearing an old pair of jeans that clung to his
body like a second skin. Hastily averting her eyes from
the powerful muscles of his thighs, she was tensely
aware of his eyes narrowing.

'What's wrong? You're as skittish as a dinghy
without a tiller.'

His fingers closed over her arm, drawing her
towards him. She could smell the familiar male scent of
his body, and felt an almost uncontrollable urge to
cling to him and let him stand between her and her
pain.

'You know coming down here always affects me like this.'

Instead of comforting her as he normally did, he released her almost abruptly.

'After ten years?' There was something almost sardonic about the way he said it. 'That's one hell of a long time to grieve, Steph.'

Before she could comment, the office door opened and a stunning blonde came out. Dressed in tight white jeans and a brief silky top, she swayed provocatively towards them.

'I've still got a few things to do down here.' Gray glanced towards the blonde. 'I'll take you up to the cottage and join you there later.'

Stephanie always stayed at the cottage when she visited Gray. The village had no hotel, and besides, where else should she stay? But now some contrariness made her glance across at the blonde walking towards them, her mouth curling slightly as she asked, 'Are you sure you want me to stay with you, Gray? I don't want to be in the way.'

She saw his mouth tighten. 'Well now, that's quite a question. What made you ask it, I wonder?'

For some reason she had annoyed him. Conscious of the blonde watching them, Stephanie took a deep breath.

'Nothing at all. I just wondered if your girlfriend might object?'

'Girlfriend?' His dark head swivelled to look at the blonde. She smiled back, teasingly. She was older than Stephanie had first imagined, and she was wearing a wedding ring, but that meant nothing these days.

'Carla won't mind. She knows that we're old friends.'

As though to prove the point he called over casually to the blonde, 'I'm just taking Stephanie back to the cottage. I won't be long.'

Stephanie had to run to keep up with his long-legged stride as he walked towards her VW. Watching him fold himself inside reminded her of how tall and broad he was, the play of hard muscles beneath his skin alienly male.

She just wasn't used to being this close to a man ... any man, she told herself as she drove the car towards the cottage; that was why she was so conscious of Gray's masculinity.

'I've put you in the far bedroom,' he told her laconically as he opened the cottage door. 'I'll leave you to get yourself settled in. I'll be back in half an hour. I've just got one or two things to finish off.'

'Half an hour. I'm sure Carla would be very flattered if she heard that.'

Suddenly conscious of how waspish and acid she sounded, Stephanie turned away from him. What was the matter with her? Gray had had girlfriends before. He was one of the most eligible men on the estuary. Physically, he was everything a woman could want in a man; he was also kind and gentle. Strange that at thirty-four-odd he should still be unmarried, and stranger still that she had never questioned his lack of a wife before.

'Oh, I'm sure I could think of a way to make amends.' He said it so softly that the words shivered across her skin, the look in his eyes as she turned to stare at him making her own widen with shocked pain.

Gray was her friend. He knew how much she loathed anything that had the slightest sexual connotation, and yet here he was deliberately making her aware of his sexuality, of the very masculine side of him that he had previously held in check.

Before she could protest he said bleakly, 'Don't provoke me, Steph, I'm not in the mood for it.'

As he turned away from her she recognised that she was not the only one who had lost weight; he too was slightly thinner, his profile carved in slightly harder lines. Was something wrong? Was that why he wanted to see her? Was that why he was acting so oddly? From the time of Paul's death he had been her friend, he had supported and protected her, and she had come to lean on him, to trust him, as she knew she could never trust anyone else, but now . . .

He paused at the door and turned towards her.

'Not everyone's like you, Steph,' he told her harshly. 'We haven't all abdicated from the human race, and the needs and emotions that go with being human.'

Stephanie recoiled as though he had hit her. In all the years they had been friends, Gray had never once spoken to her like that. Never once looked at her the way he was looking at her right now, with his mouth twisted and his eyes hard and accusing.

'Gray . . .' Panic filled her voice and her eyes. What was happening to them? She was losing him . . . losing his friendship . . . she could sense it, feel it almost . . .

'I'll see you later.'

He was gone before she could object. Numbly she stared at the closed door. What was happening? A tiny frisson of fear trembled through her. She wandered uneasily round the small sitting-room. The cottage was very old, the rooms low-ceilinged and beamed. She sat down in one of the chintz-covered chairs and stared unseeingly into the empty fireplace. The horse brasses, collected by Gray's mother, shone against the butter-milk-coloured walls, the soft salt-laden breeze flowing in through one of the open lattice windows. The room was as familiar to Stephanie as her London flat, although she could count on the fingers of one hand the number of times she had been here since Paul's death. The house had been let while Gray lived with Paul's parents, but as soon as he was eighteen he had announced that he was moving into his parents' old home. There had never been the rapport between Gray and Paul's parents that had existed between them and their own child. Many, many times he must have felt shut out, but to his credit he had never let it show ... never resented Paul in the way that the younger man had resented him. They had never discussed Paul's animosity towards him; the past was a closed book and one which she had assumed neither of them wished to open.

She had never thought of Gray in any male or sexual sense, but today, shockingly, she had looked at him and seen not her friend, but a man with sexual desires and drives like any other.

A curious, aching pain built up inside her and spread tormentingly through her body. What was wrong with her? Was she really so insecure that she feared the thought of sharing Gray with someone else? She had always known that he didn't live the life of a monk . . . but until today she had never come face to face with the reality of his sexuality, and she was shocked by her own reaction to it. Instead of feeling nothing, she had felt a surprising degree of jealousy. But why?

And why had Gray been so offhand, almost angry with her? Normally he greeted her with a warm hug and a welcoming smile, but not this time—not today. Had it been because Carla had been there? It shocked her how much she had missed that brief, warm contact with his body. Confused by the chaos of her thoughts and feelings, she tried to dismiss them as a natural result of her return to the place where she had known such pain and misery, but something deep inside her refused to be convinced.

Angry with herself, Stephanie went outside to her car and brought in her suitcase. She didn't intend staying for more than a couple of days, and it didn't take her long to unpack her things and put them away. The room she was sleeping in had sloping eaves and a tiny window that overlooked the wild tangle of the cottage garden, and the hills beyond. The cottage had four bedrooms, and this one had once been Gray's.

Now he slept in the large double bedroom which had once been his parents', and as she stepped out on to the landing something made her hesitate and then slowly push open the door to Gray's room.

He had an experienced sailor's neatness. Nothing was out of place. An old-fashioned four-poster bed dominated the room, and against her will Stephanie's eyes were drawn to it. How many women had shared it with Gray over the years? None of them would have been like her, frigid and undesirable. A lump gathered painfully in her chest, a familiar sense of anguish enveloping her. She didn't want to be the way she was. She . . .

'Looking for something?'

The unexpectedly harsh sound of Gray's voice behind her made her jump. She turned round sharply, stumbling in shock. She hadn't heard him come in.

Instantly his arms came out to steady her. Although it had been months since he last held her, she was immediately aware of a sense of homecoming and security. Without being aware of what she was doing, she snuggled up against him, sighing faintly.

'For God's sake, Stephanie!'

Instantly she stiffened in his arms, suddenly conscious of the hard thud of his heart and the heat coming off his body.

'What the hell are you doing? Dreaming about Paul? He's dead, Stephanie. Dead. And for all the living you do, you might as well be, too. Hasn't there been anyone in these last ten years?'

'I don't want that sort of relationship in my life. You know that.' She had to turn her head so that he couldn't look at her.

As his arms dropped away from her, he said flatly, 'We . . . you can't go on living like this, Steph. It's not . . .'

'Not what? Not "natural"? Is that what you're going to say, Gray? That *I'm* not "natural"?'

Her overwrought nerves shrieked in protest as she flung the words at him.

He seemed to be looking at her with an odd mixture

of pain and defeat in his eyes. Her breath locked in her throat, tears not far away. What on earth was happening to them? She and Gray had been so close, such good friends, and now . . . and now they seemed to be teetering on the brink of destroying all that they had shared.

He made a slight movement, a reaching out towards her from which she immediately recoiled, her expression proud and tortured as she cried out painfully, 'You want the truth, Gray? All right, I'll give it to you. I don't have the least interest in sex.' She took a deep, rather shaky breath. 'I'm frigid, Gray.' There, she'd said it; she'd admitted at last the agonising lack of sexuality that had caused her so much pain.

'Steph!'

She heard the shock in Gray's voice, but she couldn't respond to it; couldn't listen to any more questions now, however well meant. Gray cared for her as a friend, and would want to help her, but this was one problem that no one else could help with.

Suddenly she had an overwhelming need to be alone.

'I . . . I think I'd better find somewhere else to stay tonight, Gray, I . . .'

She saw from the look on his face that she had hurt and angered him. So many gulfs were springing up between them, so many barriers that couldn't be crossed.

She made a dash for her room and privacy, coming to an abrupt halt as Gray's fingers tightened round her wrist, holding her prisoner. Shock had darkened his eyes to dense sapphire, his mouth a hard line of disbelief as he shook her.

'What the hell is this, Steph? Is that really what you think? That you're frigid?'

'Isn't it what *you* think?' As she stood there, trembling, Stephanie wondered frantically what on earth had happened between them to promote this conversation. Talking about her relationship with Paul and the flaws in her femininity wasn't something she had ever wanted to do, least of all with Gray, who, friend though he was, was also so undeniably male that he made her acutely aware of the pathetic shortcomings in her own personality. Instinctively, without knowing how she possessed that knowledge, she knew that as a lover Gray would be both skilled and tender.

Dragging her mind away from such provocative thoughts she saw that he was frowning.

'I don't make those kind of assumptions without some hard facts to back them up. As I haven't been to bed with you, I don't know, do I?'

It was what he hadn't said rather than what he had that shocked her speechless.

'I'll wash and then we'll have something to eat. I've got a lot to talk over with you.'

His calm words broke the spell that had held her silent.

'Won't Carla object to your spending the evening with me?'

His eyebrows lifted. 'Why should she? She knows that we're old friends.'

To her chagrin, Stephanie realised that he was looking amused.

'Why don't you go down and make us some coffee?

And then over dinner I'll show you the plans of the new boat I'm working on.'

This was the Gray she knew ... her friend. The tension that had engulfed her earlier eased. Feeling relieved, she hurried downstairs to the kitchen.

Mrs Ames, Gray's daily, had left a casserole ready-prepared in the fridge, and one of her famous apple pies.

Although the cottage had a pretty dining-room, normally when she came to stay they ate off trays in the sitting-room. It was more cosy.

It didn't take long to make the coffee and, wanting to make amends for her earlier childishness, Stephanie poured some into a mug for Gray and took it upstairs.

His bedroom door was open. She could smell the clean, pine-fresh scent of his soap, and from behind the closed door of his bathroom she could hear him singing.

Her mouth curved into a brief grin as she recognised the familiar sound of an old sea shanty. It was one Gray only sang when he was feeling particularly happy. Perhaps she had been wrong about there being some serious problem with the boat-yard.

Knocking briefly on his open door, she walked into his bedroom. She had been silly to get so upset simply because he had asked about her as a friend. Not knowing the truth, he had simply thought that she had grieved for Paul for long enough.

But now that he did know the truth ... he had not exhibited the shock she might have expected. Lost in thought, she gnawed worriedly at her lower lip.

The door to Gray's bathroom opened and he walked into the bedroom, plainly unaware that she was there.

His hair was damp and he was towelling it roughly. The rest of his body . . . Scarlet faced, Stephanie stood rooted to the spot, totally unable to move, as she slowly absorbed the details of his nude body.

Gray only realised that she was there when he threw down the towel. Transfixed with shock and embarrassment, Stephanie gulped as he walked past her and gently closed the bedroom door.

'I . . . I brought you a cup of coffee.'

Her voice was a thick, unfamiliar croak, but at least speaking freed her from her momentary paralysis. She turned to flee and discovered that somehow Gray was standing in front of the door.

'Thank you.' He said it gently, casually reaching out to take the mug from her. Hideously embarrassed, Stephanie looked everywhere but at him. Why, oh why had she walked into his bedroom in the first place? She had *known* that he was having a shower.

'What's the matter, Steph?' His voice was as soft as silk, but still she couldn't look at him. 'You've seen me working on the boats wearing not that much more.'

'That . . . that was different.' She was having difficulty in swallowing.

'Not that much surely. I'm the one who should be embarrassed, you know.'

Maybe he *should* be, but he certainly wasn't. Why on earth didn't he put some clothes on?

As though he read her mind, he moved to one side, opening a drawer and casually pulling out socks and underpants.

'Pass me that shirt on the bed, will you?'

He sounded so casually at ease that Stephanie found

she was doing what he asked almost without thinking. By the time she had handed it to him, he was already wearing the brief dark-coloured underpants.

'The sight of a nude male surely can't be so shocking, can it? After all, there was Paul . . . the two of you were married, even if you are claiming that his death made you frigid. You must have known what boys look like.'

The hint of teasing in his voice made her skin burn. She was too stunned to correct his mistaken assumption that her frigidity was the result of Paul's death. 'Boys, yes, but . . . but you aren't a boy, Gray.'

He didn't say anything, but Stephanie had the distinct impression that he smiled faintly before he pulled his shirt on.

Watching his fingers move deftly over the buttons, securing them so that the tanned expanse of his torso with its shadowing of dark silk hair was hidden from her, aroused the most curious sensation in the pit of her stomach. He walked over to his dresser and pulled out a set of cuff-links.

'Damn, I can't seem to manage these. Come and give me a hand will you, Steph?'

Numbly she walked over to him, trying to focus her eyes on the sinewed strength of his wrist as he bared it for her inspection. The contrast between his dark, tanned skin and the crisp whiteness of his shirt cuff was curiously disturbing. She wanted to put her fingertips over the strong pulse she could see beating under his skin, and feel its heat. She wanted the comfort and security of his arms, in the same way she had wanted them when Paul was killed.

It seemed to take a lifetime to secure both cuff-links,

but at last it was done. When she stepped back from him she was surprised to see how shaky she felt.

'I'd better go down and check on dinner.'

As she stepped away from him, Stephanie thought she heard him laugh softly.

What was happening to her? she wondered numbly as she went downstairs. She already knew she was sexless, incapable of arousing a man, so why was she so suddenly and inexplicably experiencing this odd desire to reach out and touch Gray? She had been shocked and embarrassed by his nudity but she had felt something else as well: a purely feminine recognition of the powerful masculinity of him, an intensely female responsiveness to his maleness. But surely that was impossible? She couldn't experience those sort of feelings. Could she?

Thoroughly confused, she tried to concentrate on preparing their meal, and to direct her thoughts to whatever it was that Gray wanted to discuss with her, but irrationally they kept straying to Gray's earlier assertion that he wasn't qualified to judge whether she was frigid or not.

Could Paul have been wrong? She frowned. But surely if he had been she would have known about it before now? In the ten years since his death she had never once experienced the slightest desire for any man. The phone rang, and she went to answer it.

It was Carla, asking for Gray. As she called him to the phone Stephanie was gripped by the most painfully acute sensation of jealousy. Jealousy? But she had no right to be jealous of Carla's place in Gray's life. No right at all.

Thoroughly confused, she went back to the kitchen, trying to dismiss her painfully intrusive thoughts.

When he came into the kitchen Gray was frowning heavily. Whatever Carla had had to say to him it couldn't have been to his liking. Had the blonde perhaps objected to *her* presence at the cottage, after all? If Gray was *her* lover ... *Gray* her *lover*? Shock ripped through her unprepared body—the body she was so convinced could never respond sexually to any man. What on earth was happening to her?

'Stephanie ... what is it? Are you ill?'

She looked up, her eyes still dark with shock. She opened her mouth to speak, but no words emerged. She was looking at Gray and yet it was almost as though she was looking at a stranger.

He reached out for her, warm hands gripping her rigid arms, his face creased in lines of concern.

'You're trembling. What is it? What's wrong?'

Another minute and she would be cradled against the hard warmth of his body ... the body that, like the man, belonged to someone else. Immediately she tensed, and Gray let her go.

She felt sick with shock as she realised what she was feeling. She was jealous. Jealous of Carla. No, not of Carla, she amended hastily ... she was jealous of their relationship, because it threatened her own friendship with Gray. Yes, that was it ...

Shakily she let her mind absorb her thoughts, like a swimmer frightened by the depths, now reaching out for the safety of the shallows where they could touch the ocean floor.

'I'm all right now, Gray ...'

It was obvious that he wasn't totally convinced. 'What happened?'

She shrugged carelessly. 'Oh, nothing. I just felt cold, that's all.'

It was plain that he didn't believe her, but fortunately he didn't press the subject.

'I'll fix the trays. Will you check on the casserole?'

Everything was as it had always been, she thought thankfully, obeying his instructions. Or was it? She risked a covert glance at him. She was terrified of losing his friendship . . . especially to another woman.

CHAPTER TWO

THEY had eaten both the casserole and the apple pie before Gray broached the subject of Stephanie's visit.

'I'll wash up if you make the coffee,' he suggested, bending to take the tray from her lap. 'No one else makes it quite the way you do.'

'Oh, no? I'll bet you say that to all the girls.'

Instead of making him smile, her flip answer drew a sharp frown. Now what had she done to offend him? she wondered unhappily as she followed him to the kitchen. Something was different; something had changed between them. She felt different than she had ever felt before, buoyed up and excited one moment, and miserable and on edge the next.

Amazingly, Gray managed to unfasten his cuff-links much more easily than she had put them in. Watching him as he rolled up his shirt-sleeves and started washing up their dishes, Stephanie felt a burning tide of awareness sweep over her body. His forearms were tanned and strongly muscled. She wanted to reach out and touch him, to stroke her fingertips through those thick, dark hairs.

'I asked you to come down here because I need a favour.' The abrupt words cut through the hazy sensuality of her private thoughts, jerking her back to reality. What on earth had come over her?

'I'm having some problems with the boat-yard.

Business has fallen off quite sharply lately. I'm working on the design for a new boat which I'm hoping will be successful. If all goes well I plan to show it at next year's Boat Show, but launching a new boat is a pretty risky business, especially for a yard like ours.'

For no reason at all, a cold spiral of fear had invaded the pit of her stomach. Gray had stopped washing the dishes and had turned round to face her. The atmosphere in the kitchen was tense, almost stiflingly so.

'I'm entering this year's Fastnet, Steph,' Gray told her quietly. 'If I can win, and I think I can, the publicity would give the new boat a boost that nothing else could match. Winning the Fastnet will give us more publicity, more credibility than we could get from any amount of advertising.'

Stephanie knew that every word he said was true. A boat designed and made by an acknowledged winner of a race as prestigious as the Fastnet would sell better than a tennis racquet endorsed by a Davis Cup champion, but nothing could silence the words of protest from tumbling from her lips. Since Paul's death she had been left with a morbid fear of the sea. She knew that he was himself to blame for the accident by his rash disregard of the safety rules, that did not quell her fear, there was more to it than that.

She could hardly bear to look at the sea, even on a calm day and, as Gray well knew, coming down here to the estuary was purgatory for her.

She had once loved sailing. It was her father's hobby and, like him, she had been thrilled about his transfer to this part of the coast which had a reputation of being an idyllic spot for small boat enthusiasts.

She had been more grateful than she could say when her father had been transferred to an inland posting shortly after Paul's death, and never once since that time had she set foot in a boat herself, even though she had once crewed enthusiastically and knowledgeably both for her father, and for Paul.

Now Gray was telling her that he intended to enter one of the most dangerous races of all, and she shook with fear for him.

'Gray . . . please don't,' she pleaded huskily.

'Stephanie, I have to. Don't you understand?' he demanded harshly. 'If I don't, I stand to lose the boat-yard . . . I have no other choice.'

She could see that, but she still longed to beg him to change his mind. Instead, she said shakily, 'Gray, please . . . I don't want to lose you as well.'

'You won't, I promise you you won't.' She felt him move as he gathered her against his body, bracing himself against the unit as he rocked her gently in his arms.

Tense with fear, Stephanie buried her face against his chest, soothed by the heavy thud of his heart.

'If I'm to go ahead I'm going to need your help, Steph.' His voice was muffled slightly by her hair, and slightly unsteady, as though he was under a tremendous strain. 'I want you to move into the cottage, and take over the day-to-day running of the boat-yard for me until after the race. You could work from here on your illustrations, just as easily as you do in London . . .'

'Run the yard!' She jerked away from him, horrified. 'I couldn't do that.'

'Yes, you could. You did it when you and Paul were married.'

It was true that she had helped out at the yard all those years ago, organising the office along more practical lines.

'Stephanie, when have I ever asked you for anything?' His voice was rough, grating against her tense nerves. It was true, in their relationship he had always been the giver, she the taker. Although he didn't say it, she felt that he was reminding her that she owed him a debt—a debt he was now calling in. How could she explain to him how much she feared and loathed everything that reminded her of Paul? He thought she was still grieving for a husband she had loved and adored. How could she tell him that what she felt was guilt—that there was no love ... that the reality of marriage had woken her from what had only been an adolescent's dream?

'I ... I need time to think ...' Implicit in her husky words was an acknowledgement of all that she owed him.

He had stood by her when she felt everyone else was against her, accusing her of pushing Paul to his death, because of their quarrel. How could she deny his request for help? She knew how much the boat-yard meant to him.

Almost on a sigh she heard herself saying, 'I ... I've made up my mind. I'll do it ... I ...'

She didn't get the opportunity to say any more. She was in Gray's arms, held tight in a crushing grip that drove the breath from her lungs and brought a surge of blind panic as her body remembered how often it had been imprisoned with similar force by Paul.

She fought frantically against his constraining hold, until she felt him releasing her. Breathing deeply, she staggered back against the wall, her eyes dark with fear.

'For God's sake! What the hell did you think I was going to do . . . Rape you?'

As she raised her shocked eyes to his, Stephanie saw him rake angry fingers through his hair.

'I know how you feel about Paul, Stephanie, but you can't cling to those memories for ever. Christ, if that's how you react when someone else touches you, I'm not surprised there hasn't been anyone else.'

The look in his eyes chilled her, she felt like a child abandoned by its parents, and longed to cry out to him to understand.

Instead she moved away from the wall, and turned away, shivering with the inner bleakness possessing her.

'Stephanie . . .' She felt his fingers touch her arm and this time she didn't move away.

'Look, I'm sorry. We're both wound up. I should have remembered how much you hate being touched.'

Her expression gave her away and he grimaced wryly.

'Did you think I didn't know? You freeze every time I come near you.'

Did she?

'Has it ever occurred to you that there's something dangerously obsessive about your determination to remain faithful to Paul's memory? Do you think he would have done the same if the positions had been reversed?' he demanded harshly. 'It's time to put the past behind you, Steph. Nothing's going to bring Paul back. You've got to start learning to live again. You told me not long ago that you were frigid.' His hand slid to her face cupping it, lifting it so that he could look down into her eyes.

'I don't think you are, but I think you've convinced yourself of it because it makes it easier for you to escape from the pain of loving anyone else. It's easier to tell yourself you're frigid than to risk loving someone whom you might ultimately lose.'

She wanted to tell him that he was wong, that she *was* frigid, that Paul himself had told her so; but somehow she was mesmerised by the magnetic glitter of his eyes as his head bent slowly towards her own.

Slowly, shockingly she realised what he meant to do, and by the time that knowledge had infiltrated her brain it was too late to move away. His lips were moving gently and softly over her own, their commanding impact making hers cling bemusedly to his warmth. Shock held her unmoving within his embrace, her breath obstructed by what was happening to her. She could feel her heart racing.

'Stay with me, Stephanie. Stay with me and help me . . .' Gray whispered the words against her mouth, and they brought her back to reality, releasing her from the trance imposed by his totally unexpected kiss. She drew away shakily and he let her, watching her through half-closed eyes.

'Yes . . . Yes, I will.' Her lips framed the words slowly, still quivering from the silken pressure of Gray's kiss. Thoroughly bemused, she was barely aware of what she was saying. She heard him laugh softly, deep in his throat, as he stepped back from her.

'You kiss like a little girl, do you know that?'

Pain pierced her. What on earth was she thinking of? To let Gray kiss her? And as for Gray himself . . . Her claim that she was frigid must have piqued his male curiosity, but now he knew the truth for himself he was hardly likely to kiss her again, she reflected flatly, still trying to recover from the blow of his soft-voiced taunt.

Her pride demanded some recompense and so, turning her back on him and busying herself with the coffee, she said coolly, 'We're friends, Gray, not lovers, and that's how I kissed you—as a friend.'

She was a little surprised by the anger in his eyes when he reached past her to relieve her of the heavy coffee jug. She and Gray had often had arguments in the past and he had never seemed to harbour any resentment on those occasions when she won. In fact, Gray had always encouraged her to think for herself and to form her own views. He had never been the sort of man who preferred women to be obedient, quiet echoes of their men's views.

'If I'm going to stay on to look after the yard I'll need to go back to London to collect my paints and some extra clothes.'

'I'll run you back on Monday morning. I've got some business to deal with, so I'll stay at your place Monday night and then we'll come back together on Tuesday. I'm not going to give you any opportunity to back out of this, Steph,' he warned her, before she could speak. 'I need your help too much for that.'

He wasn't saying so but Stephanie also knew that he had every right to ask for and expect her help. He had, after all, given her his in those dark months after the accident. Without his support ... She shuddered slightly, remembering the accusations she had flung at him then; the demand that he leave her to simply die. There had been plenty of times when she hadn't wanted to go on living, when she had thought that there was no longer any point to life, but Gray had refused to let her go, to let her abandon herself to that sort of self-destruction.

Yes, she owed him a lot, but how on earth was she going to cope with living so close to the sea; with knowing that every day Gray himself was out there, sailing on it; that Gray was going to enter one of the most dangerous sailing races in the world? The cup she was holding slid from her fingers to crash down on to the stone floor, her hands going up to cover her face.

In a tortured voice she pleaded, 'Gray, please don't do it! There must be another way.'

Tough, work-scarred fingers pulled her hands away from her eyes so that he could look at her.

'I have to do it,' he told her grimly. '*Can't* you understand that? The yard's been losing money steadily over the last few years—you know that ...'

She had, of course, but she had not realised how intensely Gray was worrying about it.

'There's still money coming in from the moorings you let out to summer visitors.'

'Yes, they're just about keeping us afloat, but it's not enough. I want this yard to be again what it once was. There's no cash available for development and invest-ment ... to do the things I want to do. You know that the design and production of small craft has always been

more important to me than the day-to-day running of
the yard.'

'But the Fastnet . . .' she protested weakly. 'Gray . . .
What . . . what does Carla think about it?'

The words were out before she could stop them. A
curious expression, half-pain, half-pride, crossed Gray's
face.

'She knows that it's something I have to do,' he told
her quietly, and she was pierced with a poignant sense of
loss, so totally did his voice and expression exclude her.

In those few words Gray had condemned her to the
periphery of his life; had shown her that there was
someone else in his life far more important to him than
she could ever be.

She swallowed hard against the pain.

'You love her a great deal.' Her voice trembled and
she saw Gray's brief smile.

'Can one quantify love? I don't think so.'

'Did you know the moment you met her that . . .?'

'That I had found the woman I was going to love for
the rest of my life?' he submitted for her.

Something quivered and hurt inside her, some deep-
lodged pain that, like a tiny splinter buried deep in one's
flesh, festered and irritated. *Why* had she never known
before how possessive she felt about Gray? *Why* had it
taken another woman to open her eyes to how desirable
a man he was?

'You're looking very pale. What's wrong?'

'I just don't like the thought of you entering the
Fastnet.' It wasn't a lie, but it wasn't the entire truth
either. It was the thought of losing him to Carla that had
driven the blood from her face, just as much as the

thought of losing him to the sea had frozen her heart in ice.

'Come and have a look at the plans, I've got them here in my study.'

Something in the firm purposefulness of his voice calmed her a little. Gray knew the sea . . . he did not take risks . . . he never had. She remembered how thrilled she had been on the rare occasions she had sailed with him. Even then he had been fascinated by the problems of designing safe racing craft. His uncle had called it time-wasting. He preferred the more mundane side of the business. He had wanted to sell off part of the boat-yard to form a huge marina, but Gray and the local council had opposed him, and rightly so. It would have completely spoiled the atmosphere of the small village.

Somehow she found herself being guided into the study and sitting down alongside Gray while he unrolled plans for the hull of the new racing craft.

Soon he was lost in enthusiasm for what he was doing, pointing out to her how the design could be modified to fit into a family market; how the utilitarian interior of the prototype racing craft could be turned into comfortably luxurious accommodation for a small family.

At the moment, Stephanie was working on the book cover for a novel set in the Caribbean, and in her mind's eye she saw Gray's sleek new craft swinging gently at anchor in the background.

For ten years she had turned her back completely on sailing but now, poring over the plans Gray had spread out on the large partners' desk in the study, she felt all the old enthusiasm and excitement of her teenage years come rushing back. A single glance had been enough to show her the grace and potential of Gray's new boat. Without even having to strain her imagination to the slightest degree, she could already see the boat's sleek lines as she sped over the water; she could almost feel the old thrill of racing against other small craft, the salt-laden breeze stinging her skin and lifting her hair. Those had been good days . . . happy, carefree days, before . . .

'These new compounds mean that we can make the hull lighter than ever before, and these sails——' Gray's finger indicated one of the sketches, and Stephanie pushed aside the past to concentrate on what he was showing her.

Unlike many of the entrants in the Fastnet Race, Gray's yacht would only be sailed by him. Apparently, the fact that it could be handled by one man alone was one of its potential selling points in its racier form.

'The sails will certainly give it plenty of speed,' Stephanie remarked.

Her fear must have shown in her voice, because Gray said lightly, 'Yes, and the special buoyancy tanks we've fitted will make it virtually unsinkable. The beauty of this design is that it can be fitted out as anything from a racing yacht to a sea-going cruiser, depending on what the customer wants. More and more people are sailing these days, and they're demanding a wider and better equipped range of craft at the right price. I need that business, Stephanie, and I'm determined to get it.' He rolled up the plans. 'So far we're very pleased with the way she's tested out. I'm hoping to do the final sea trials in the next couple of weeks.'

She shivered slightly, unaware of the way the light from the lamp highlighted the rich copper tone of her hair. In the last ten years she had changed from a pretty girl into a beautiful, although somewhat haunted woman, Gray thought, watching her. He had a momentary impulse to reach out and watch her hair glide through his fingers, to see if it felt as warm and vibrant as it looked. Her mouth curved as she smiled uncertainly at him, and he got up abruptly.

'You stay there, I'll go and make us both some coffee.'

The clipped way he spoke broke the mood of relaxed friendship between them. It was almost as though he didn't want her company . . .

Stephanie turned her head to one side automatically, hiding her expression from him. It was idiotic to feel hurt, but they had been getting on so well, and then for no reason at all, or so it seemed, Gray had suddenly retreated from her.

After he had gone into the kitchen for their coffee, Stephanie hunched her arms round her knees. The light from the lamp illuminated the haunting pensiveness of her face. Gray was right, it was time she learned to come to terms with the past, but every time she thought about Paul, every time she remembered his cruel words, every time she remembered how quickly their love had died, pain engulfed her.

It was safer to love a man the way she loved Gray, as a brother, rather than to love one the way she had loved Paul. And yet . . . She frowned, and chewed anxiously on her bottom lip. There was something different about Gray. She was aware of a tension within him that she had never noticed before. Gray was always so calm and

controlled. She had rarely seen him lose his temper,
never heard him raise his voice. He was a man of infinite
resource and capability, adept at concealing his
thoughts and his feelings, and yet today she had sensed
that that control was slipping. Was it just because he was
worried about the boat-yard?

She was still puzzling over a change in him when he
came back with their coffee. A quick look at his face
revealed that he was smiling at her, and Stephanie
expelled a faint sigh of relief, without really knowing
why she should do so. All she could think was that she
didn't want to be at odds with Gray, whatever the
reason, and yet in the past they had quarrelled mightily
over various issues on which they had taken opposing
stances without it damaging their relationship in the
slightest. So why was she so afraid now? Was it perhaps
because of Carla? Did she fear that she might lose his
friendship? That somehow his relationship with Carla
threatened his relationship with her? But surely that
was silly; she and Gray were friends, Carla and Gray
were lovers.

'Penny for them?'

Instinctively she bent her head so that a silky swathe
of hair hid her expression from him. It was the first time
she had ever felt the need to be defensive with Gray, and
part of her mourned the fact that this should be so.

'They aren't worth it.' She smiled up at him and
wondered if her smile looked as forced as it felt. 'I think
I'll go up to bed, if you don't mind, Gray. I'm tired—it
must be the hot weather.'

She had to avoid looking at him as she gave voice to
the small lie. She never went to bed early on the first

night of her visits. She and Gray normally stayed up until the early hours of the morning, catching up on one another's news, teasing each other, talking ... But tonight, for some reason, she was conscious of an air of constraint between them, and almost every time she looked at Gray, she couldn't help mentally picturing him with Carla, his body as magnificently nude as it had been earlier, its muscled hardness covering the blonde's more delicately female shape.

Gray didn't say a word about her unusual decision to go to bed early, but as he walked her to the door and opened it for her, Stephanie glanced up at him and saw that his dark eyebrows were drawn together in a heavy frown.

Instinctively, without thinking what she was doing, she raised herself up on tiptoe, and pressed her fingertips to the frown lines, tenderly smoothing them away. Her gesture was completely unselfconscious, born of her desire to restore their relationship to its normal footing, but from the way Gray reacted her touch might have burned his skin like acid.

Lean fingers clamped round her wrist, his head jerking back as though he loathed the physical contact between their skins.

The pain of his bone-crunching grip was nothing to compare with the anguish of rejection which Stephanie suffered, when she saw the look of revulsion in his eyes.

'Gray!' Shock rounded her eyes to deep violet pools of pain, humiliation sending a burning wave of scarlet across her skin. Her arm throbbed from the tightness of his grip, and a terrible feeling of nausea churned in her stomach. What was it she had done?

Blue eyes narrowed sharply on her face, a hard burn of colour darkening the taut thrust of Gray's cheek-bones. More than ever he reminded her of a beast of prey, a dangerous jungle cat, waiting to pounce on its victim.

'What did I do wrong?'

The words whispered past lips trembling slightly with the aftermath of shock.

Stephanie saw Gray's lips twist. 'Twenty-eight years old and you have to ask me that? You haven't done the male sex any favours by living like a nun since Paul's death, Steph.'

The violet eyes betrayed bewilderment and he made a sound of self-derision deep in his throat, caught midway between anger and amusement.

'For God's sake, do you want me to spell it out for you?'

Something dangerous had been let loose in the room: Stephanie could sense it and yet she didn't know where the danger came from. She touched the tip of her tongue to her trembling lips, moistening them, in an acutely nervous gesture, blinking a little as she saw the flat hardness compressing Gray's mouth as he watched her movements like a hawk.

Her voice in a husky whisper she protested, 'Gray, I only touched you. I've touched you before.'

'Now it's different.' His voice was flat, metallic almost, as though he'd deliberately forced every iota of emotion out of it. 'Then I wasn't suffering from the frustration that's eating into me now.'

The shock of it tensed her muscles. Gray had never spoken to her like this before, never mentioned his physical desires, or the women he shared them with.

She wet her lips again, conscious of a strange heat burning through her veins. She didn't want to hear about Gray's sex life, but for some reason she heard herself saying slowly, 'Carla . . .?'

'Carla's married, Steph.'

Numb with shock, Stephanie heard him swear. For some reason her heart was racing, her nerve-endings pulsingly conscious of Gray's tension. She saw him move and stiffened with shock as his fingers bit into the tender flesh of her upper arms.

'You don't even know what I'm talking about, do you?' His voice was thick and unfamiliar, and for the first time since she had known him, his movements were less than perfectly controlled. She could actually hear the fierce thud of his heart as he closed the distance between them, so loud that it drowned her instinctive gasp of shock.

'This is what it's all about, Stephanie. This, and this.' He pulled her so close to his body that she could feel its heat; so close that, shockingly, she was aware of his physical arousal. If just the thought of Carla could affect him like this . . . Icy cold with shock, she shuddered. Instantly Gray released her, an expression of cold withdrawal icing over his eyes.

'I'm sorry.' His voice was curt. 'I shouldn't have done that.'

He turned his back to her, and part of her ached to reach out and comfort him. Instead she said shakily. 'It's all right, Gray. I . . . I . . . understand. At least, I think I do.'

'Do you?' He turned to look at her, searching her face

with hard eyes. Stephanie made herself hold that searching gaze.

'I think so. You love Carla, but she's married to someone else. You love someone who's out of reach.'

'I certainly do.' The look he gave her was wryly sardonic. 'Go to bed, Stephanie,' he told her tiredly. 'I don't think there's any point in discussing things any further.'

Despite her original claim that she was tired, Stephanie couldn't sleep. It had come as a shock to learn that Gray was in love with Carla, and it hadn't been a pleasant shock. In fact, she was stunned to discover just how resentful and unhappy she felt. She loved him as a friend, as a brother—so why did she feel like this?

Of course, it was because Carla was married. That was the explanation! Poor Gray, what a terrible situation for him. She knew how devastating jealousy could be, and he *must* be jealous of Carla's husband—jealous and frustrated. Her face burned as she remembered the way he had demonstrated that frustration to her. She had never known Gray behave with anything other than calm, brotherly affection; had never before seen him like this, driven, and almost aggressive towards her. She hated the thought of their relationship changing; of another woman coming between them.

She told herself she was being unrealistic, selfish even, but it didn't help.

'I'm sorry about last night—things got a little out of control.' Gray grimaced faintly as he handed Stephanie her breakfast. 'I don't normally let go like that.'

He was watching her covertly, as though expecting

... expecting what? Despite her own complicated feelings last night, Stephanie had made a vow that she would give Gray all the emotional support she could to sustain him during what she knew from her own experience would be a very traumatic time.

'Carla's husband and I are financial partners in the boat I'm sailing for the Fastnet—that's how I met her.'

Stephanie knew that her disquiet must have shown in her eyes, because Gray's mouth twisted. 'We can't *all* love to order,' he told her, curtly turning away from her. 'We'll leave for London this afternoon to collect your stuff. We'll stay at your place overnight.'

'You'll have to sleep on the settee,' she warned him.

'It won't matter for one night, and besides, I'd never get an hotel room at this time of year.'

'No. London is packed with tourists. Have you much business to do?'

Gray shook his head, pouring them both a second cup of coffee. 'No, I should be through it by lunchtime, and then we can head back here in the afternoon. By the way, you'll need a room to work in while you're here. There's an empty office down at the yard, will that do? I could show you it later.'

This was more like the Gray she knew, and although it hurt her that he didn't want to discuss Carla with her, part of her was glad. She was growing to hate the sound of the other woman's name.

She thought she'd been successful in keeping her thoughts hidden from him until he said softly, 'What is it, Steph?'

'I'm worried about you—about your involvement with Carla.'

For some reason her admission alarmed her, and she looked down at her plate, missing the look of brooding pain he gave her.

'Why?'

'I don't know. Perhaps it's because I know you're not the sort of man who'd really want to be involved with a woman who's married to someone else,' she offered lamely. 'You're always so honest in everything you do, Gray.'

'Think you know me well, don't you? Well, don't be too sure, love. The pain of an almost unendurable physical desire that you know can never really be satisfied makes a man do irrational things. Remember that, Steph.'

What was he trying to tell her? A faint shiver of apprehension held her in a cold grip. Instinctively she reached out to cover his hand with her own. His hands were large and well shaped with long fingers, clever hands . . . caring hands.

'Does she feel the same way about you, Gray? Will she . . .?' She swallowed, knowing it hurt to say what she had to say. 'Will she leave her husband for you?'

'No to both questions. Alex is a very wealthy man. Carla would never leave him.'

Her heart ached with pain for him, her huge eyes violet-shadowed with the intensity of her emotions. Wanting to offer him comfort, she moved closer to him, leaning her head against his shoulder and placing her hand against his chest. The neck of his shirt was open and her fingertips accidentally grazed against his warm skin. Instantly, hot colour flooded her face as she remembered how she had seen him yesterday. Shocked by her mental picture of his nude body she started to move away, but Gray's hand clamped down over hers, imprisoning it against his chest. The sensation of bone and muscle moving beneath her palm was faintly unnerving.

She hadn't touched a man voluntarily since Paul's death. 'Give her up, Gray,' she pleaded softly, trying to drag her thoughts away from the strange tension that seemed to have sprung up between them. 'Stop seeing her.'

'I can't.' His voice was harsh, his chest rising sharply as though he was finding it hard to breathe. When she looked up into his face it was closed and set, his nostrils slightly flared. He looked like a man in the grip of a fierce and unwanted emotion. 'Alex is financing me in the Fastnet,' he told her starkly. 'Without him I couldn't even contemplate entering it. He's provided the money for the new ketch we'll be using. I've built her, and we've got a first-rate crew of local volunteers. I can't stop seeing her, Steph, not without making Alex suspicious.'

Stephanie shivered. 'It must be awful to love someone so much and know that you'll always be apart.'

'Awful?' Derision grated through the word. 'It's hell on earth!'

Stephanie looked up at him, shocked by the bitter intensity in his voice. His mouth curved in an unfamiliarly hard line. He had a very nice mouth, she thought absently, the top lip firmly drawn, the bottom one fuller.

As though it possessed a will beyond her control, her hand lifted, her fingertip gently touching that full bottom lip. She felt Gray tense, his fingers fastening round her wrist, his eyes furiously dark, as he looked down into the surprised violet innocence of her own.

'What the . . .?'

'I'm sorry, Gray.' Her eyes clouded, confusion spreading through her, almost as though she spoke the words for herself rather than him. She said huskily, 'I don't know why I did that . . . I just thought how nice your mouth was.' She frowned, breaking off incoherently. 'I . . .'

'It's OK.'

The anger was gone from his voice and she looked at him in relief. The expression in his eyes was shielded from her by twin fans of thick, dark lashes. She had always known that Gray was an attractive man, but until now she hadn't realised how attractive. The temptation to reach out and touch his lashes in the same way she had touched his mouth was almost too much for her. While she was still grappling with the strangeness of it, the dark lashes lifted and for a moment dark blue eyes looked relentlessly into vulnerable violet.

'It's all right if you want to touch me, Steph. I'm just not used to it, that's all. You're not a very touching person, are you?'

Wasn't she? Gravely she considered it.

She looked back at Gray, trying to interpret the expression in his eyes, but he veiled them from her, turning his head.

The sudden brief contact of his lips against the soft tips of her fingers in a butterfly kiss sent quivers of sensation racing from her nerve-endings, but before she could analyse why she should be so shocked, he was releasing her, and standing up.

'Come on. It's time we set off for the yard.'

As she moved past him towards the open door he watched her with an expression in his eyes that would have shocked her to the depths of her soul had she seen it. It was the look of a hungry, aching man fighting to hold on to his self-control.

Eleven years he had wanted her, from the day she had turned seventeen. She only had to touch him for him to go up in flames. When he had looked down at her and seen her looking at his mouth . . . God, but he had come close to betraying himself. She didn't have the slightest idea how he felt about her, and she never would, but sometimes the strain of maintaining their sexless friendship when he wanted . . . He swallowed hard, trying not to let himself imagine what it would be like to have her softness in his arms, to bury himself in her and love her in all the ways he ached to do. It was utterly pointless yearning for her; she loved Paul and she always would, he knew that. He had tried every way he knew how to stop loving her, to stop aching for her and wanting her, but none of them worked. It didn't matter how many other women he took to bed, in the end there was only her.

There were times when he almost wanted to take hold of her and *make* her respond to him; when he was almost driven mad by the torment of having her so close to him and yet so unattainable.

The day he knew he loved her, he had planned to wait until she had grown a little, until she knew enough about life to make her own decisions; but Paul had beaten him to it, Paul who had never waited for anything in his life, Paul who had seen the way his older cousin watched Stephanie's slender, copper-haired figure; Paul who had deliberately and knowingly taken her from him.

Grimacing faintly as he fell in step behind her, Gray reflected that it was just as well that she believed he loved Carla. He would have to have a word with Carla. She and Alex adored one another ... she had also guessed, in that infuriatingly intuitive way that women have, how he felt about Stephanie. In fact, the only person who didn't seem to know was Stephanie herself.

He shouldn't have given in to his own weakness and asked her to come down here. How on earth was he supposed to concentrate on working for the Fastnet, with Stephanie providing a constant distraction, a constant torment? A muscle beat betrayingly in his jaw as his body tensed. God, when she walked into his bedroom yesterday ... He had had to to turn away from her so that she wouldn't see. How on earth he had managed to get his body under control before it betrayed him, he still didn't know.

For one split second he had almost been on the point of begging her to touch him.

'Gray?'

Stephanie turned to wait for him to catch up with her. Under his tan, his face looked strained, and she ached to comfort him. She hated seeing him like this, but not as much as she hated the cause of his pain. How could Carla do this to him? Had she no compassion? But if Carla was free to marry Gray ... Stephanie shivered, knowing that she didn't want the other woman to have such a permanent place in Gray's life. She told herself that she wasn't jealous, that there was no reason for her to be, but knowing that Gray loved someone else somehow disturbed her.

CHAPTER THREE

THE ESTUARY was on one of the prettiest parts of the Channel coastline, and although Stephanie couldn't quite repress a shudder as they walked into the boat-yard, part of her couldn't help being aware of what an attractive picture the variety of boats made as they clustered around the marina just beyond the yard.

Out in the mouth of the estuary where it joined the sea, a dinghy race was taking place, and she paused automatically to watch them tack in and out of the buoys, remembering how much pleasure she had once gained from sailing.

She had learned to sail almost as soon as she could walk, and she and her parents had spent many happy holidays indulging their love of the sport.

Since Paul's death, she hadn't set foot in a boat of any kind, and linked with her deep guilt over his death was her own almost phobic dread of anything connected with the sea.

'You've got quite a lot of work in hand,' she commented to Gray as she walked at his side.

He shrugged. 'Repairs mostly, and they don't bring in an awful lot. I've taken on an agency for one of the national small yacht builders, and that brings a reasonable amount in commission, but it isn't enough.'

He left her for a moment to go over and speak to the two men working on an upturned hull.

The clean, salty tang of sea air assailed her nostrils.

Almost against her will, Stephanie found her gaze drawn to the far horizon. It was a perfect day for sailing, just enough brisk wind . . .

'Fancy going out?'

She hadn't heard Gray coming back and she jumped, shocked that he could even make such a suggestion when he knew how she felt about the sea. She shook her head, and felt his fingers bite deeply into her arm.

'Paul's dead, Stephanie,' he told her harshly. 'Nothing's going to bring him back. Sooner or later you're going to have to face up to that fact and start re-building your own life. You've been living in a vacuum since he died,' he accused roughly. 'You've got to . . .'

He broke off, his eyes narrowing as a car drove into the yard.

Stephanie turned to look at it, and her heart plummeted as she saw Carla stepping out of the passenger seat of a racy-looking Jaguar car.

'Hi, there . . .'

The other woman was an excellent actress, she acknowledged grudgingly. No one could have guessed from the way she was smiling to include them both that she and Gray were anything other than merely friends.

A tall, fair-haired man extricated himself from the driver's seat of the car and put his arm round her shoulders. He was older than Gray, somewhere in his forties, but lean and bronzed and very fit-looking.

'That's Alex, Carla's husband,' Gray murmured to her.

For some reason she found that she was moving closer to him, almost as though she wanted to protect him. *Her*, protect Gray? She grimaced to herself as the other couple came over to them.

'Alex darling, I don't think you've met Stephanie before, have you?' Carla introduced.

Alex Farlow's handshake was as firm as Stephanie had anticipated it would be. He did not look like a man whose wife was being unfaithful to him, and Carla certainly did not look like a woman who was cheating on her husband. Her arm was tucked through his and she was smiling up at him in a teasing, loving way, that made Stephanie unable to look at Gray, standing so tensely at her side.

This must be purgatory for him, to see Carla with her husband, playing the part of a loving wife.

'No, we haven't met before.' Alex Farlow smiled. 'But I certainly have heard a lot about you, Stephanie.' He grinned at Gray as he spoke, and to Stephanie's astonishment she saw a dull burn of dark colour stain Gray's cheekbones. Gray was embarrassed ... but why ...?

'See, I told you that Gray wouldn't be in the mood for work today,' Carla announced, smiling up at her husband.

'We're on our way to Southampton, and I just thought I'd call in to tell you that a guy from *Yacht Owner* will be coming down to interview you about the new boat—that should give us some good publicity.'

The two men talked for a while about the progress on the boat, but then Carla tugged her husband away, exclaiming playfully, 'Alex, Gray doesn't often get the chance to spend time with Stephanie, and I'm sure he doesn't want to waste any of it talking boats ...'

Stephanie frowned as Carla drew her husband away. What was she trying to imply? That *she* and Gray were more than merely friends? Why? Did Alex perhaps suspect her relationship with Gray?

There had certainly been nothing remotely lover-like in their attitude to one another that she could see, and yet she couldn't help noticing that Gray was quick to detach Carla from her husband's side, as he walked with them towards their car. While Alex eased himself into the driver's seat, Carla and Gray stood talking, their voices too low for her to catch what they were saying, their heads close together. The pain inside her startled her. She was jealous . . . jealous of Carla! She shivered and told herself it was just the freshening breeze but, as Gray waved off the departing couple and came back to her, she felt as though somehow the brightness of the day had been inexplicably dimmed.

Gray took her into the office. Nothing had changed; the same old battered filing cabinets, the same ancient typewriter. The paperwork generated by the business was minimal and shouldn't take too much of her time.

She saw Gray glance at his watch.

'The new boat will have to wait for another time. We'd better get moving if we're going to collect your stuff.'

He was right. He was also withdrawn and almost distant with her, and her throat ached with compassion for him. Carla's brief appearance had done this to him.

She reached out to touch his arm, and immediately he tensed, frowning down at her.

'Gray, is there nothing I can do to help?' she asked him awkwardly.

For a moment she thought he was actually going to deny knowing what she meant, but then his frown eased slightly to be replaced by an expression of such bitter cynicism that she could have cried for him.

'It's no good. She'll never leave Alex. I know that now.'

Stephanie bit her lip. It was wrong of her to feel so relieved, but she couldn't help it. That must have been what they were talking about. Carla must have told him their affair was over. Odd, but she hadn't struck Stephanie as the type of woman to indulge in casual affairs. If she hadn't known better, on this morning's showing she would have judged her as a woman who was deeply in love and perfectly happy with her husband.

'They've got two children . . . both boys . . . They're away at boarding school but . . .'

Stephanie pressed his arm in mute sympathy.

'Did you really mean what you said about . . . about wanting to help?'

Gray's voice seemed to have become unfamiliarly thick. She glanced up at him, and saw that his skin was slightly flushed. It tore at her heart to see him looking so vulnerable, to have him in need of her help instead of the other way round.

'Anything,' she told him softly, meaning it. 'You know that.'

His mouth twisted in a strange smile.

'It's hell on earth wanting a woman who doesn't want you. I need something or someone to strengthen my will-power . . . to stop me from doing something crazy . . . You could be that someone, Steph.'

For a moment she could do nothing but stare at him. When she did manage to speak, her voice was a muffled croak.

'Me . . . but how?'

His mouth twisted again.

'By the oldest method in the book. You could pretend to be my lover ...'

For a moment she was too shocked to speak.

'But that wouldn't stop you wanting her,' she said at last.

'No,' Gray agreed bleakly, 'but it would help to salvage my pride ... and the boat-yard. Don't you see, Steph?' He grabbed hold of her arms, pulling her so close to him that she could see the dark irises of his eyes, the pupils enlarged with emotion and pain.

'Having you as my make-believe lover will erect a barrier between us. It will help to stop me from running after her and making a complete fool of myself. And it will stop Alex from finding out ...'

'That you're in love with his wife.'

Why did saying the words cause her so much pain? She gnawed on her bottom lip, knowing there was no way in a hundred years she could play such a role convincingly.

As though he read her mind, Gray released her and stepped back from her.

'It's all right. I shouldn't have asked you. It's expecting too much to ...'

'No!' Her own denial startled her. She gave a shaky laugh and went on. 'I *will* do it, Gray. I owe you that much—and more ... much more than I can ever repay. But I'm not sure that I'll be very convincing.'

The pain in his eyes was almost too much for her. She felt her throat close up against the tears forming. She hurt for him.

He had his back to her, but there was no mistaking the sarcasm in his voice as he said cruelly, 'You can remember how it was with Paul though, can't you ...?'

The pain of his words shut off her breath. She wanted to cry out against it, but the agony inside her was too great. She made a sound in her throat, something between a cry and a moan, and instantly Gray was at her side.

'Oh God, Steph. I'm sorry.' He was rocking her in his arms, holding her so closely that she could feel the heat coming off his skin, and instantly she remembered how it had felt to have the aroused pressure of his flesh against her own.

Immediately she tensed and recoiled from him, shocked by the surge of sensation engulfing her own body. She felt Gray release her, his expression shuttered as he looked down at her.

'I'm sorry.' His voice was clipped. 'I didn't mean to hurt you.'

And she wasn't sure if he meant physically or emotionally.

They set out for London and Stephanie's flat after a snack lunch. Gray was driving his Range Rover. It was a pleasant change to make the journey with some degree of comfort. Her VW wasn't designed for long journeys.

Conversation between them was desultory. Stephanie asked about his progress with the development of the new boat and how he and Alex intended to market it. There was a constraint between them that had not been there before, and when at last they were on the outskirts of the city, Gray said curtly, 'Look, if you want to change your mind and recall your offer of help, you only have to say so.'

'I don't,' Stephanie told him quietly. 'Unless, of course, *you're* having second thoughts.'

A muscle twitched betrayingly in his jaw as he clenched his teeth and Stephanie knew how much it must be costing him to go through with the farce of pretending he no longer loved the other woman.

'There'll be a certain amount of talk—gossip about us,' he warned her. 'It's unavoidable, living in such a small place.'

Stephanie was startled. 'Why should there be? Everyone knows . . .'

'That you're still mourning the death of your husband,' he jeered unkindly. 'Stephanie, that was ten years ago. You're an adult woman and you'll be living under the roof of an equally adult male. People are bound to jump to conclusions.'

'I've stayed with you before and . . .'

'This time it's different,' Gray interrupted.

Stephanie had lived in London for too long to be concerned about the threat of unfounded gossip. She shrugged her shoulders. 'Does it really matter what people think? You and I . . .'

Gray looked at her. 'Well, if *you're* not concerned, I don't suppose there's any reason why I should be. I just thought I'd warn you.'

'That people will look on me as your live-in lover?' She shrugged again. 'I can't believe that that's going to occasion much gossip these days!'

She glanced across at Gray and was surprised to see that he was frowning as though for some reason her comment displeased him. Was he secretly still hoping that Carla would change her mind, and was this the reason for his reticence?

She felt unable to question him too closely on a subject that was obviously intensely painful to him.

They reached her flat without incident, parking outside the Victorian villa in which it was situated. Stephanie's flat was on the top floor, where the attic windows had an excellent north light, ideal for her work.

The flat comprised a hall, sitting-room, dining kitchen, bathroom and two bedrooms, the smallest of which she used as a workroom and in which she had set up her easel and reference books, plus a desk and filing cabinet.

As she had already warned Gray, he would have to sleep on her rather small bed-settee.

Because she hadn't anticipated returning quite so soon, her fridge was empty, and Gray offered to go out and find them something to eat while she started to pack. She had taken the precaution of storing several heavy-duty cardboard boxes in the back of the Range Rover and Gray carried them upstairs for her, following her into her bedroom with them.

She had decorated the room herself in muted neutral shades, livened with a sunny yellow and deep blue, and Gray glanced round appreciatively, his eyes lingering briefly on the narrowness of her single bed before he commented drily, 'No frills and feminine furbelows, that's my Stephanie.'

For some reason his remark hurt her and she turned her back on him, snapping, 'I suppose Carla's bedroom is all pink and white with miles of lace!' And then she broke off, her face scarlet with mortification. What on earth had come over her? She bit her lip and looked uncertainly at Gray. 'I'm sorry, I . . .'

'I don't know what her room looks like,' he told her flatly. 'I've never been in it, but somehow I can't see

Alex having a taste for pink and white, can you?'

Oh God, how cruel of her, to remind him that the woman he loved did not sleep alone but shared her bed with her husband.

She went over to him, laying her hand on his arm. 'Gray . . .'

Immediately he jerked away from her.

'Save it,' he advised her curtly, opening the bedroom door. 'I'll go out and see what I can dig up in the way of food.'

After he had gone, Stephanie opened her wardrobe doors, and then stared blindly at the contents. How could she have hurt him like that? But she simply hadn't thought. She had been so . . . so hurt by his laconic comment about her bedroom that she had simply lashed out at him without thought.

But *why* had she been hurt? He had only spoken the truth. Why all of a sudden did she find her celibacy such a burden? Surely she had taught herself years ago to accept the fact that sexually she was a failure. Why now, of all times, did she have to start feeling like this?

Like what? she asked herself wryly. Like she was jealous of Carla . . . jealous of the fact that Gray loved and desired her? She had always known that Gray didn't live the life of a monk, why on earth should it only start to bother her now?

Perhaps because in the past Gray had never mentioned any of the women he was involved with, never introduced her to any of them, never intimated in any way at all that his mode of life was any different from her own.

Was she so damaged that she actually resented the closeness of others? Was that what was wrong with her?

Was she envious of Gray's ability to both give and receive the sexual fulfilment that had always been denied to her, or was her jealousy of a more intimate and dangerous nature?

Such as ... Immediately she stiffened, refusing to allow her thoughts free rein, flinging herself into a fever of activity to stop herself from pursuing trains of thought she knew instinctively would lead to danger.

Gray was gone less than half an hour, returning with a Chinese take-away which they ate in front of her sitting-room fire.

It was no longer possible to burn real fuel in the grate, but she had splurged on a very effective fake gas fire, which gave off both heat and the illusion of flickering flames.

'Good, but not as good as the real thing,' Gray commented, looking at it. 'But then, nothing ever is.'

There was something in his eyes as he looked at her that made her stomach churn with restless aching tension, although she didn't know what it was.

She looked away from him and got up clumsily. 'I'd better get these things washed up.'

'I'll do that. You carry on with your packing. I'd like an early start in the morning, if that's OK with you. We'll get all your stuff packed in the car tonight, and then we can leave right after breakfast.'

Stephanie had no objections to his plans and, while he washed up from their meal, she continued with her packing, leaving Gray to carry the heavy boxes downstairs and store them in his car.

By nine o'clock everything was in. Straightening her aching back, Stephanie grimaced. 'I don't know about you, but I'm whacked—and stiff as well.'

'A hot bath will get rid of that.' Gray glanced at his watch. 'You go and have one, I'll make us both a hot drink.'

There was no reason for her to feel self-conscious, and yet for some reason she did.

She felt far too on edge to linger in the bath, getting out and drying herself quickly, and then pulling on clean clothes.

Gray looked surprised when she emerged so quickly.

'I thought you'd have a good long soak. You still look very tense. Where is it sore? Here?' He reached out quite naturally, spreading his hand over her shoulder, his fingers gently massaging the back of her neck where the tension was the greatest.

For one weak moment she thought about relaxing against their stroking pressure; about closing her eyes and . . . Her eyelashes flickered and she felt the warmth of Gray's breath against her face as he bent towards her.

'You're losing weight.' His free hand cupped her face, pulling her round to face him, his thumb gently probing the shadow beneath her eye. 'I shouldn't have let you work so hard.'

A dangerous lassitude was creeping over her, an aching need to simply lean against Gray's strength both emotionally and physically.

'Gray . . .'

His hand slid into her hair, soothing away the tension locking her muscles. She closed her eyes, relaxed by the proximity of him where before she had been alarmed by it, her senses soothed by the familiar scent of him.

'What is it?'

She looked up to smile at him, and then suddenly remembered Carla.

When he held Carlà in his arms, it would not be just to comfort her ... like a child.

Abruptly she pulled away from him, terrified of pursuing the thought any further. She was becoming almost obsessed by his relationship with the other woman. Her skin burned with the intimacy of her thoughts and she felt as guilty as though she had actually observed them making love. In her thoughts she *had* pictured the two of them together ... and to her that was almost as bad ... almost as much of an intrusion into their privacy.

'Gray ... I'm tired. I think I'll go straight to bed.'

He let her go without a word, but as she walked to her room she was conscious of him watching her ... conscious that somehow, by drawing away from him so abruptly, she had created a coldness between them that had not been there before.

CHAPTER FOUR

STEPHANIE was awake early, her sleep disturbed by a tension she couldn't put a name to, until consciousness flooded back and she remembered the events of the previous day.

Now, lying in her nun-like single bed, watching the grey dawn break over the London roofs, it seemed incredible that she had allowed Gray to persuade her to move back to the estuary—even if it was only temporarily. And worse still . . . she shivered involuntarily as she remembered the additional folly she had agreed to.

She couldn't blame Gray for wanting to uphold his pride, nor for his fears that the boat-yard could become bankrupt if Carla's husband chose to withdraw his support, but how on earth could she have been stupid enough to agree to play the part of his new lover?

It seemed incredible. She was the least likely candidate for such a role, and she was sure she would never be able to play it convincingly. But she had given Gray her word.

Soberly she showered and dressed, knowing that there was no going back. She had given Gray a commitment and her pride would not allow her to withdraw from it.

A dry throat drove her into the kitchen in search of a cup of coffee.

Gray was still asleep, and she hastily averted her eyes from his bare torso, tanned and darkened with a covering of fine hair. Would it feel as silky as it looked? Shocked, she stared unseeingly at the filter coffee machine, wondering where on earth such an alien and dangerous thought had come from.

She had several minutes to wait for the coffee and she moved restlessly back to the door, her eyes drawn immediately to where Gray lay fast asleep on her bed-settee.

Although a reasonably respectable size, there was no way it was big enough for Gray. He dwarfed it, looking oddly youthful and almost vulnerable, with his dark hair untidy, and his eyes closed in sleep.

Long, dark lashes lay against the sharp rise of his cheekbones. He made a small sound and moved in his sleep, twisting the already dishevelled bedclothes round his lean body as he rolled over.

Something stronger than logic impelled her forwards until she was standing looking down at him.

Her heart was beating extraordinarily fast and she felt as though she were on the edge of some dizzyingly frightening discovery—and then Gray moved again, his eyes opening abruptly.

When he reached out and cupped the back of her head, she was too stunned to move. The smile he was giving her was like no other she had ever seen. It curled his mouth with a languid male appreciation of her as a woman that made her pulses pick up and race frantically. His eyes had closed again and he levered himself up slightly, pulling her down towards himself at the same time.

The sensation of his mouth moving against her own, the sleep-warm scent of his skin, the rough rasp of his night's growth of beard against her face were all things that should have jerked her out of his arms immediately, but somehow her senses refused to respond in that way. Instead she found herself melting against him, her mouth softening beneath the gentle pressure of his.

She might have gone on melting mindlessly if his hand hadn't suddenly strayed towards her breast. Instantly she tensed.

His eyes opened, widened as they saw her face, and then grew shuttered, leaving her in no doubt that he had had no idea whom he had been kissing. But *she* could quite easily imagine who he had hoped it had been! Pain, sharp and bitter, pulsed inside her.

'Stephanie.'

She knew from the tone of his voice what he was going to say, and suddenly she didn't want to hear the words; didn't want to hear him saying he thought she had been Carla.

'I've just made some coffee,' she told him, trying to control the tremor in her voice. 'Would you . . . would you like some?'

She thought she saw an expression of pain darken his eyes but then it was gone, his mouth bleak, his voice devoid of all expression, drained like that of a man tired of fighting against impossible odds, as he accepted quietly.

'That would be fine. Thank you.'

'I didn't mean to wake you, but you did say you wanted an early start, and there's nothing to keep us here.'

Stephanie knew that she was babbling, just as she knew that for the first time that she could remember she felt uncomfortable with him. It had been a shock to feel his mouth moving against hers ... but it had been something more than shock that she had felt. And she tensed against remembering that dangerous softening, the yielding sensation that had spread through her body at the touch of his lips.

He had been kissing *Carla*, she reminded herself fiercely. Not her.

She took him his coffee, taking care not to look at his body as he sat up and straightened the bedclothes.

'You can look now,' he told her drily, destroying her hope that he was not aware of her discomfort. He was looking at her, his eyes cool and determined, and Stephanie swallowed nervously.

'Stephanie, I ...'

He was going to apologise for kissing her; she knew it! She stumbled into speech before he could do so, telling him huskily, 'I know you thought I was Carla. It ... it must be very frustrating to see so much of her, but to know that she ... that she prefers to stay with her husband ...'

Her cheeks were pink by the time she had finished. She had said far more than she intended, and she cursed herself for inadvertently bringing up a subject that could only cause Gray pain.

He was watching her with a peculiarly brilliant intensity that made her lose her thread and feel as though every muscle in her body was locked in some kind of unbreakable vice.

'Hellish frustrating,' he agreed flatly, refusing to let

her look away. 'Shall I prove to you how much?'

Shock hit her first, followed quickly by pain, and then fear. She was backing away from him even before she had had time to form any conscious decision.

As though he had looked into her mind and saw what haunted her there, his hand suddenly dropped away, his face changing.

'For God's sake, Stephanie,' he demanded savagely, 'you didn't think I was going to *hurt* you, did you?'

What could she say? She knew of course that Gray would never hurt her, but briefly, for that soul-tormenting moment in time, she had forgotten this was *Gray*, and remembered only that he was a man.

The fear that he would start questioning her drove her into saying petulantly. 'I'm not like you, Gray. I don't play those sort of games.'

Anger gave way to incomprehension as he continued to look at her.

'What do you mean? *I* don't play games, Steph. You should know me well enough for that.'

Her colour high, Stephanie said bleakly, 'I meant your remark about me ... about ...'

'About my physical frustration,' Gray supplied grimly, as realisation dawned. His mouth thinned as he said curtly, 'Don't worry about it, Steph. For a moment I forgot that you don't suffer the same feelings as the rest of us mortals.'

He sounded angry with her and Stephanie felt herself shiver.

'Tell me something,' he demanded bitterly. 'If the positions had been reversed, if you had been the one to die, do you honestly think that Paul would have lived the rest of his life as a monk?'

She made a small agonised sound at the back of her throat and instantly Gray leapt out of the bed, enfolding her in his arms, and rocking her against his hard frame, even though she struggled to break free of him.

The tears she hadn't been able to conceal poured from her eyes, soaking his shoulders.

He wasn't completely nude. He was wearing a brief pair of underpants, but he might as well have been, Stephanie reflected shakily, as she shivered in his arms.

Against her ear she could hear him crooning words of apology and comfort. There was nothing sexual in the way he was holding her; this was the Gray who had held and comforted her after Paul's death, the Gray she loved and respected as she did no other human being. But still lingering in the shadows was that other Gray ... the Gray who had looked at her with something approaching hate in his eyes when he opened them to see that she wasn't Carla. The Gray who had brutally made her aware of the fact that he was a man with all man's natural desires.

Now, gently, he held her away from him, using his knuckles to brush the tears from her face.

She felt herself shudder, and longed to be back in his arms, comforted by his bulk, protected by his caring. She felt cold and intensely alone, and yet, as she made a move towards him, he released her and stepped back, chiding her gently.

'I'm not made of stone, Steph.'

And he wanted a woman who was out of reach. She had learned the hard way from Paul, that the male sex could want and take women for whom they felt nothing emotionally.

'What's happening to us, Gray?' she asked him tearfully.

'Do you really need me to answer that?' He looked at her with brooding eyes. 'We're two people who know each other too well in some respects and not well enough in others. Come on, let's get some breakfast and then get out of here.'

Common sense urged her to tell him that she had changed her mind; that she wasn't going to go with him, but for some reason she said nothing. Why? Did she *want* to go back to the estuary with him?

Thoroughly confused, Stephanie set about making them both breakfast, while Gray went to have his shower.

The first thing Gray did when they arrived back in the village was to drop Stephanie outside his cottage, with the explanation that he wanted to go down to the yard to make sure nothing needed his attention.

Stephanie watched him go, her mouth drooping slightly with sadness and bewilderment. Gray had changed. Hitherto she had perceived him as being slightly remote, above the trials and tribulations that beset the rest of the human race, but now . . .

But now she was being forced to confront the reality of his sexuality, she told herself unkindly, and she was jealous; jealous of Gray because he was able to experience those pleasures that were denied to her, and jealous of Carla because she was the woman who aroused the need for them within him.

Almost sick with self-disgust, she let herself into the

cottage and took the cases Gray had dropped off for her up to her room.

What was the matter with her? She was developing a selfish dog-in-the-manger attitude towards Gray that made her feel uncomfortably guilty about her own motives. Was she really so weak-minded that she resented Gray loving someone else?

Immediately her mind shied away from the question, her hands stilling for a moment as she tensed and stared unseeingly out of her bedroom window.

Gray had asked her for her help, and she had agreed to give it, but wasn't some part of her secretly pleased that Carla had given him up in favour of her husband?

Her mind fought in panic against the hardness of the accusation. She had been concerned for Gray, of course she had. Carla was a married woman. And if she hadn't been? A shudder of tension convulsed her body, a fine sheen of sweat dampening her skin. She was trembling violently, shivering so much that she had to wrap her arms round herself. Her thoughts were taking her along paths, raising spectres that she wasn't prepared to face.

The shrill sound of the telephone ringing was a welcome relief. She went downstairs to answer it. The caller identified himself as a 'Mac Weston', and asked for Gray.

She explained that he was down at the yard.

'Could you get him to give me a ring, as soon as possible? Tell him it's about the Fastnet. He knows my number.'

The Fastnet. Stephanie's hands were trembling when she replaced the receiver. Only the previous year bad weather had caused many of the entrants to withdraw from the race. Those who had persevered had battled against monstrous seas—several had capsized—some had lost their lives.

Her guilt over the failure of her marriage was somehow inextricably caught up in her fear of the sea. She shivered again, suddenly remembering the very last time she and Paul had gone out sailing together.

It had been after their relationship had started to deteriorate, not long before Paul's death. They had taken his boat out with the intention of sailing it to a small, uninhabited island off the coast. It had been Paul's idea; a way of making amends to her for their quarrel the evening before.

He had come in late—and drunk. He had hit her, she remembered, touching her cheek automatically, as though her flesh still bore the imprint of that blow.

They had set out early; she had packed a picnic. It was a perfect day for sailing, and Paul had been in high spirits. Almost like the old Paul; the Paul she had fallen in love with.

They had made good time to the island and had spent a couple of hours there, swimming and then having their lunch. It was mid-afternoon when they set off back. Paul's mood seemed to change immediately they got back on board.

The breeze had picked up and a stiff, fresh wind had been blowing, Stephanie remembered. Paul had sailed the small boat almost recklessly close to the wind, crowding on too much sail. When she cautioned him against it, he had lost his temper with her, delivering a furious tirade that had destroyed all her earlier pleasure in the day. Neither of them was wearing safety-jackets.

She had wanted to put hers on, but Paul had called impatiently that he was ready to leave, and now, as the small boat raced dangerously across the waves, she was beginning to regret the lack of this safety precaution.

She had called out to Paul to take in some of the sail, but he had ignored her, tacking so abruptly that she was flung to one side of the yacht as it keeled over. Instinctively she had clung to the side, closing her mouth against the incoming swell of sea water, waiting for the small craft to right itself, furious with Paul for putting them both in so much danger, and then ...

It had been years since she had let herself remember this particular incident, and part of her didn't want to remember it now, Stephanie acknowledged, her body as cold as though it was still immersed in sea water. Even without closing her eyes, she could remember the scene in minute detail, feel the cold clamminess of her wet clothes, the numbness of her fingers, and the anger that had turned horrifyingly to fear as she realised that Paul was not going to help her; that he was deliberately trying to ...

To what? she asked herself now. To drown her? Anxiously, she gnawed at her bottom lip. As she had learned after their marriage, Paul had an uncontrollable temper when aroused, but had he actually been trying to drown her that day, or had it simply been an accident ... a misjudgement ...?

While she was still clinging grimly to the side of the boat, a coastguard craft had come within hailing distance to them and, seeing her plight, had instantly come to her rescue.

Paul had explained away the mishap with his usual

charm, and although the coastguard had frowningly
pointed out that he was carrying far too much sail for
such a brisk wind, he had made no other comment.

Once they got home, Paul had been surly and
uncommunicative. He had left her there to go to
Southampton, she remembered, and she might have
thought no more about the incident, had it not been for
the fact that during a particularly vicious row some
days later, he had said, 'I want to be free of you,
Stephanie, and I will be—whatever I have to do to do it.'

Even now there were still occasions when she
dreamed about the incident, the cunning, almost
triumphant look in Paul's eyes as he watched her
struggles to maintain her grip on the boat. Had he
actually tried to drown her, or had it only been an
accident? She would never know.

Just as she would never know whether his death had
been an accident or . . . or a deliberate decision to escape
from her once and for all.

That haunted her, too; that she might have been
responsible for his death. It was like a sickness that she
carried round inside her; a poison that tainted her
whole life.

Jerking herself back to reality she pushed the bitter
memories away. She had to go down to the yard and
give Gray his message.

She saw the car first; a long, sleek Jaguar that looked
oddly out of place among the shabby boats and Gray's
rather battered Range Rover. She recognised it
immediately of course, a mixture of anger and pain
obliterating her earlier tension as she realised that Carla
was visiting the yard.

She saw them the moment she rounded the corner of the building, standing together, with barely an inch of space between them. Gray's dark head angled almost protectively over Carla's bent one. Her hand was on his arm, her finger-nails dark with polish. She was wearing a suede skirt with a toning silk blouse. Every blonde hair was in place.

As she watched, a small breeze sprang up and teased the smooth blonde bob. Gray reached out and tucked several silken strands behind her ear.

The ground beneath Stephanie's feet actually felt as though it moved as she watched the small, betraying tableau. Carla's hair looked like spun silver against the tanned masculinity of Gray's hand. She looked up at him, and although she couldn't hear what they were saying or see their expressions Stephanie had no doubt that she was watching an intimate moment between two lovers.

Off to her right a small movement caught her eye. She raised her head and then tensed as she saw Alex striding towards the other couple, still both oblivious to the fact that they were no longer alone.

Immediately Stephanie started to move, her one instinct to protect Gray.

She reached the engrossed couple several yards ahead of Alex, her hand reaching out to clutch Gray's arm, her eyes unknowingly dark with shock and fear.

'Stephanie. Is something wrong?'

Immediately Gray swung away from Carla, the hand that had so intimately touched her hair now covering the place where Stephanie's lay against his tanned forearm.

The sun was dazzling her, preventing her from seeing his expression, but she was aware of Carla stepping away from them to greet her husband, and her body tensed in dread, wondering if he had witnessed what she had seen and placed the same interpretation on it. If he had . . .

She forgot that the last thing on earth she wanted was for Gray to sail in the Fastnet, and immediately reached up on her toes, clutching at his shoulder to balance herself as she planted a kiss against his jaw and said huskily, 'No, nothing at all. I . . . I was just lonely without you . . .'

She could feel Gray's tension, and understood the reason for it, but by now he too was aware of Alex's presence, and as naturally as though they were indeed lovers he slid one arm round Stephanie's waist, curving her against his side, swinging her round so that the sunlight no longer dazzled her.

'Now that's what I like,' he responded in teasing tones. 'A woman who's not afraid to say she wants me.' The look in his eyes was that of an ardent lover, who could scarcely wait to be alone with his woman, and it threw her, confusing her, making her forget that she was still clinging to him like a fragile vine.

'I . . . I have a message for you . . .' She relayed it to him, stumbling over the words as she realised that his attention was focused on her mouth. The way he was looking at her was causing the most extraordinary sensations inside her. She realised of course that he was simply doing it for Alex's benefit; that it wasn't real.

The heat of his arm resting against her body seemed to burn right through her clothes. She could feel the imprint of his hard hip against her softer flesh, and where the side of her breast was pressed against his body a fiery ache was developing that was having the most devastating effect on her senses.

'I suspect that you and I are most definitely *de trop*, darling,' she heard Alex say laughingly to Carla.

'You two must come round and have dinner with us one night. What about next week? We should have the results of the sea trials in by then, shouldn't we, Gray?'

Without taking his eyes from her mouth, Stephanie heard Gray saying almost abstractedly, 'Yes . . . yes . . . I'm more than satisfied with her tests so far. I intend to take her out a couple more times—all I'm waiting for is a good gale.'

Numbly Stephanie stared up at him, her eyes going dark with shock and fear. She couldn't bear to think of losing Gray to the sea. She wanted to scream at him and beg him not to take such a risk. All her normally logical responses were swept away in the fierce tide of fear that burned through her.

Somewhere in the distance she was aware of car doors slamming and an engine starting, and that small part of her mind that was still functioning properly recognised that Carla and her husband must have left them; but all her concentration, all her attention was focused on Gray and the way he was still looking at her mouth.

A thrill of some dangerous and alien emotion raced through her. Without being aware of the provocation of what she was doing she touched her tongue-tip tentatively to the dry outline of her lips.

Someone shuddered. Herself, or Gray? She looked up at him, and trembled beneath the expression in his eyes.

'Do that again and I won't be responsible for what happens next,' he warned her in a curiously rusty, hoarse voice, that trapped her attention, focusing it on the shape of his mouth.

'For God's sake, Stephanie, do you *know* what you're doing? You're looking at me as though you can't wait to feel my mouth against yours.'

The words reached her, shocking her out of her momentary trance. She fought to break free of his enclosing arm, but instead of releasing her Gray pulled her hard against his body, his free hand sliding into her hair, trapping her so that she couldn't move.

She watched the downward descent of his head with a strange sensation of calm and disbelief.

His mouth touched hers, and she closed her eyes automatically. 'No ...' She felt the harsh objection against her mouth, and opened her eyes instinctively.

'I want to see what you're feeling when I kiss you.'

'Gray. No ... don't ...' She struggled to free herself, squirming against the almost painful hardness of his body, until she realised the effect her frantic movements were having on him.

He watched the hot colour scorch her skin with cynical detachment, demanding acidly, 'You're not that naïve, surely, Stephanie. Rub yourself against any normal man like that and you'd get exactly the same response.'

When her embarrassed colour deepened he smiled sardonically and bent his head to her ear and mouthed softly, 'I'm a man, Stephanie, and not a machine, and what you're doing to my body right now is driving me right out of my mind.'

His grip had slackened slightly and Stephanie pulled back, sickened and shaken by his bluntness. This wasn't the Gray she knew; the Gray who was always so courteous and careful of her, never allowing his masculinity to embarrass or disconcert her. This was another Gray, a Gray she was not familiar with. *Carla*'s Gray, she acknowledged achingly.

'What *I'm* doing to you?' she threw back at him bitterly. 'Don't you mean what seeing Carla has done to you? I'm not blind, Gray, I saw the way you were looking at her before. I saw how you touched her . . .'

Tears started up in her eyes, and she brushed them away impatiently, torn between misery and anger.

'I won't be used as a substitute for her, Gray. You told me it was all over between you. You . . .'

'It is,' he interrupted quietly, stepping back from her, his eyes watching her with cool dispassion.

'Alex saw the two of you together as well,' Stephanie told him uncertainly. 'That was why I . . .'

'Acted as though there was nothing you wanted more than my body against yours, my *mouth* against yours?' Gray derided savagely. 'Oh, you don't have to explain that to me, Stephanie. I know the score. For God's sake, you can't spend the rest of your life grieving over Paul.'

He was angry now, and she couldn't understand why, or how Paul had been dragged into the conversation. What did her relationship with Paul have to do with their present discussion?

She drew in a sharp breath, and remembered the way he had looked at Carla, with both tenderness and compassion, and she said bitterly, 'Why not? That's what you intend to do over Carla, isn't it?'

She saw him reach out towards her, but she moved back, turning on her heel and almost running out of the yard.

Once she was outside it, she slowed down to a more normal walk. Her chest felt tight and hurt, her eyes were smarting with unshed tears; her whole body was gripped with tension, and the turmoil of emotions inside her was something she had not experienced for years.

As she walked back to the cottage she tried to calm herself down a little. A group of fishermen stood by the harbour wall, chatting; one of them called out a greeting to her and she returned it.

How did the wives of these men cope? she wondered. Only last year there had been a terrible disaster, the entire crew of a trawler lost in heavy seas; some women had lost both husbands and sons. And yet she had heard one of them say on television that if her only surviving son should want to go to sea she would not try to stop him.

Where did such courage come from?

CHAPTER FIVE

STEPHANIE waited tensely for Gray's return, anticipating a confrontation following the way she had run
out of the yard, but none was forthcoming.

Gray simply came into the kitchen where she was
preparing their supper, and calmly started to help her as
though nothing had happened.

It took her several seconds to realise that the feeling
she was experiencing was something akin to disappointment, as she forced herself to follow his lead and respond
to his casual conversation.

'With a bit of luck I'll be able to take the boat out
tomorrow for more testing. They're forecasting heavy
weather. Just what we need at this stage.'

She could almost feel herself blench as she listened to
him, and he frowned, putting down the bowl of salad he
had been preparing, and taking a gentle hold of her
shoulders.

'Look, Steph, I understand how you feel about the sea,
but it wasn't the sea that caused Paul's death, it was his
own recklessness,' he told her bluntly. 'I'm sorry if that
hurts you but it is the truth. Paul disregarded the safety
precautions and that was why he drowned. You used to
love sailing. I remember when your family first came to
the estuary; you were never away from the yard.'

'Sailing was my father's hobby,' Stephanie told him

stupidly, as though they were strangers and he knew nothing about her.

'I know, and he taught you well. Too well for you to give it up completely. I used to see you handling that small dinghy of his. You were a pleasure to watch.'

Gray used to watch her. She stared at him. As a teenager he had seemed very remote and adult, a man while she and Paul were still little more than children. He had been kind to her though, she remembered that . . . kind and patient . . .

She remembered Paul teasing her once that Gray 'fancied' her . . . How embarrassed she had been, and how she had resented Paul's teasing remark. How could a man like Gray ever want a girl of her age? She remembered now that Paul had often made similar remarks to her about his cousin; after they were married those remarks had taken on a gloating, unpleasant nuance she had instinctively shied away from.

The memory was a very selective thing; for instance, in the early days after Paul's death she had forgotten his cruelty, both mental and physical, and remembered only her adoration of him.

She had also forgotten how much Paul had seemed to resent Gray at times . . . how much he had railed against his older cousin's influence with his parents.

Her parents had moved to the estuary when she was fifteen; she had been eighteen when she married Paul, and yet she had learned less about him in all those three years than she had in three months of marriage to him.

Paul had confessed to her once that Gray had been against their getting married. She had thought nothing of it at the time apart from being a little hurt that Gray, whom she looked upon as her friend, had chosen to align himself with their families.

'Come back . . .'

Gray's deep voice brought her back to the present, his eyes hardening slightly as he told her. 'I won't ask who or what you were thinking about, but whatever it was, it was obviously unpleasant. It's time you got over this phobia you have about the sea,' he added abruptly. 'What is it you fear so much? That you might drown?'

She shook her head forcefully, unable to explain to him that her fear was somehow linked with Paul's death, and those awful, terrifying moments alone in the yacht with him when she had thought he was going to let her drown. Ever since his death she had battled to keep those memories at bay, and she knew that to go sailing again would be to unlock the doors she had barred against them.

But weren't they already unlocked? Today, this afternoon, she had relived those traumatic moments and had found that, while the fear and panic remained, the dreadful soul-wrenching agony of fearing the man that she loved wanted to kill her had gone.

Not that she thought that Paul had deliberately and cold-bloodedly tried to drown her. It was just that she had seen in his face such a look of triumph and delight that she had sensed in him a wild desire to destroy her; that same desire she saw in him whenever he lost his temper with her and struck her. Paul had had an extremely volatile temperament, his emotions constantly see-sawing. Sometimes she had even wondered if he had perhaps been slightly unbalanced in some way. After all, he had been the one to persuade her into marriage, and he had been the one to grow tired of her once they were married, so quickly that in retrospect his feelings seemed to have changed overnight.

By mutual consent, she and Gray decided on an early night. She was tired, Stephanie admitted as she prepared for bed, but it wasn't a healthy tiredness, it was a mixture of strain and mental exhaustion.

What had happened to the Stephanie and Gray who used to stay up until all hours of the morning, talking animatedly to one another? It was as though Carla was proving to be a catalyst whose presence was causing her to dig deep into the past and re-evaluate very many things in her life. She was causing ripples on the surface of Stephanie's life that were nothing when compared with the deep and complex currents eddying dangerously, far below that surface.

Tomorrow she would start work at the yard, familiarising herself with its procedures, and thus freeing Gray to concentrate on testing his boat.

She fell asleep on that thought.

She was dreaming. She was sailing on an impossibly blue sea; and the bright sails of the small craft were silhouetted against an impossibly blue sky. It was warm, and there was a teasing, dancing breeze. She could see it billowing out the striped sails, filling them, sending the boat skimming across the water.

It was an exhilarating sensation, and automatically she lifted her face to the sun, her blood singing with pleasure and excitement.

She wasn't alone in the boat. There was a man with

her. He was controlling it. She felt safe and happy with him, free to enjoy the golden brilliance of the day and to give herself over to the thrill of matching her skills against those of the elements.

Sailing ... She had always loved it. She leaned forwards to tell Gray so, and he turned his head. Only he wasn't Gray, and she felt a scream of panic rise from her throat as she recognised Paul's face contorted in a grimace of hatred.

Suddenly both the sky and the sea turned black, and she was filled with fear.

She screamed out, and felt Paul lean towards her, taking hold of her.

'Stephanie ... Stephanie, wake up ...'

Shuddering, she opened her eyes. Gray was bending over her, his fingers biting into the soft flesh of her arms as he shook her.

He was wearing a robe and his hair was all tousled as though he had been woken abruptly from sleep.

'You were having a nightmare,' he told her curtly.

The lamp beside her bed had been switched on, its soft glow warming the dark room.

'You called out for Paul. You sounded terrified.'

She had been. She shuddered violently, remembering her dream. It had been so real ... so traumatic. Often in those first months after Paul's death she had dreamed, but in those dreams she had always been overwhelmed by guilt, and had always been reaching out to him, trying to save him.

It didn't take super-intelligence to understand why she had had this particular dream tonight though, but what she did find disturbing was her remembrance of how happy and safe she had felt when she had thought she was with Gray.

She sat up awkwardly, snatching at the sheet as it slipped away from her body. The nightdress she was wearing was a fine cotton lawn and, although she knew that Gray was hardly likely to be concerned about any momentary glimpse of her breasts, her gesture was the instinctive protective one of a woman not used to sharing intimacies with members of the opposite sex.

'I'm sorry if I disturbed you——' she began to apologise, but Gray cut her short, his mouth compressing, and twisting oddly as he interrupted sardonically, 'Are you?'

His reaction puzzled her, and she reached out automatically, her hand on his arm as he made to get up.

'Gray . . .'

'You're *never* going to get over him, are you, Stephanie? You're never going to let him go. You carry him about in your head with you . . . he shares your bed at night . . .' He broke off abruptly and said in a different voice, 'When you touched me this afternoon— were you pretending then that I was him?'

His accusation stunned her. Her eyes widened as she stared at him, pain forming a hard knot in her throat.

'No . . . no, of course I wasn't. I did that to protect you, to . . . Carla's husband had seen the two of you together. I . . .'

'You were only thinking of me, is that it? Well, perhaps it's time I repaid the favour, and reminded *you* exactly what it is you're turning your back on by clinging to your memories of a dead man.'

Before she could move, his hands were on her

shoulders, pushing her back against the pillows, his head descending so that it blotted out all the light.

She froze beneath the hard pressure of his mouth as it took hers in fierce determination. She could feel the sharp pressure of Gray's teeth against her lip and taste the rusty salt of her own blood. She made a muffled sound of protest and, as abruptly as he had taken hold of her, she felt him release her.

She was quivering with the shock of his unexpected attack. Never in a thousand wild imaginings had she ever believed that Gray would treat a woman like that. If she had given any thought to it at all she had supposed that he would be a considerate, caring lover, not . . .

Her fingers touched her swollen mouth, tears flooding her eyes.

'Stephanie, for God's sake, I'm sorry. I shouldn't have done that.'

Incredibly he was taking her back in his arms, and even more incredibly she was not resisting him. She felt the roughness of his robe beneath her cheek as he eased her against his shoulder. 'I . . .'

'I never thought you'd do a thing like that, Gray. I never thought you were the sort of man who . . . who liked . . . hurting women . . .'

Fresh tears brimmed from her eyes, and she heard him curse. It seemed incredible after what he had just done that she should have no fear of him. Perhaps her marriage to Paul had robbed her of the ability to experience any more sexual fear.

She heard Gray curse, and jerked back instinctively when his fingers slid along her jaw, cupping and tilting her face.

'Stephanie, I'm sorry. I'm sorry . . . I didn't mean to hurt you.' As he whispered the husky words of apology his lips moved caressingly against hers, imparting comfort and warmth. His arm tightened around her, and as his tongue started to trace the tender outline of her mouth she felt as though she were falling through space, helplessly spinning out of control; floating in a sea of sensations she could no longer understand.

Quite when her lips parted to the subtle persuasion of his tongue she didn't know.

It seemed as though one moment he was kissing her as though he was comforting a hurt child and the next the touch of his mouth had aroused such a storm of passion within her that she was clinging helplessly to him, responding to every passionate movement of his mouth against her own with a responsiveness that her conscious mind could only observe with awe and disbelief.

His robe had come open and her breasts were pressed against his chest, only the thin cotton of her nightdress between them.

His hands moulded her body, caressing her back, his touch making her spine arch, making her . . .

Abruptly she realised what she was doing, and in that same moment he released her, moving back from her. Both of them were breathing hard.

'*Were* you remembering Paul then, when I held you in my arms?' he demanded thickly. '*Were* you . . .?'

Shaken by the realisation of how much he had affected her, Stephanie cut across his raw demand with a shaky question of her own.

'Why not? After all, I know that *you* must have been thinking of Carla.' Her mouth twisted bitterly.

Gray got up abruptly and stood towering over her.

'Are you trying to tell me that you *were* pretending I was Paul?'

She didn't answer him. She couldn't. Not without lying, so instead she simply averted her head, and prayed for him to leave. She had experienced too much in far too short a space of time. Her emotions were in turmoil, her whole world had been turned upside-down and she needed to come to terms with what had just happened . . . with the fact that in Gray's arms she had responded to him in a way that she had never responded to any other man, and that included Paul.

When she had married Paul she had been little more than a child, in love with the idea of love. She had been happier exchanging kisses with him than she had making love, but just now in Gray's arms, for the first time in her life she had experienced the reality of physical arousal and need.

She had wanted Gray to go on touching and kissing her. She had wanted . . . She drew a shuddering breath, and her senses relayed to her the fact that he was moving away.

He opened the door and she turned her head to look at him, praying that he wouldn't read what was in her eyes.

'I'll leave you to your dreams of Paul, then,' he told her harshly. 'It seems that you get more satisfaction from them than you do from reality.'

She wanted to cry out to him, to stop him and tell him the truth, but what was the point? He loved Carla.

And she loved him!

It hit her like a sledge-hammer blow, knocking her

whole world out of focus, while she grappled with the enormity of it.

Of course she loved him, she tried to reason with herself, but as a sister . . . as a friend . . . but her body and her heart mocked her for her cowardice; they wanted him as a man . . . as a lover.

'Oh, God!' She wasn't sure if she said the words out loud or not. What on earth was she going to do? The sensible thing would be to pack her bags and leave first thing in the morning, but how could she do that? She had given Gray her promise to help him, and if she hadn't realised it already, his out-of-character behaviour tonight must have shown her just how much he was suffering.

Loving Carla was tearing him apart. So much so that he had been tempted to vent his physical frustration with her, Stephanie.

The pain that followed that admission was appallingly enlightening. It was a shock to a woman who considered herself to be lacking in sexuality to discover how wantonly her body was reacting to the thought of Gray as her lover.

But he wouldn't have been *her* lover, she reminded herself bitterly, he would have been Carla's and she would have been her substitute.

They were friends, and she would have to content herself with that. Maybe one day . . .

Maybe never, she told herself hardily. She would be a fool if she spent the rest of her life longing for a man who could never be hers. Gray loved Carla, he had told her so.

It took her a long time to get to sleep. Perhaps it was

only her emotionally heightened senses, she didn't know, but the scent of him seemed to cling to her skin, disturbing her, making her ache and yearn for things that could never be.

At last she drifted off to sleep but, although she longed to do so, she did not dream of Gray.

During the night the weather changed. Stephanie heard the wind the moment she woke up. For several minutes she simply lay drowsily listening to it. It was a comforting, noisy sound—when one was tucked up warmly in bed.

Through her open window she could smell salt, and deep down inside she felt a flicker of long-forgotten excitement. She and her father had spent many blustery days out in the Channel, before Paul's death and her own guilt had crippled her with fear.

Gray had been right about the weather, and now he would be able to undertake sea trials on his boat.

Gray! Instantly she sat up in bed, colouring hotly as she remembered how he had kissed her last night and how she had responded.

He had been trying to make her forget Paul, but he didn't know the truth about Paul or their marriage. He thought she was still deeply in love with his cousin.

Even before she went downstairs, some new sixth sense she had developed overnight told her that Gray had gone out. She found a note propped up against the kettle, informing her that he had left early and would be spending the day testing the boat.

The house felt empty without him and she felt restless. The phone rang just as she was setting out, and the shock of hearing Carla's voice on the other end of the line made her freeze with pain.

'Gray isn't here,' she managed ungraciously when she eventually found her voice.

'I was ringing to arrange that dinner date.'

Carla was ignoring her comment and Stephanie realised that the other woman might not be alone, and that her husband might be able to hear her conversation. Or was the dinner party simply an excuse she was using because Gray wasn't there?

'What about next Wednesday? Are you both free that evening?'

Making small talk with the woman that Gray loved was like trying to speak after her throat had been rubbed raw with sandpaper, but since Gray had made no objection to the invitation, she felt she had to go along with it, and confirm the arrangement.

Part of her longed to demand that Carla leave him alone, to ask her if she knew what the game she was playing with him was doing to him, but she knew that Gray would not thank her for her interference.

How could he love a woman like that? A woman who saw him only as a diversion from her marriage. A woman who frankly admitted that she preferred to stay with her wealthy husband. Had Carla no feelings, no compassion? She couldn't love Gray. If she did . . .

It was several minutes after the phone call had ended before Stephanie was able to bring herself to set out for the yard. She had dressed sensibly, in comfortable faded jeans, a cotton shirt and a warm jumper.

The wind buffeted her the moment she stepped outside, rain-clouds racing across the sky, driven by its surging gusts. Beyond the estuary the sea looked choppy, with white-capped waves further out to sea.

She had intended to listen to the shipping forecast before leaving the house but Carla's telephone call had driven it from her mind.

The men working in the yard called out a greeting to her as she walked past and let herself into the office. The phone was ringing as she walked in, and it seemed to go on ringing all morning, so that it was almost lunchtime before she had time to switch on the portable radio she had found on the muddled desk.

She was just in time to catch the last of the gale warnings, and her stomach heaved with nervous anxiety as she heard the newsreader announcing a gale and heavy seas off the Channel.

Gray would have taken the boat out into the open sea, she knew that. How would he be able to test its rough weather endurance without doing so? She knew enough about sailing to understand the reason behind his early-morning start.

She heard a car outside and glanced out of the window, her heart dropping as she recognised Alex's Jaguar.

Resentment stabbed through her. What did Carla want? Hadn't she hurt Gray enough already?

Only it wasn't Carla who got out of the car, it was Alex himself. He strode towards the office and she went to let him in.

'The weather's worsening,' he commented as he came in.

'Yes, I've just heard the shipping forecast.'

He was a good-looking man, she acknowledged, with an air of calm dependability.

'Try not to worry, Gray knows what he's doing. I've got one hell of a lot of money tied up in that boat he's out in, and you don't think I'd let him handle it if I didn't have absolute faith in him, do you?'

Her eyes widened as she read the message in his eyes. He *knew* that she was frightened. How? Had Gray told him about her hang-up about the sea?

She frowned. She wouldn't have thought that he and Gray would be that close—not with them both loving the same woman.

Her private knowledge about Gray's love for Carla made her feel acutely uncomfortable with Alex. He seemed such a pleasant man; a strong man too, not one she would have thought who would be drawn to a woman as faithless as Carla.

'I've a radio at home, Gray's just called in to say he's on his way back. I thought you'd like to know. He should be back about seven,' he added, glancing at his watch.

Stephanie cleared her throat. She was stunned that Alex had taken the time to come down here and reassure her about Gray's safety, and then she remembered that as far as Alex was concerned, she and Gray were lovers.

'I . . . thanks for letting me know,' she said lamely, adding awkwardly, 'Is Gray pleased with today's tests?'

She hardly knew what to say. She felt uncomfortable and ill at ease with Alex, even while she appreciated his kindness. She hated feeling that she was in any way a party to Carla's deception of him, and she wondered bitterly how on earth Gray managed to work alongside him. Perhaps his own love for Carla freed him from any normal feelings of guilt.

'Very,' Alex responded, apparently unaware of her constraint. 'We're using a revolutionary new keel—something along the lines the Australians used for the America's Cup—but I expect Gray's told you all about that. It's his design—it gives the boat greater speed and manoeuvrability. With a little bit more research and development, it could be modified for use with smaller, more commercial craft, but of course you know all about his plans for the development of the yard. It's fortunate that your own career is such that you can work almost anywhere. Carla gave up hers after our first child was born and I felt very guilty about it. She'd always loved her work.'

Carla working? Stephanie tried to visualise what line of work the glamorous blonde had been in. Modelling seemed the most likely choice.

'What exactly did she do?' she asked, unable to restrain her curiosity.

'She's a psychiatrist. She worked mainly with adolescents. It was very demanding, but I know she misses it.'

Stephanie looked at him in stunned disbelief. A psychiatrist! So Carla had brains as well as beauty. Brains, beauty, but no heart, she reflected acidly.

'I'd better be on my way, but I promised Gray I'd come down and give you the good news.'

She watched him walk to his car through a blur of angry tears. Gray's concern hadn't been for her; he had simply wanted to make sure that Alex didn't suspect anything.

His behaviour was so at odds with the Gray she had

thought she knew, and yet she couldn't despise him for it, even though she knew that she would have condemned his behaviour in any other man.

Had she ever known him at all? Had she ever known herself? she wondered bitterly. After all, she hadn't known that she loved him until last night.

She moved, restless, wanting to forget the physical sensations he had aroused in her the previous night. She wanted to forget the sensation of his mouth possessing her own, his hands . . . With a taut sound of anger, she spun round on her heel and started to attack the large pile of filing stuffed into one of the metal trays.

By mid-afternoon it was raining, and her nerves were stretched to breaking-point as she looked out at the angry sea. There were no small sails out in the estuary now, and Bob, the oldest and most experienced of the boat-yard's employees, an ex-trawlerman who had lost a leg in a fishing accident, prophesied that it would get worse before it got better.

At five o'clock the men went home. She had done all the filing, the post was up to date, and she was sick of prowling restlessly round the confining office. She might as well go back to the cottage.

It was only a matter of a hundred yards or so walk, but she was glad of the heavy-duty jacket she had taken from the laundry room on her way out, as she tugged the collar up against the sheeting rain.

The jacket belonged to Gray, and whether it was the dampness in the air or her own imagination, she didn't know, but it seemed as though the scent of his body clung tantalisingly to the heavy wool.

When he came in he would be tired, cold and hungry,

and because it was easier to busy herself with practical things than to sit anxiously counting the minutes until his return, she went upstairs to check that there were plenty of fresh towels in the bathroom and that the water was hot.

The woman who normally took care of the house was on holiday, but Stephanie had enough experience of sailing herself to know exactly what Gray would want to eat once he got back—something fast and hot.

She opted for chilli, knowing that it wouldn't spoil if he got back later than expected.

At half-past six, a whole half-hour before Gray's earliest time of arrival, she was tense with nervous anxiety. Over and over in her mind, like a video played in slow motion, she saw him being swept overboard, destroyed by the seas as Paul had been. She told herself that Gray was a far better sailor than Paul had ever been, that he had more experience, more caution, that he was perfectly safe—but none of it mattered.

If this was what she was like when he was simply out testing the new boat, what would she be like when he actually took part in the Fastnet?

She shuddered visibly, chafing her goose-pimpled arms with tense hands. Despite the fact that the central heating was on, she was cold.

On impulse she went outside, the strength of the wind whipping back her hair and making her catch her breath. There was a store of dry logs kept just outside the laundry room and she filled a basket with them.

Lighting a fire would keep her hands occupied, even if it did nothing to relieve the tension of her mind.

The crackle of the logs as the dry tinder caught fire

betrayed how tensely silent the room had been. She sat in front of the flames, staring unseeingly into them, Gray's face dancing in the yellow glare.

A door slammed and she stiffened, remembering that she had come in without locking the back door. She had lived in London for long enough to be aware of the danger of unwanted intruders.

She stood up, every nerve-ending alive with tension. The sitting-room door opened and her tension evaporated in a sob of relief as she saw Gray framed there.

He was still wearing his oilskins, the hood of his jacket pushed back to reveal the wet unruliness of his hair.

For a moment she was too choked with emotion to speak. He was back. He was safe. She wanted to run to him and be caught up in his arms. She wanted . . . She swallowed, feeling the tension within her increase.

'A fire—great. I'm frozen.'

Unlike her, Gray was completely relaxed.

'You . . . you're back early. Alex told me seven or later.'

'Yes, I asked him to. I knew if I was more than five minutes late you'd be worrying yourself silly.'

For no reason at all tears filled her eyes. Gray saw them.

In three strides he was at her side, filling the air around her with the clean, salty scent of the sea and cold, fresh air. She could smell the wind and the rain on his clothes and she wanted to reach out and touch him.

'There's nothing to cry about.'

He reached for her and would have wrapped her in his arms if she hadn't stepped away. Stephanie saw him frown and gnawed miserably at her bottom lip.

'You're all wet,' she complained huskily. 'There's plenty of hot water, and I've made a chilli.'

She was gabbling idiotically, she knew, but she couldn't stop herself. It was her only defence against flinging herself into his arms and confessing to him just how she felt.

Before, she had longed to experience love, to feel what other women felt, but now she wished wholeheartedly that she could return to her earlier companionable friendship with Gray. Loving him and knowing that he could never love her put a strain on her nervous system she wasn't sure it was able to bear.

CHAPTER SIX

AFTER supper, Gray rang Alex and spent some time on the telephone telling him how pleased he had been by the yacht's performance.

Supper had been a quiet meal. Gray had eaten his chilli hungrily, with the appetite of a man who had been out in the open air all day, but Stephanie had only been able to nibble at hers.

Her appetite seemed to have deserted her completely. She was tired as well. Not the healthy tiredness that came from enjoyable physical activity, but the draining, exhausting lassitude that followed intense emotional trauma.

One of her favourite hobbies was tapestry work. She used her own designs, which appealed to the artistic side of her nature, while the practical work of stitching the designs was very soothing.

A London friend had commissioned from her a set of six chair-seats for her rambling Cotswold cottage, and she was half-way through the work. Each seat-cover depicted a scene that had some relevance in her friend's life, and while Gray was on the telephone she went upstairs to collect her work. It took her longer than usual to become engrossed in what she was doing, at least half of her concentration unashamedly focused on Gray's conversation.

When he eventually hung up he was smiling

contentedly as he walked over to join her.

'You're pleased with your progress so far then?' she asked him as he sat down opposite her and picked up a book from the coffee table.

'Yes, very.'

Her heart sank. Only now was she prepared to admit to herself that she had hoped that somehow the yacht would not pass muster and he would change his mind about the Fastnet.

The silence wrapped round them as Stephanie worked on her tapestry, and Gray read his book. It should have been a companionable silence, but it wasn't.

Stephanie was acutely conscious of every movement he made; every time he turned a page she looked up; every time the fire crackled and spat she used it as an excuse to study him.

At last she couldn't stand it any longer. Putting aside her work, she got up.

'I'll go and make us some coffee.'

'No, you sit down, I'll do that. You made the supper, it's my turn now,' Gray told her easily, putting down his book and pushing her gently back into her chair.

The moment she felt his fingertips touch her arm, she flinched. She couldn't help it. The shock of him touching her, when she had yearned so much for some contact between them, had her cowering back in her chair petrified that she might betray herself in some way and that he would see how she felt about him.

Immediately, his expression changed, his smile turning to grim surveillance of her tense features. His hands locked round her upper arms, causing her to tense even more.

'What's the *matter* with you?' he demanded bitterly. 'I'm not going to hurt you, Steph.'

But he already was, and although he didn't know it, his words were an exact echo of the ones Paul had used to her so often after he had lost his temper with her and was trying to coax her round.

Immediately, it was as though she were back in the past, and it was Paul who was holding her so tightly, Paul who was looking down at her. Paul . . .

She gave a small moan of panic, and cried out hoarsely, 'No, no, please don't hurt me . . .'

Immediately his hands dropped away, his face registering his shock. 'Hurt you? For God's sake, Steph, I *wouldn't* hurt you.'

He sounded so tortured that her fear dropped away, leaving in its place a need to comfort and reassure him.

'No . . . not you . . . I . . . for a moment, I thought you were Paul.' The husky words seemed to hang on the air while they stared at one another. It seemed to Stephanie that they were seeing each other properly for the first time.

'*Paul* used to hurt you?' Gray demanded incredulously.

Too late, Stephanie realised the trap she had set for herself. She moistened her lips with the tip of her tongue, her throat dry with nervousness.

'Stephanie?'

'No . . . no . . . I . . .'

Her denial was so obviously a lie that she didn't blame Gray for the hard look that tautened his face.

'You're lying to me,' he gritted. 'I want the truth, and I intend to have it—no matter how long it takes. For ten years you've been acting like a tragedy queen, who's lost everything that made life worth living, and now you tell me . . .' He shook his head and she caught the bleak bafflement in his eyes before he lowered his gaze.

'I always knew that Paul had a wild streak—he could be violent as a child, but I never imagined . . . He did hurt you, didn't he?' he demanded thickly. 'And yet despite that you loved him. You all but fell apart when he was drowned.'

'No . . . no, I didn't love him,' Stephanie heard herself whispering, her own shock as great as Gray's, as his eyes mirrored the stunned expression in hers.

'I fell apart because of my guilt. Can't you understand, Gray? He had already told me how much he hated being married to me. He wanted to be free.' She moistened her lips again, not seeing the man standing in front of her, her thoughts back in the past. 'When he got angry . . . his tempers . . .' She shook her head in despair. 'I thought he might have deliberately let himself drown to escape from me.'

She heard Gray make a bitter, derisive sound in his throat and her eyes lifted to his in tragic entreaty.

'Not Paul,' he told her roughly. 'He loved life and himself far too much for that. Don't blame yourself for his accident, Stephanie, you mustn't do that. I know he had a bad temper, and probably said . . . unkind things, but he did love you.'

'No.' She marvelled that she could say it so calmly, 'No, Gray, he *didn't* love me,' she repeated quietly. 'He wanted me, and the only way he could have me was through marriage. I was so naïve, I didn't really understand. I thought he did love me, but he soon grew tired of my inexperience, of my——' She flushed deeply and forced herself to look directly at him. '—my lack of sexuality.'

She could feel the tension surrounding them and realised that it wasn't coming from her, but from Gray. He was looking at her as though he was on the point of erupting into blazing anger, and for a second she automatically flinched.

He reached out and touched her arm, keeping his eyes on her face. 'I promise you you have nothing to fear from me, Stephanie. Do you believe that?'

His voice was deep, and reassuring; she felt as though she could drown in the intensity of his eyes. A flood of relief and warmth swelled up inside her, and she smiled shakily at him.

'Paul used to say that I wasn't really a woman, that sexually I was still a child. I . . . I bored him. I . . . I didn't like it when we made love. He had someone else, I think, in Southampton. He used to go there a lot.'

Suddenly she wanted to tell him everything; she wanted to unburden herself of the secrets she had kept for so long. But most of all she wanted to look into his face and see there the knowledge that he refuted Paul's accusations; that in Gray's eyes, she *was* a woman . . . that she *was* desirable.

That knowledge brought her to an abrupt halt, hot colour flooding her skin, until it burned with painful intensity. Immediately, her lashes dropped, concealing her expression from him, in case he read what she was thinking. What was happening to her? What could she possibly gain from manoeuvring Gray into telling her she was a desirable woman?

If he had desired her she would have known it before now; he would have betrayed it to her without the need for any words.

A feeling of desolation swept over her, making her droop slightly in unconscious defeat.

'And despite all that you went on loving him . . . mourning him.'

She couldn't look at Gray. It was enough to hear the condemnation in his voice.

She shook her head, her voice husky and unsteady.

'No . . . I realised very quickly that what I loved was the idea of being in love. I had been playing at being an adult. Once Paul realised how . . . how disappointing I was in bed he soon destroyed all my illusions. He told me he had only married me because it was the only way he could get me into bed.' She drew a shaky breath. 'I think we'd been married less than a month when I realised what I'd done.'

She heard Gray swear, but she couldn't look at him. She felt too ashamed. This was his cousin she was talking about. He must hate her for saying these things about Paul.

'You *knew* that, but you stayed with him?' His fingers dug into her arms as he grabbed hold of her and swung her round to the light. 'Why . . . why, Stephanie? Did your parents know what he was doing to you?'

She shook her head, her throat choked with tears. 'I couldn't tell them. Don't you *see*, Gray?' she cried desperately, reading the grim lack of comprehension in the hard line of his mouth. 'It was *my* fault . . . *mine* . . . If I'd been better in bed . . . more responsive . . . less frigid.' She shuddered as she dragged out the word.

Instantly Gray released her, turning his back towards her, and she sensed that he did not want her to see his expression.

Her whole body went rigid. It was just as she had thought. He *was* angry with her, he was blaming her for Paul's death.

'*Why* haven't you ever told me any of this before? *Why* did you let me think you loved him . . . that you mourned him?'

He delivered the questions in rapid succession, in an even, careful tone, as though he was frightened of doing something violent.

Her throat went dry. 'I . . .'

Suddenly he spun round, catching her off guard as he grabbed hold of her. His eyes were blazing with emotion, his muscles straining under the control he was exercising over his body.

His anger swamped her fear and sparked off an answering response within her, freeing her from the thrall of her guilt.

Firelight illuminated both their faces as they stood opposite one another—like adversaries, Stephanie thought achingly.

'Because I *couldn't* . . . I couldn't tell anyone.' She saw his eyes harden, and continued bitterly, 'You can't imagine what it was like. Knowing that I was a failure as a woman . . . knowing that my lack of response frustrated Paul so much that it made him violent. And people wonder why there have been no other men in my life,' she added wildly. 'Well, now you know . . .'

'Because you're frightened that another man would hurt you—use violence against you?'

She shook her head despairingly. Had what she just said made so little impact on him!

'No, not that. Paul only hit me because I failed him as a woman. I told you, Gray, there's something wrong with me. I . . .' She avoided looking at him and swallowed thickly. 'I don't like sex.'

There was a long, tense silence that sawed at her fragile nerves, and eventually she risked looking at him. He was staring into the fire, his face averted from hers.

When at last he spoke, his words caused a shock that thundered through her.

'Have you ever thought that Paul might have been the one at fault? That he might have been responsible for your inability to respond to him? Have you ever tried to find out if any other man affects you in the same way? Have you never even *tried* to love someone else, Stephanie?'

The words hit her like blows. She opened her mouth to deny them and then closed it again, her eyes widening as she took in their full, shocking impact.

Of course she loved someone else. She loved *him*, but how could she tell him that? Gray had enough problems of his own without taking on the burden of hers, and she knew him well enough to know that he would try to do so.

'I . . .' She shook her head. 'I . . . no . . .'

A strange expression crossed his face as she voiced

the lie; one she found it impossible to read.

'Paul couldn't have been the one at fault,' she went on quietly. 'I . . . I know there were other girls, both before and after we were married.'

'I'm sure there were,' Gray conceded grimly. 'But knowing my hot-headed, selfish cousin, if he gave them any more pleasure than he gave you I should be extremely surprised.'

'You're . . . you're not angry with me, then?'

She had to ask the question, had to know if he still accepted her.

'Angry?' He frowned and looked at her as though the meaning of the words was unfamiliar to him.

'Paul was your cousin,' she elucidated. 'You . . . I . . .'

'For God's sake!' Suddenly he seemed furious. 'And because of that, you expect me to condone what he did to you? I thought you knew me better than that, Stephanie,' he said bitterly. 'I am angry, yes, but not with you. Paul always was a selfish little b . . .' He broke off, quite obviously fighting for control. 'It's just as well for his sake that he isn't alive. Because if he was . . . I'm not a violent man, but when I think of what he's done to you . . .'

He swore briefly, shocking her, his face contorted with rage and pain.

Slowly, like dawn creeping in on a winter morning, gladness was replacing the fear in her heart. Gray *hadn't* rejected her! He still cared about her. He was still her friend. She started to tremble, slow tears gathering in her eyes and rolling down her face.

She heard Gray make a muffled sound deep in his

throat and then she was in his arms, her face pressed against his neck.

'What is it? What did I say?'

'Nothing. I'm just so happy that you're still my friend.'

She felt his whole body tense as he held her away from him. 'Your *friend*?'

There was an odd note in his voice, a combination of acceptance and almost bitterness. 'Does my friendship mean that much to you then, Stephanie?'

'Everything,' she assured him truthfully. 'Much, much more than I can ever put into words.'

It was only later that she realised she might as well have been making a declaration of love, but, at the moment the words were uttered, all she was conscious of was the tenderness of Gray's smile and the warmth in his eyes as they stood together in front of the fire.

'How does all this fit in with your phobia about the sea?' he asked her some minutes later.

His question stunned her. She had opened her heart to him and told him so much, but there were still some things she could not bring herself to voice. Panic flared briefly in her eyes, and she shook her head.

'I . . . I don't know.'

She suspected he guessed that she was lying, but he didn't press her. It was only later when they were both on their way to bed that he referred to their conversation again. She was walking towards the door when he stopped her, saying softly, 'You know, Steph, there's a school of thought that says there are no frigid women, only inept men. Next time you get an attack of guilt over Paul, I should try thinking about that if I were you.'

She smiled shakily at him from the doorway. She had reached the door, but his words stopped her. Before she could stop herself she heard herself saying huskily, 'It's just as well you're in love with Carla, Gray, otherwise I might ...' Appalled by her own stupidity, she broke off in mid-sentence.

'Might what? Want me to prove that statement with actions and not words?'

Hot colour spread betrayingly over her skin at his quick grasp of her thoughts.

'Would you like me as your lover, Steph?'

The words seemed to hang on the air, tormenting her. What would he say if she told him? She swallowed hard, and wondered if he knew how weak and shaky she felt. It was her own fault; she should never have uttered what had, after all, been an openly provocative remark.

'I ... I ...' She was looking everywhere but at him, but even so she was still aware of him coming towards her.

'We're just friends, Gray. You love Carla!' she managed to blurt out just before he reached her, instantly turning on her heel and almost running upstairs.

In her room she sank down on to the bed, her hands cupping her hot face. Dear God, what had come over her? She had practically begged Gray to make love to her. Had she no pride? No self-respect?

She was deeply asleep when Gray's hand on her shoulder shook her awake. It was just barely light and she stared groggily up at him. He was dressed in jeans and a fine cotton shirt. Alarm spread through her as she realised how early it was, a sudden spiral of fear replacing her initial embarrassment as the events of the evening came rushing back.

'What's wrong?'

'I need you down at the yard.'

He looked so grim that she didn't even think of asking what for, but simply dived out of bed, showering and dressing quickly, the moment he left her room.

In the kitchen he had coffee and toast ready for her, barely giving her time to eat and drink before bustling her outside. No one else was about; it was too early. The tide was just on the turn, and the sea lay still and calm under the lightening sky. During the night the storm had died, and already the sky was flushed with the promise of a fine day.

Gray was walking so fast it was hard work keeping up with him; she was too breathless to question him when they reached the yard, and instead of heading for the office he swung off in the direction of the deep-water moorings.

The yacht he was using for the Fastnet lay at anchor. Stephanie caught her breath as she glimpsed the beautiful craft. Fear mingled with admiration for her sleek lines.

Gray was walking on to the wooden pier, expecting her to follow him. She hesitated momentarily and then went after him. He stopped alongside the yacht and turned to wait for her. What was so important that he had rushed her down here almost before it was light?

She saw that he was frowning and felt a familiar tug of anxiety. 'Gray, what's wrong?' she demanded as she caught up with him.

'That's what I'm just about to find out.'

She was taken off guard when he bent down and picked her up in his arms. When she realised he was carrying her on board the yacht she cried out in protest, struggling to break free, but his grip on her body only tightened.

Like all racing yachts, its cabin was strictly functional and full of equipment. A life-jacket lay on one of the two bunks and as he put her down, Gray said, shockingly, 'I think that should be your size, put it on.'

And then, before she could object, he turned his back on her, leaving her to hammer helplessly on the closed door as he stepped outside and locked it against her.

Panic and anger kept her hammering on the door long after she realised that he wasn't going to let her out. She heard the engine start, and felt the movement of the yacht as it left its mooring.

Gray was taking her out to sea! Sheer surprise held her motionless as she realised what was happening. He must have planned to do this . . . getting her up when it was too early for anyone else to see them . . . providing her with a life-jacket. And then she remembered his cryptic words as he carried her on board. He was doing this because he thought it would reveal why she was so terrified of sailing.

With that came the realisation that he was not going to allow her to go ashore until he decided that she could. There was no point in her hammering on the door any longer. She had already bruised her knuckles and broken the skin.

Full of self-pity and misery, she sank down on to the hard bunk, automatically pulling on the life-jacket. Old habits died hard, and her father had taught her to be cautious and safety-conscious.

The jacket wasn't a new one. It smelled elusively of perfume, a perfume she had smelled before, Carla's perfume, she recognised, with a renewed spurt of rage.

Had Gray and Carla made love here on the yacht? She looked round at the cramped quarters and grimaced to herself. Hardly. It was amazing what fantasies the jealous mind could conjure up, and yet she knew that if Gray came to her now and said he loved her, she wouldn't care what their surroundings were.

But that was the difference between herself and Carla. She loved Gray, and she was convinced that the other woman did not.

They were well out into the Channel before Gray put the yacht on automatic and came down and unlocked the door. They stared at one another in silence.

'I thought you were my friend,' Stephanie said almost childishly at last.

His face grim, Gray replied, 'I am. Why else would I be doing this? There's something you're not telling me, Stephanie. Something that's festering inside you like poison.'

'And you think kidnapping me and bringing me on your yacht will release it, is that it?' she demanded angrily.

'You used to love sailing,' Gray responded obliquely.

'I remember that as a teenager you used to have such an intense love of life. Paul destroyed that.'

'And you think by bringing me out here you can restore it?'

'I don't know,' he said quietly. 'You tell me, can I?'

She didn't answer him. How could she? How could she tell him that her morbid fear of the sea was a two-pronged thing. She didn't just have Paul's death to contend with, she had her own far-too-vivid memories of icy sea water closing over her head, of numb fingers slowly loosing their grip on a slippery surface; of a man's face contorted into a mask of bitter determination as he watched her slowly lose her grip on life.

'Why don't you come up on deck and help me sail this lady?'

She didn't want to, but to stay down here alone with her memories and fears would be even worse. Numbly she followed him, hating him almost as much as she loved him.

She had never been on such a sophisticatedly equipped craft and she froze to an abrupt halt when Gray called out sharply to her, wondering what on earth she had done wrong.

'Safety lines,' he told her when she looked at him. 'Come over here and I'll fix it on for you.'

A safety line. She stared at the nylon rope and then back at Gray, feeling as though an enormous weight had suddenly been lifted from her shoulders.

With a safety line she couldn't slide overboard and be drowned. She would be safe! Trembling with relief, she let Gray clip on the sturdy harness, immediately awash with a feeling of gratitude.

'Feeling better now?' Gray asked her when he was sure the harness was secure.

'Yes . . . Yes.' She smiled shakily at him. 'I feel much better.' Her fear of the water receded and she lifted her face into the breeze, breathing in lungfuls of the clean, salty air.

Suddenly she felt exhilaratingly alive. More alive than she had felt in years. She wanted to laugh and cry at the same time. She felt free, she realised. Free of Paul, free of the past, and most of all, free of fear.

CHAPTER SEVEN

THE HOURS that followed had an almost magical quality about them. It was as though by some special power Gray had transported her back to the past, to a time before she had experienced reality and pain.

He was an expert sailor, taking no unnecessary risks even in such placid seas as they had today. Her fear gone, Stephanie was free to enjoy again something that had always given her special pleasure.

At lunchtime Gray dropped anchor and hauled out a watertight picnic box.

'You planned all this deliberately, didn't you?' Stephanie accused, watching him unpack foil-wrapped chicken, and garlic-flavoured bread to put in the small oven. There was fruit, cheese and fresh salad, too, and her mouth watered, her appetite sharpened by the sea air.

'Yes,' Gray admitted without hesitation. 'After what you told me about Paul it struck me that your fear of the sea might not have sprung quite so much from his death as from a desire to punish yourself for it.' He held up a hand to stop her when she would have interrupted him.

'I know it's the easiest thing in the world to play amateur psychiatrist, but hear me out, Steph. You loved sailing. When Paul was drowned, ending the fiasco that your marriage had become, it was like a prison door opening for you, but like anyone else in the same circumstances you felt guilty—more so perhaps because

Paul had already taught you to feel guilty—to shoulder the blame for the problems in your relationship. And because you felt guilty you had to punish yourself, just as Paul used to punish you, so you took away from yourself one of the things you enjoyed the most . . .'

He watched as she plucked tensely at the wool of the blanket he had put down on the hard bunk. She wasn't looking at him, and he wished desperately that she would so that he could see her reaction. Was she strong enough to take what he had just thrown at her? Or . . . or was the damage Paul had done to her so severe that . . .?

He got up abruptly, unable to endure thinking about his cousin. It was just as well he was dead. When he thought of what Paul had done to Stephanie, of how he had destroyed her as a woman and left her with a legacy of pain and fear . . .

'Stephanie, look at me. I don't want to hurt you—in any way.' The raw urgency in his voice made her lift her head. His eyes were brilliant with compassion and concern, and she felt the shock of what he had said to her recede, leaving in its place a warmth that seemed to spread throughout her body.

Gray cared. Perhaps he didn't love her in the way she loved him, but he still cared enough to want to break down the barriers imprisoning her. Enough to believe what she had told him without question. Perhaps enough to . . .

To what? Free her from her repressions by making love to her?

The thought whispered seductively through her mind, almost paralysing her with shock. She couldn't speak or move. *Gray* make love to her? She shivered,

unaware that his eyes darkened with strain and fear for
her.

How long had the desire for Gray to make love to her
lain dormant in her subconscious? She shivered again,
suddenly and quite illogically remembering the spring
before Paul had started to pursue her in earnest.

She and her father had been sailing. Gray had been
there when they came back. He had helped her off her
father's small craft, lifting her bodily out of the boat.
The memory of how he had held her—the sun on her
back, the smell of salt and fresh air, the flurry of
excitement beating through her veins—came back to
her in startling detail.

That had been the moment she first became aware of
Gray as a man and herself as a woman. She had haunted
the yard for days after that, but Paul had been there and
not Gray. And then Paul had started pursuing her and
. . . and she had forgotten until now that all those years
ago she had looked at Gray and wanted him.

'Stephanie, what's wrong?'

She blinked and was back in the present, suddenly
aware of the rough urgency in Gray's voice. Her eyes
focused on his face, surprised to see how strained he
looked.

The smile she gave him was brief, her eyes still
clouded with memories.

Paul, he thought savagely, hating his dead cousin.
She had been thinking about Paul.

After that the day seemed to change; the sparkle
dying out of it. It seemed to Stephanie that Gray was
suddenly preoccupied and distant, and she wondered if
he was wishing that Carla was with him.

Had she been, they wouldn't have been sitting primly

opposite one another in the rugged intimacy of the cabin. She glanced at the narrow bunks, her face suddenly burning with colour as she realised that she was mentally visualising Gray making love on them. But it wasn't Carla's body she visualised entwined with his. It was her own ...

Where had it come from, this sudden surge of hunger after so many long years of cold uninterest in everything sexual? How had she gained this instinctive knowledge that as a lover Gray would be both demanding and tender? How was it that her very skin seemed to know already what it would be like to experience his touch? It seemed impossible that she, who had known nothing but pain and degradation through the physical side of her marriage, suddenly knew exactly how she could feel in Gray's embrace.

But that knowledge wasn't enough. She wanted the reality of Gray's lovemaking, she wanted ... She wanted the impossible, she told herself angrily as she cleared up after their alfresco lunch.

Gray was on deck, and she deliberately delayed before going up to join him.

The wind picked up as they headed back, and by mutual consent they concentrated on sailing the sleek yacht.

It was dusk when Gray finally brought her alongside the jetty. The yard was empty, and suddenly, as she unclipped her safety harness, Stephanie realised how utterly exhausted she was.

Perhaps it was that exhaustion that made her clumsy, or perhaps it was another and higher authority that directed her movements.

As she went to follow Gray on to the jetty, a wave

caught the yacht and she lost her balance and fell into the water.

The moment she felt its cold émbrace she panicked, forgetting that she could swim, and remembering only that this natural harbour was deep. She heard a splash and then felt an arm tighten round her, and immediately her panic intensified.

She screamed out in fear, gulping in salt water as she fought against that constraining arm. She had to hold on to the boat. She mustn't let go . . . if she did . . . if she did, Paul would let her drown . . .

She screamed again, fighting against the swift, shocking curtain of darkness swooping down on her even as she knew she could not avoid its deathly embrace.

She was lying on the ground. She could feel its hardness underneath her. She was desperately cold and her chest hurt. She shivered and tried to sit up, and was immediately overwhelmed by nausea.

As her stomach rebelled against its intake of salt water she closed her eyes and retched desperately.

Someone was holding her head, speaking to her, but she felt too desperately unwell to respond. As the nausea faded she opened her eyes and saw Gray crouching at her side, watching her.

'All right now . . .' she managed to whisper. 'What happened . . .?'

'You missed the jetty and fell in.'

He was frowning, and soaking wet, she realised, and then memory flooded back, and she remembered for herself what had happened.

'Do you feel well enough to make it to the cottage?'

She nodded her head and struggled to get up, but Gray wouldn't let her, bending to lift her in his arms.

Through the wetness of their clothes she could feel the warmth of his skin, and instinctively she tried to get closer to it. She could feel the hurried thud of his heart as he carried her down the road. Weakly she suppressed a hysterical giggle. If anyone were to see them now . . .

But the road was deserted, and they reached the cottage without incident. Once inside, Gray paused briefly in the hall, without putting her down.

'I'm going to take you upstairs and put you in a hot bath, then I'm going to come down and ring for Doctor Fellows . . .'

Immediately Stephanie felt panic shudder through her. She remembered that Doctor Fellows had seen her after Paul's death. He had prescribed tranquillisers for her, but she had never taken them. She didn't want to see him now.

'No . . . No doctor,' she managed to croak, her throat sore from the salt and sickness. 'I'm all right, Gray. Promise me, no doctor.'

Her panic showed in her eyes and he frowned. She seemed to be all right. It had given him a shock when she slipped and fell overboard, but that had been nothing to the shock he had received when she had fought against him, calling out Paul's name with terror. Had she thought he was Paul come from a watery grave to claim her? She seemed calm and lucid enough now.

'We'll see how you feel after a hot bath,' he temporised, and she was too shaky and exhausted to argue any further.

Too exhausted, in fact, to raise anything more than a token protest when Gray started to fill the bath and then

sat down with her on his lap, undressing her as though
she was a helpless child.

There was nothing remotely sexual in his touch, and
why should there be? she reflected ruefully, catching a
momentary glimpse of herself through the steam
obliterating the bathroom mirror.

She hardly represented the epitome of female
desirability. Her skin was turning blue and covered in
goose-bumps. Her hair was hanging in soaking rats'
tails, and her dunking in the sea had made her mascara
run in dark streaks over her pale face in a way that
made her look like an apology for a circus clown. All in
all, hardly a tempting sight!

She sat, completely passive, as Gray stripped off her
outer clothes, flinching only briefly when his hand
accidentally brushed against the side of her breast. She
saw his mouth tighten and wondered what he was
thinking. Probably that she was a poor apology for a
woman ... and nothing like Carla.

He twisted sideways to turn off the taps and test the
water, frowning slightly as he asked curtly, 'Can you
manage the rest yourself?'

Since all she had on was her briefs and bra, she
nodded her head. He was still wearing his own wet
clothes, and must be anxious to get under the healing
warmth of the shower himself. She scrambled awkwardly off his lap and reached behind her for the catch
of her bra, but her arms ached from the unaccustomed
exercise, and her fingers were still numb.

After she had fumbled the fastening twice, Gray
made an explosive sound of impatience deep in his
throat and turned her round, swiftly dispensing with the
recalcitrant fastening. Feeling as chastened as an

awkward child, Stephanie stepped out of her briefs and turned to get into the bath.

Gray was standing by the door watching her, a tense, unreadable expression on his face.

All at once she was acutely conscious of her deficiencies and limitations.

Tears of exhaustion and unhappiness burned her eyes, and she wondered if she actually had the strength to get into the warm water.

Any other woman worthy of the name could have managed events better than this. Here she was, alone in a potentially provocative situation with the man she loved, and all she could do was to shiver and move clumsily about as though she had suddenly developed two left feet.

Almost as though concurring with her own opinion of herself, Gray moved impatiently towards her, picking her up bodily, his hands on her waist.

'I don't know if it was a good idea letting you persuade me not to call the doctor. I'm going for a shower, and don't you dare to try and get out of that bath until I come back.'

As he lowered her into the water she had an insane urge to cling to him and beg him not to leave her. She had been through too much in too short a time, and now she was paying for it.

The water lapped blissfully at her chilled skin, and she made a small murmur of pleasure, her movements unconsciously sensual as she wriggled under the warmth.

Gray stood watching her for a moment, his mouth grimly compressed, and she wondered again what he was thinking—probably regretting ever asking her to come down to the estuary in the first place. She had been more of a hindrance than a help, she felt sure.

He opened the door and said brusquely, 'Now remember, don't you dare move until I come back.'

The thick, rough quality of his voice made her look curiously at him. His face was slightly flushed, his eyes very dark. He seemed to be unable to tear his attention away from her breasts. Her throat suddenly went dry. Could he . . . did he . . .? But then abruptly he looked away, and she knew that the intense desire she thought she had read in the tense line of his body had been nothing more than a product of her own fevered imagination.

And then the door opened and he was gone. Voluptuously she gave herself up to the soothing heat of the water as it turned her skin from blue to warm pink. A great wave of tiredness washed over her but she fought it back, reaching for the shampoo, and vigorously soaping her hair.

An impulse she wasn't sure she wanted to investigate made her add scented bath oil to the water when she topped it up, the heat releasing a delicious smell of roses.

She was out of the bath and wrapped in a huge, warm towel when Gray came back.

He frowned when he saw that she had disobeyed his instructions. 'I thought I told you to stay put?'

Stephanie smiled tremulously at him. He was barefoot, wearing a towelling robe that exposed the crisp, damp hair curling on his chest.

'I'm all right now, Gray, I promise you. I'm hungry as well,' she told him, watching the frown disappear and relief take its place.

In actual fact she was feeling exhausted, but the

memory of those moments when she had actually thought she was back with Paul and he was trying to drown her were still too strong and she didn't want to be alone with them.

'All right. You get dressed. I'll go down and light the fire and make us both something to eat.'

She was too exhausted to make much of an effort, simply pulling on clean briefs, and an all-in-one peach jumpsuit with buttons down the front and an elasticated waistband.

Sliding sandals on to her feet, she combed through her wet hair and left it, knowing that it would dry quickly in the heat of the fire.

As she went downstairs she could hear Gray in the kitchen. He had closed the sitting-room curtains, and flames from the burning logs illuminated the attractively furnished room.

Stephanie extinguished the main lights and switched on two lamps. Immediately the room took on an air of intimacy. She heard Gray behind her and swung round, watching his eyebrows draw together as he studied the subdued lighting queryingly.

'My eyes are a bit sore. It must have been the salt water . . . the main light's too bright.'

'It's all right, Stephanie. You don't have to make any excuses to me,' he told her roughly, putting the tray down on a small table and cutting right across her stammered explanations. 'After all, we both know you're hardly likely to have set the scene with anything intimate in mind, don't we?'

There was a barbed quality to his words, an acid backlash, almost as though he wanted to hurt her, and he had. Her nerves quivered painfully under his flint-eyed scrutiny and she wanted to cry out in protest that she couldn't help it if she wasn't Carla.

Instead she looked blindly at the supper he had prepared and said huskily, 'Is there anything to drink? Wine? Somehow tonight I don't think I'm going to find it easy to sleep.'

She saw his eyebrows go up, his voice terse as he said curtly, 'I'll go and get a bottle from the kitchen, although if you really think that you should have let me phone the doctor.'

'No, I couldn't take any more tranquillisers, Gray. They remind me too much of . . .'

'Of Paul,' he said, suddenly grabbing hold of her arm in an almost painful grip. 'What happened to you today, Stephanie? Did you think he had come back from the dead to claim you?'

She went white with shock and pain. She couldn't believe this was actually Gray speaking to her like this, with bitterness and contempt.

He released her almost immediately, swearing under his breath, and she watched him blankly as he opened the door.

She was still standing in the same spot when he returned with a bottle of wine and two glasses.

'It's red,' he told her curtly. 'I hope that's all right.'

She shrugged, not really caring, too hurt to make any comment as her mind still grappled with the shock of his verbal attack on her.

He had heated up the chilli left from the previous night and it was deliciously warming, but Stephanie was in no mood to appreciate its spicy taste. She gulped down her wine, and poured herself a second glass. She was thirsty—a legacy from her intake of salt water, no doubt.

The intimacy of the room seemed to have been replaced by a brooding silence. Gray was watching her in a way that unnerved her, although she couldn't have said why.

She saw him frown slightly and make to check her as she drained her second glass of wine. It was smooth, filling her with pleasant heat, driving away the ghosts that haunted her.

'Do you think you ought to have any more?' he asked her drily when she reached for the bottle again.

She never normally drank more than the odd glass, but now she pushed out her bottom lip as rebelliously as any child and said huskily, 'Why not—after all, I'm not going anywhere, am I?'

'You could regret it in the morning,' he warned her, but made no move to stop her from refilling her glass.

In point of fact she was already beginning to feel distinctly hazy, but she welcomed the woolly anaesthetising sensation.

Gray had finished his meal and he watched in silence as she toyed with what was left of her chilli. He had bought in a pot of coffee and he poured them both a cup. She ignored hers, drinking her wine instead.

He waited until she was half-way down it before taking it away from her. 'I think you've had enough of that, don't you?'

She wanted to protest, but the room was swaying disconcertingly around her.

She tried to stand up and sat down again almost immediately, as she felt the floor tilt beneath her feet.

'Why did you think I was Paul, Stephanie?'

Gray's quiet voice seemed to reach her from a long way away. She opened her eyes wide and tried to focus on him.

'Because it was like it was before when he tried to drown me,' she said calmly, proud of the way she managed not to slur her words. She smiled at Gray in her pride, but he wasn't smiling back. In fact, the icy look in his eyes almost dissipated her alcoholic daze.

'Paul tried to *drown* you?'

Didn't he believe her? She frowned in indignation. 'Yes, when we were out sailing. He swung round to quickly and I went overboard. I held on to the side, but he tried to prise my fingers away. I was frightened.' Suddenly her face crumpled and she shivered. 'The coastguards came, and Paul let me get back on board. He wanted to kill me, Gray. He wanted to kill me.'

She repeated the words in a whisper, her brain suddenly clearing of the wine fumes, her expression stark with remembered pain and fear.

'Oh, my God!'

She heard the words and felt their anguish, and then suddenly she was in his arms and he was cradling her trembling body, murmuring soft words of comfort against her ear. She was sobbing out her terror against the warmth of his throat, letting the heat and security of his body engulf her.

'*Why* did you never tell me this before?'

'I couldn't ... I couldn't tell anyone what our marriage was ... I wasn't even sure myself. I used to dream about it after ... after Paul was drowned ... and I sometimes thought I was making excuses for myself ... trying to give myself a reason for not loving him any more.'

'He hated me, Gray. He really hated me towards the end. He wanted to be free. We should never have got married . . .' Her voice died away and she felt a tremendous sense of release sweep through her. She yawned tiredly and stretched in Gray's arms, burrowing into his warmth, suddenly exhausted.

Her eyelashes fluttered down, her eyes closing.

'I think it's time you were in bed.'

She could feel the reverberations of his voice deep in his chest and she snuggled closer to him, giggling deliciously. 'Only if you promise to come with me.'

She felt the tension invade his body, but her own was still too affected by the aftermath of her ordeal and the wine she had drunk to be aware either of what she had said or Gray's reaction to it.

'You're going to regret this in the morning.'

She opened her eyes wide and smiled up at him, seeing her image reflected in the dense blue depths of his, as his eyes darkened and his pupils dilated as though he was held fast in the toils of some intense emotion.

He stood up with her and she curled her arms around his neck, smiling sleepily as he carried her upstairs.

Her room was warm, and when Gray pushed back the bedclothes and sat her down on her bed, she refused to let him go.

'You've got to get undressed,' he reminded her, his eyes narrowing slightly as he added sardonically, 'if you can.'

If she could? What on earth did he mean, of course she could! She'd show him.

Her fingers fumbled over the buttons of her jumpsuit, suddenly seeming ridiculously unable to obey the command of her brain. She heard Gray make a snort of ironic sound beneath his breath as he pushed her fingers away.

'Here, let me. You'll never get out of the thing, the state you're in right now. I should have known better than to let you drink three glasses of that wine. You'll have to manage your own underwear, although I don't suppose it will do you any harm to sleep in . . .' His voice was silenced abruptly as he eased down the top of her jumpsuit, and saw for himself that she was unlikely to face any problems removing her underwear, since all she was wearing was a pair of minute silky briefs.

For a moment he could only stare at the smooth perfection of her body, her skin warm and supple now; her feminine shape reminding him tantalisingly of how long it had been since he had held a woman in his arms.

He was past the age when he could enjoy sex simply for sex's sake. Unable to share his life with the woman he wanted, his conscience hadn't allowed him to give false encouragement to the ones who would have liked to take her place. He could feel the blood beating through his veins, feel the heat building up inside him. He breathed deeply, feeling the pain of his cramped lungs. He wanted her so much, and Paul and her love for him no longer came between them.

With a sudden gesture of revulsion he moved back from the bed. Sensing that he was about to leave her, Stephanie reached out and clutched his arm, her eyes pleading with him not to go.

'Don't leave me, Gray,' she begged huskily. 'Please stay with me, I need you.'

For a moment he let the words fill his senses, drinking them in, absorbing them greedily into his heart, and then reality intruded. She wanted him as a *friend*. She was more than a little tipsy, and hardly knew what she was saying.

'Stephanie, no . . . I . . .' His voice was rough with all that he dared not betray to her, and the harshness of it brought weak tears to her eyes.

Stephanie heard him swear and then say thickly, 'For God's sake, don't cry. You don't know what you're *asking* me, what you're *doing*!'

'I can't bear to be alone tonight.' She was really crying in earnest now and he felt his resolve weakening.

'You lie down. I'll be back in a minute.'

With those few words he had committed himself and he knew he could not go back on that commitment—did not want to go back on it.

Alarm thrilled through Stephanie. He was lying to her, trying to soothe her. He *was* going to leave her and he wouldn't come back. She cried out in protest and clutched desperately at him.

'No . . . no . . . you mustn't go.'

In a voice almost suffocated with anguish Gray said harshly in protest, 'Stephanie, I'm not wearing a damn thing under this robe. I *can't* stay with you like this.'

She was beyond listening to reason, driven almost insane with the fear that still haunted her, and it showed in her face and eyes. She whimpered helplessly and clung to him, pleading with him not to leave her, babbling that she was frightened that if he did Paul would come back.

One part of her brain knew that she was exaggerating and that she really wanted him to stay because she wanted him close to her, because she wanted to have this one night, even if it was all only a pretence; but she refused to heed it, and Gray, with a sudden, savage exclamation of despair, gave in.

'All right, I'll stay,' he told her grimly, reaching out to snap off the lamp and plunge the room into darkness.

He had kept his robe on, Stephanie felt the roughness of the towelling brush her arm as he slid into the bed next to her and pulled up the covers.

She felt him begin to turn away from her and instinctively snuggled closer to him, wrapping herself around him with a determination she could never have shown when she was quite sober.

Part of her registered the shock go through him as Gray felt the warmth of her body against his own, but before he could protest she begged in a tremulous whisper, 'I just want you to hold me, Gray. Please, just hold me.'

He wasn't proof against such a plea. With a groan of submission he turned round and took her in his arms, pillowing her head against his shoulder.

He could smell the clean, fresh shampoo scent of her hair and the faint rose fragrance that still clung to her skin. Beneath his fingertips her body felt like silk. He wanted to touch her so badly ... to drive out for ever her memories of Paul.

It was bliss, sheer bliss being held in Gray's arms like this, thought Stephanie, even with the thick blanketing fabric of his robe between them, preventing her from enjoying the sensual delight of feeling his flesh against her own.

Stephanie scarcely knew what had happened to her. It was as though another, different Stephanie had suddenly stepped out from behind the old, a Stephanie who knew instinctively all that it meant to be a woman; a Stephanie who ached for the touch of the man she loved, who felt no fear or inhibitions about expressing such feelings; the Stephanie she might have been had she never married Paul.

She felt positively light-headed, delirious almost; and dangerously free of all past repressions.

The wine still sang dizzily in her veins; she tugged impatiently at the lapel of Gray's robe and trembled as her fingertips encountered the male heat of his skin. She felt the silky texture of the hair on his chest and stroked her fingertips through it until the tie belt of his robe prevented her from going any further. Dreamily she dragged her nails lightly back again, excitement spiralling through her as she heard Gray's indrawn gasp of protest, and his hand clamped down over hers, trapping it against his body.

'*What* the hell do you think you're doing?'

His voice sounded thick and unsteady. Beneath her hand she could feel the wild pounding of his heart.

Her fingertip touched the hardness of his small, flat nipple and he groaned out loud, pushing her flat against the bed and leaning over her, his face contorted in an expression of savage rage.

Poised above her in the darkness, he reminded her of a pagan god. She felt small, fragile and unbelievably feminine, and all her instincts told her that despite his anger she had aroused him.

She ignored the tiny voice that reminded her that he loved Carla; she ignored the cautionary voice of warning telling her not to do anything she would regret. His fingers still manacled her wrists either side of her throat where he had pinned her to the bed as he pushed her away from him. She could see his chest rising and falling as he breathed raggedly. His body, where it was exposed by the gap in his robe, gleamed slightly as though it was damp.

'Stephanie, I can't . . .' He leaned closer to her, his anger starting to fade, and without even thinking of the consequences she lifted her head and placed her lips delicately against his nipple, enveloping it with their softness and caressing it experimentally with the moist tip of her tongue.

She heard him cry out, a thick, tortured sound that reached her ears, but not her consciousness, which was given over fully to the pleasure of touching him so intimately. When he wrenched away from her, dragging her into a sitting position and holding her at arm's length from him, she felt so acutely deprived that her body ached and trembled.

'Do you *know* what you're doing?'

As though it was someone else who said the words she heard herself replying calmly, 'Yes, I'm touching you the way I want you to touch me. Make love to me, Gray. Make love to me tonight. Let me believe tonight that I'm a desirable woman, that I'm not what Paul said.'

He should stop her. He knew that. She didn't know what she was saying . . . what she was asking. She was still in shock, still traumatised by what had happened. He tried to resist the lure of her words, to deny the surge of feeling that poured through him. He had wanted her, loved her, for ten years. But for her sake . . . She didn't want him really. She just wanted to exorcise Paul's ghost, to prove to herself that she was finally free. He closed his eyes and remembered the feel of her soft mouth against his body. A hot tide of need convulsed him.

'Gray, I know I'm not Carla . . . but don't reject me, please . . .'

Stephanie heard him groan, a low, tortured sound that tore at her own nerves and she tensed, waiting for the words that would end her secret fantasy of being with this man, being the woman she had never allowed herself to be.

Gray moved, shifting his weight so that he could take her fully in his arms. She shivered in a mixture of shock and delight as she felt his mouth moving against her skin—her forehead, her eyes, her cheek and down her jaw. She tilted her throat eagerly, quivering beneath the hungry ferocity of his kisses as his lips caressed the taut, smooth vulnerability of her skin.

Her head fell back against his arm, her body trembling with frantic pleasure as his mouth closed over the pulse thudding erratically at the base of her throat.

It was beyond her wildest dreams; as though he was as desperately hungry for her as she was for him.

Her fingers scrabbled for purchase against the thickness of the terry robe, and with a thick sound of impatience Gray shrugged his upper torso free of it.

His skin was hot, smooth like satin or velvet, she thought hectically, almost kneading it in her pleasure, tiny muted sounds of delight emerging from her throat.

Gray tilted her head, his mouth moving from her throat to her lips, biting gently and then not so gently at their softness, inflaming her until she wrapped her arms impatiently round him, dragging his head down so that he couldn't pull away.

The sensation of his mouth on hers, his tongue tasting, exploring, and finally thrusting passionately within the softness of hers, was a delight beyond anything she had known or dreamed of knowing. She clung to him, offering herself to him with reckless abandon.

His mouth released hers, his thumb rubbing softly over its swollen contours. His breath filled her ear, making her squirm in renewed pleasure.

'I want you to touch me the way you were doing before. I want to feel your mouth against me here,' he murmured huskily.

She quivered with joy that she could make him want her touch, scattering eager kisses against his skin until he moaned and dragged her head down against his chest, his whole body shuddering as she repeated the provocative caress she had given him earlier.

The tiny nub of flesh seemed to swell and harden, and as he cried out her name in a voice rough with need, she felt her own body swell and tighten almost shockingly.

'See how you make me feel when you touch me like that? And I'm going to make you feel the same way.'

His voice was thick and unfamiliar, and she shivered under the sensual rasp of it.

Paul had never particularly enjoyed touching her breasts. He had been too young and impatient to indulge in caresses, she recognised now, and then her whole mind went numb and her body arched in ecstatic pleasure as she felt Gray's lips against her breast and then her nipple as it swelled eagerly to meet the raw heat of his mouth.

The slight drag of his teeth, instead of bringing pain, brought only a fresh upsurge of pleasure. Her soft moans were almost lost beneath the harsh staccato of his breathing as he gave in to the need that had burned in him for too long, cupping both her breasts in hands that trembled slightly, pampering their swollen crests with the erotic lash of his tongue until they were so sensitised that merely to feel the warmth of his breath against her skin was enough to convulse her with the aching need to have his mouth against her body.

The euphoria created by the wine had faded, leaving her completely sober, but it was too late to go back now, Stephanie thought recklessly. At this moment in time she no longer cared that he loved Carla. He was here with her ... and in her arms, he was hers; he wanted her.

She cried out as his mouth tugged at her breast and she felt the sharp edge of his teeth.

Instantly he released her. 'I'm sorry, I didn't mean to hurt or frighten you ... I was forgetting ...'

'Paul never ...' She swallowed hard, missing the moist contact of his mouth against her skin. 'Paul never wanted to ... to make love to me like this.'

She heard Gray say something under his breath and then he said, 'I shouldn't be doing this ...'

'I want you to.' How easy it was to say. 'Neither of us is hurting anyone else by making love, Gray. I need you to make love to me to ...'

'To what? Free you from the past? Show you that you really are a desirable woman?'

'Both those.' And much much more than he would never know, she tagged on silently. 'I need the memories tonight will give me, I need something to hold on to in the dark days ahead.'

He had turned slightly away from her and she sensed that he was having second thoughts. She shivered and instantly he reached out and touched her comfortingly.

'I ... I can't promise that I won't hurt you.' His voice sounded oddly strained. 'I'll try not to ... but it's been a long time for me, too. Do you understand what I'm trying to say?'

She did, and it shocked her. What did he mean by a 'long time'? Surely he and Carla had been lovers at some point; but now was hardly the time to remind him that he loved another woman, nor to dwell on it herself.

'Paul hurt me because he liked hurting me. I was frightened of him, which made me . . .' She felt herself flush as she tried to put into words what she felt. 'I'm not frightened of *you*, Gray. You won't hurt me.'

He made a thick, choking sound in his throat and suddenly she was back in his arms, his hands shaping and moulding her, pulling her hard against him so that she could feel his arousal through the thick folds of his robe.

She moved impatiently against him and felt his chest rise and fall at his quick, indrawn breath. Her fingers encountered the knot fastening his robe and she tugged on it.

'Stephanie, no.' His voice was thick and slurred. 'No . . . not yet. I want to give you all the pleasure you never had with Paul before. I . . .'

His words made her skin prickle with sensual heat, but she still cried out protestingly, 'Gray, I want to feel *all* of you against me. *All* of you.'

She felt him shudder just before he buried his mouth against her skin, tasting the smooth tenderness of her shoulder where it joined her neck. His hand stroked her body, cupping her breasts, spanning her waist and then caressing the feminine curve of her hip before moving to cover the soft swell of her stomach and stroke tantalisingly along the edge of her briefs.

She was torn between wanting to touch him with the

freedom with which he was caressing her, and giving herself up to the pleasure he was inciting. She ached for them both to be completely free of their clothes. The only covering she wanted was the heat of his body.

His hand covered her over the silky fineness of her briefs and she moved protestingly against him, lifting her hips and nipping frantically at the smooth flesh of his shoulder. His hands lifted her, moulded her, pulling her tightly against the hardness of his body, and she sobbed out loud as she twisted against him.

This time her anxious fingers managed to untie the towelling knot and she made a soft, feminine sound of triumph deep in her throat, a feline purring noise that accurately mirrored her feelings as she pushed the robe away and yielded to her need to feel all of him against her.

Only she had forgotten she was still wearing her own briefs. But as she made to remove them with a muted sound of self-disgust, Gray stopped her. 'No . . . let me.'

She quivered expectantly, eager to be held against him, knowing from the arousal of his body that he wanted her as much as she wanted him, but instead, Gray pushed her flat against the bed and arched over her as he eased the silky barrier away.

Impatiently she waited for him to join her, dreading reading in his hesitation that he had changed his mind; that he had remembered that she wasn't Carla.

Dreading feeling him move away from her, she cried out huskily, 'Gray, please I . . .'

'Paul starved you,' he said softly, as though he hadn't heard her. 'He deprived you of love and pleasure. I can't make that up to you, but tonight I want to give you a banquet, the memory of which will stay with you for ever.'

He cupped her heel in the warmth of his palm as he spoke, rubbing it caressingly. Her skin started to tingle as his fingers stroked up her calf and his mouth explored the sensitive hollow behind her knee. His teeth nibbled gently at her inner thigh and she quivered dizzily, her finger-nails digging protestingly into his arm.

'No . . . no, you mustn't,' she cried out weakly, but he ignored her, stroking fingers that were supposed to soothe, but in reality only inflamed, over the taut swell of her stomach.

His hand cupped her and his mouth closed over the swollen areola of her breast, sucking erotically. Her body arched beneath the darts of fire engulfing her, her skin damp with a soft dew of sweat. His fingers stroked and aroused, and she felt herself moving helplessly against them, pierced with such a sweet pleasure that she couldn't help crying out against him.

She could hear Gray breathing, a harsh, laboured sound that betrayed his own arousal. His mouth left her breast and moved hotly over her skin, caressing her stomach, leaving it quivering with nerves, then moving on to her inner thigh.

His hands held her prisoner, as helpless in their grip as she was in the grip of the need aching inside her. She felt his mouth on her body, caressing it with deliberate intimacy and, although she cried out in shock, she couldn't stop herself from responding to its insistent demand.

Ripples of sensation gathered and bunched tightly inside her. Her throat was rigid with tension, her body bathed in moist heat. She had never, ever experienced anything like this with Paul.

As her body began to explode in tiny shock waves of passion she felt Gray move and then lift her, fitting her to the taut hardness of his own.

She absorbed the shock of his first controlled thrust with a sense of awed disbelief, feeling her body soften and expand to welcome the powerful strength of him.

The pain she had known with Paul might never have existed. With each thrust of his body Gray was bringing her to fresh heights of pleasure; fresh knowledge about herself.

She arched eagerly against him, wrapping her arms and legs round him, crying out in spontaneous delight until he took the sound into his mouth, kissing her with an almost feverish intensity that was rapidly mirrored by the uncontrollable surge and demand of his body.

She felt as she had never felt in her life before— powerful, almost mysterious, and yet humble at the same time in the knowledge that she was the one who had aroused him to this pitch; that hers was the body in which he sought release. And then, as the circles of pleasure started to tighten again, she stopped thinking and gave herself over entirely to feeling.

She cried out his name as the world exploded around her, almost delirious with pleasure as she felt his body achieve fulfilment within her own.

It took her a long time to float back down to reality and when she eventually did, she discovered that Gray was fast asleep. She laughed weakly, tears of joy running out of her eyes. Paul had been wrong. She hadn't been frigid. Her heart overflowed with gratitude and love towards the man who had shown her the truth. She wanted to tell him how she felt, but she hesitated to disturb his sleep.

Besides, she was tired herself. She closed her eyes and let her tired body relax. They could talk in the morning.

CHAPTER EIGHT

ONLY in the morning, when Stephanie woke up Gray had gone, and to judge from the coldness on his side of the bed he had been up for quite some time.

And in the cold light of day things seemed rather different. Stephanie's skin burned hotly as she remembered her abandoned response to him. Her response to *him*? She groaned out loud as she remembered begging him to make love to her.

How could she face him? What on earth could she *say*? *How* could she have risked prejudicing their friendship?

She dressed reluctantly and went downstairs.

The scent of freshly brewed coffee led her to the kitchen. Gray was sitting down at the table reading his paper. He looked up as she walked in, his expression cloaked and distant.

Stephanie bit her lip, gnawing at it. There was no easy or polite way round this.

'Do you still want me to stay after . . . after last night?' she asked baldly.

For a moment she thought he wasn't going to reply and then, without looking at her, he said coolly, 'Why not? We both know it wasn't me you were making love with. We both know *why* you felt the need to physically exorcise Paul's ghost. It happened, and if anything, I'm the one to blame. You had been drinking—a notorious relaxer of inhibitions as any number of unfortunate young women will testify. I suggest we both put the entire incident behind us.'

To say that she was shocked was putting it mildly. Whatever she had expected, it certainly hadn't been Gray's cool dismissal of the entire incident as though it was so unimportant as to be barely worthy of comment.

Was this the same man who last night had whispered so passionately to her that he wanted to give her a banquet of passion? Was this the same man who had kissed and stroked every inch of her body, who had . . . Her skin burned, and she shuddered tensely. Gray was right. If they were to continue as friends, she would have to pretend that nothing untoward had ever happened. That was, of course, if she *could*.

'Carla's been on the phone,' Gray continued casually. 'She wanted to remind us that we're expected there for dinner tonight.'

Stephanie went icy cold. So that was why he was trying to pretend nothing had happened between them! He had spoken to Carla, and hearing her voice had no doubt reminded him that *she* was the one he loved.

'Coffee's freshly made if you want some. I'm taking the yacht out again today.' He glanced at his watch. 'In fact I'll have to be on my way in a few minutes.'

'I . . . I'll follow you down to the yard later,' Stephanie told him, fighting hard not to let her voice tremble. This was dreadful, awful . . . impossible. But she mustn't *let* it be impossible, an inner voice warned her. She must somehow find the strength to follow Gray's lead, otherwise she would end up embarrassing them both.

Without looking at him, she went to pour herself a

cup of coffee. As he watched the downbent vulnerability of her exposed neck, Gray slowly unclenched his tightly closed fist. Last night she had given herself to him so freely . . . so innocently . . . he dared not scare her away by telling her just how much it had meant to him. He had woken up this morning and ached to make love to her again, but he had let her sleep on. When she remembered what had happened between them, would she blame him? She had been suffering from both shock and too much wine on an empty stomach. After the way Paul had treated her it was not surprising that she would want to prove her own sexuality. He didn't deceive himself that she felt any particular attraction for him. She trusted him. She looked on him as a friend, or at least she had done until last night. Maybe in time she might come to feel something more. He mustn't rush her, and yet when he remembered how she had felt in his arms, he ached to pick her up and take her back to bed, and keep her there until she moaned against his skin in the way she had done last night; frantic, passionate little moans of need.

Stephanie tensed as she heard Gray's chair scrape back. He didn't even look at her as he walked to the kitchen door. She ached to go after him, to . . .

To what? she asked herself derisively. To tell him that I love him? Hadn't she already laid enough burdens on him?

The day dragged, and it didn't help that she was both physically and emotionally exhausted. The very last thing she wanted was to have to share Gray with anyone at all this evening, least of all with the woman he loved.

She couldn't even frame the words within her mind without them hurting her, but she made herself do it. There was no point in hiding from the truth. Gray loved Carla. Oh, he loved her, too . . . as a friend.

At four o'clock there was a sudden flurry of telephone calls and enquiries, and it was almost six before she was free to leave the yard.

The yacht was already tied up at the jetty, signalling that Gray was back. He must have returned while she was busy in the back office, and it hurt that he had gone straight back to the cottage without stopping off to see her.

He was on the telephone when she walked into the cottage, and he replaced the receiver as she came in. With a twist of pain in her heart Stephanie recognised the constraint between them. She wondered if he had been talking to Carla; if he felt guilty about last night because he felt he had betrayed the woman he loved.

As she was beginning to discover, no one act or incident could be taken in isolation; everything in life interlocked or reflected on everything else. She had wanted to keep her memories of last night shining and untarnished, but already she was recognising that to do so would be next to impossible.

'You look pale, are you feeling all right?' Gray frowned as he looked at her. 'You know you don't have to come tonight, if you'd rather not . . .'

She read in his eyes the message that he would rather she did not come, and instantly she was on fire with jealousy.

Her voice burned with acid as she responded angrily, 'Surely that would defeat the whole purpose of either of us going? Unless, of course, Carla has had a change of heart and is now prepared to leave Alex for you?'

'No, she won't leave him.'

Shrugging, Stephanie countered curtly, 'Then it would be better if I were there, wouldn't it? You don't want Alex getting suspicious at this stage, with the Fastnet so close.'

She thought she saw a flicker of shame darken Gray's eyes, and for a moment she longed to reach out and comfort him, but her hand fell away even as she raised it, her pale face flushing as she realised how open to misinterpretation any gesture of affection on her part might be now.

'We're due there at seven,' she said instead. 'I'd better go up and change. How formal an occasion will it be?'

'As formal as any dinner party you might attend in London,' Gray advised her coolly, almost as though they were enemies and not friends.

The dress she chose was black, underlining her mood as well as the pallor of her skin. It made a striking contrast to her rich chestnut hair, and with it she wore silk stockings and high-heeled shoes. The dress was a Jean Muir in heavy silk jersey, cut to mould and flatter her shape. She was too tired and depressed to do anything with her hair other than catch it back with tortoiseshell combs. Large, pearl costume-jewellery earrings edged with *diamanté* added a subtle touch of glitter. Blusher, eyeshadow and lip gloss warmed the too-pale translucence of her skin, and then she was ready.

Her dress had long sleeves and the evening was warm enough for her not to need a jacket.

Gray was waiting for her downstairs and her heart lurched as she studied him surreptitiously. He looked as much at ease in his dinner suit as he did in his jeans. He glanced at his watch and she caught the discreet flash of gold cuff-links at his wrists. He looked up and saw her, and his eyes seemed to darken and burn. She ached to fling herself into his arms and be held close against his body, but she forced herself to smile carelessly and take her time about joining him.

They drove to the Farlows' house in silence. For the first time that she could remember she had to suppress the nervous inclination to make small talk to cover the silence between them.

The Farlows lived in an attractive Georgian house several miles outside the village. It had its own drive, illuminated with traditionally styled lights that revealed the beginnings of a smooth sweep of immaculate lawn. Ivy covered the end wall of the house, giving it a settled, comfortable air.

Before Gray stopped the car she caught a glimpse of an attractive conservatory and was momentarily pierced with envy for Carla. She already had so much, and now Gray's love as well. She told herself she was being bitchy for guessing that Carla would be reluctant to give up such a beautiful home, but when Carla opened the door to them and welcomed them both with equal warmth and enthusiasm, Stephanie told herself that her bitchiness was well justified.

A woman who could greet her lover in the presence of her husband, so free of guilt and self-consciousness, had to have a core of heartlessness. But as she led them into their comfortable drawing-room and Alex served them with drinks, Carla was so pleasant and natural with them both that Stephanie found it impossible not to warm to her. She dared not look at Gray when Carla voluntarily produced studio portraits of their two children.

'I miss them dreadfully,' she confided to Stephanie, 'but we haven't lived here very long, and I agree with Alex that it would have been wrong to disrupt their schooling. Hopefully, now that we're settled here, next year I'll be able to find them both good day schools locally.'

The two men had drawn away and from the snatches of conversation Stephanie caught were deep in a discussion about the boat.

Something of her feelings must have shown in her expression because Carla touched her arm lightly, and said quietly, 'I know how you must feel, but try not to worry. Gray isn't the sort of man to take unnecessary risks.'

For a moment Stephanie bristled; longing to tell Carla that there was nothing she could tell her about Gray, and then the ambiguity of the other woman's statement struck her and she longed to demand to know how a man who did not take unnecessary risks had managed to fall in love with his partner's wife.

She still believed quite passionately that Gray would never have fallen in love with Carla without encouragement, and then a traitorous little voice whispered tormentingly to her, 'Why not? You did ... with him ...'

'The Fastnet is one of the most dangerous sea races there is,' she retorted to cover her own inner turmoil.

'Not so very long ago many lives were lost, and boats abandoned.'

'Yes, I know.' Carla looked at her and said quietly, 'Alex's brother was one of them. That's why Alex is so determined that this boat will be both successful and safe. Alex and David, his brother, designed and built the boat that was lost. Alex should have sailed in it, but almost at the last minute he broke his leg and couldn't go.' Her face clouded as though she was remembering great unhappiness, and against her will Stephanie felt a confused sort of compassion for her.

'I'll never forget his face when we got the news that David was lost. I promise you, Stephanie, that Gray will be safe.'

'Hey, what are you two girls talking about so seriously?' Alex interrupted them, adding with a teasing grin at Carla, 'I don't know about everyone else, but I'm starving.'

Altogether it was a very confusing evening, Stephanie decided. If she had met them without knowing of Carla's relationship with Gray, if she hadn't been aware that Carla couldn't possibly genuinely love her husband, she would have thought them an exceedingly happy couple and she would have thoroughly enjoyed their company. Both of them had a lively interest in the arts, and far from centring exclusively on sailing and the Fastnet the conversation covered a wide range of diverse subjects. Of all of them she seemed to be the only one who was ill at ease.

It was while they were drinking their coffee that Alex unknowingly dropped his bombshell.

'I've chartered the *Nemesis* again this summer, since

you enjoyed it so much last year, Carla.'

'The *Nemesis* is a ten-berth schooner moored in St Lucia that we chartered last year,' he explained to Stephanie. 'All four of us went and we fully enjoyed the experience. There's plenty of space and we'd love you both to join us this time.'

Stephanie felt her face go stiff with shock and suspicion. Was Carla behind this? Was this her way of ensuring that she had the company of both her lover and her husband?

One look at Gray's face assured Stephanie that he was as surprised by Alex's announcement as she had been herself but, to her shock, instead of instantly rejecting the offer he said quietly, 'That's very generous of you, Alex. I'd love to join you, but of course it's up to Steph.'

With all three of them focusing on her, Stephanie had little option but to swallow her ire and say huskily, 'Yes, it is generous of you. I'm sure I'll love it.'

How could Gray have acceded so easily to Alex's suggestion? she wondered miserably. He must *know* the temptation he would be facing in the close confines of the schooner. How on earth would he be able to endure being so close to Carla, knowing she was with Alex?

In his shoes . . . in his shoes, she couldn't have endured to watch him with another woman. It was tearing her apart being here tonight. Every time he looked at Carla, every time he spoke to her, she was consumed with jealousy.

Irrationally, as she listened to the three of them making plans for the projected holiday, she was filled with resentment. How on earth could either Carla or Alex believe that she and Gray were lovers, when he was practically ignoring her?

'You're very quiet.' Carla smiled at her, and once again Stephanie was struck by the friendly naturalness of the other woman's smile. Had she not seen for herself the faint hauteur and coldness in Carla's attitude towards her the first time they met, had she not known the truth about her relationship with Gray, she might almost have found herself liking the other woman, and that confused and distressed her.

'I'm afraid I'm rather tired,' she responded unevenly. 'Gray took me sailing yesterday, and I'm still suffering the after-effects of all that fresh air.'

Instantly she was aware of the covert look that Gray and Carla exchanged, and again she was filled with jealousy.

How *could* Alex not notice the intimacy of that shared glance?

'I'm afraid Stephanie isn't the only one who's tired,' Gray commented. 'Would you think us very provincial if we make an early night of it?'

Carla and Alex accompanied them to the front door and watched until they were both installed in the car.

Stephanie sat rigidly in her seat, aching with jealousy and tension. Last night Gray had made love to her, but tonight that intimacy might never have been.

She sat in stiff silence as he drove them back to the cottage, getting out of the Range Rover the moment it stopped.

She had intended to be upstairs and in her own room before Gray came in, too angry at what she saw as his weakness over Carla to want to talk to him, but her throat was dry, and she stopped for a glass of water.

He came in while she was still drinking it, and waited until she had put the glass down before taking both her hands in his and holding them gently.

'Stephanie, what is it? You've been tense and on edge all evening. If it's because of last night . . .'

Instantly she was furious both with him and with herself. 'No, it's not because of last night,' she told him tight-lipped. 'It's because of tonight. Because of the way you weakly fell in with Alex's plans. You told me that you wanted to break away from Carla, that you *knew* that you had no future with her. And yet tonight you couldn't wait to accept their invitation to join them in the Caribbean.'

She watched as his forehead furrowed.

'No . . . no, Stephanie, you've got it all wrong. Let me explain.'

'I don't *need* any explanations, or any lies, Gray. I can see for myself what's going on,' she told him bitterly. 'I offered to help you by pretending that you and I . . . that we were lovers because I thought you genuinely meant it when you said it was all over between you and Carla. I won't be used as a convenient screen behind which you can carry on your adulterous relationship.' Her voice was thick with biting scorn, but to her surprise Gray looked more angry than contrite.

'I am *not* having an affair with Carla,' he ground out furiously. 'Surely last night showed you that much?'

She felt as though her whole body was on fire. How *could* he refer to what they had shared last night in the same sentence as his affair with a married woman? Only to him, Carla wasn't a married woman; she was the woman he loved, she acknowledged miserably.

'I don't want to talk about last night,' she told him, childishly snatching her hands away and heading for the door. 'I'd like to forget that it ever happened.'

She was lying of course, but even so her voice rang with intensity and conviction. Gray couldn't see her face, or the tears filling her eyes. He had hurt her tonight and badly, and she wanted to hurt him in turn, she acknowledged unhappily as she headed for her room. Although how any comment of hers could hurt him, when he was so obviously concerned only with Carla, she really did not know.

CHAPTER NINE

FOR a week they shared the cottage together in an atmosphere of subdued hostility. Too proud and too hurt to back down from the stance she had adopted, Stephanie continued to treat Gray with coldness although inwardly she ached to go back to the days when they had been close.

Even his friendship seemed to be lost to her now, and several times she thought of suggesting she should leave, but she was frightened to do so, dreading hearing him agree.

It was hell living with him like this, but it would be even greater hell to be sent away.

The week stretched to ten days, time running out swifter than a rip tide as the date of the Fastnet approached.

Gray was gone most days now, testing and re-testing the boat. Hostility gave way to a cool state of armed neutrality. When he came home in the evening she asked him about the yacht's progress, but the old spontaneity of their relationship was gone. She knew that she was losing weight, growing increasingly tense.

As far as she knew Gray hadn't seen Carla since the evening of the dinner party, and part of her urged her to apologise and take back her hasty words, but she was still too hurt and jealous.

Added to that was her ever-increasing anxiety as the

days dribbled away and the race loomed ominously close at hand.

Several times she sensed Gray's frustration with the cool barrier she had put up against him, but every time he tried to recapture their earlier closeness she froze him off, panicked by the fear that if she let him get emotionally close to her again she would break down completely and reveal to him how she felt.

Once she would have said, if asked, that there was nothing she could not tell Gray, but now that had changed.

The weekend before the commencement of the Fastnet they were invited to an official pre-start party at a prestigious local yacht club, along with other entrants in the race.

Carla and Alex were also going, and on a reckless impulse Stephanie went into Southampton and spent far more than she had intended on a peach satin ballgown that did amazing things for her hair and skin.

On the suggestion of the sales assistant she also made an appointment to have her hair done in a profusion of vaguely eighteenth-century curls to compliment the formality of her gown.

Her impulsive decision to buy a new dress and have her hair done meant that she didn't arrive back at the cottage until later than she had planned.

Gray was already upstairs getting ready and she hurried into her own bedroom and quickly started getting changed.

To compliment the narrow, stiffened bodice of her dress, the saleswoman had recommended that she wear a lacy, boned basque underneath to ensure a smooth fit, and she had just finished struggling into this instrument of torture and securing fine white stockings to the attached suspenders when Gray knocked briefly on the door.

Conscious that time was running out, and her mind on the stamina of those women of long ago who submitted to being pushed and squeezed into real corsets, she forgot to respond.

When her bedroom door suddenly opened and Gray strode in, she didn't know which one of them was the more shocked.

Gray took one look at her supple, white, lace-clad body and immediately went completely still, while all she could think of was how ridiculously and deliberately provocative she must look clad in nothing but high-heeled sandals, stockings, briefs and an article of underwear that seemed to make her waist look far smaller than it had ever appeared before, and contra-dictorarily her breasts surely far fuller.

'I . . . I wasn't sure if you were back,' Gray said at last, averting his eyes from her.

'I'm sorry I'm so late.' Her fingers touched the tumbled mass of dark red curls that had been the cause of the delay. 'I bought a new dress for tonight, and then I had to have my hair done . . .'

She was babbling and she knew it, but she felt so ridiculously self-conscious. Gray was already dressed. The party was a formal one, with white tie specified.

'I've only got to do my face and put on my dress. I'm leaving it until last because the skirts are so full. I . . .' She was babbling again, she realised, and she checked herself, a sudden surge of warmth invading her body as she saw Gray look at her.

'With skin like yours you don't need make-up,' he told

her abruptly and she was conscious of a fresh surge of heat. It was almost as though he was actually touching her, smoothing and savouring the softness of her flesh as he had done the night they had made love.

'What time did you order the taxi for?' Somehow she had to break the heavy silence hanging over them.

'You've got just under half an hour.' He paused and looked at her again slowly before retreating and closing the door. After he had gone, Stephanie put her hands against her flushed face, her colour deepening even further as she saw her own reflection in the mirror.

Against the soft white of her basque and stockings, her skin glowed creamy warm. Her eyes seemed to have gone darker, almost slumbrous, and the way the stylist had done her hair gave her, even to her own eyes, an unexpected air of sensuality. Was *that* how Gray had seen her? Or when he had looked at her had he only seen Carla?

Impatient and angry with herself she quickly put on her make-up, applying it only slightly less dextrously than usual. Her dress came last and she stepped into it, grimacing as she battled with the mass of net underskirts. The three-quarter sleeves could be worn on or off the shoulders, and she left them down as she reached behind herself to slide up the zip, only when it got to her waist it wouldn't go any further, no matter how much she struggled.

In the shop she had commented on how close-fitting it was, but the assistant had assured her that a close fit on such a gown was essential. She, Stephanie remembered now, had had both hands free to close the fastener. Frightened of breaking it completely in her impatience, she stuffed her evening bag with what she would need for the evening and opened the door.

Hurrying downstairs was impossible with such wide, heavy skirts, but finally she made it. She found Gray in the sitting-room.

'I can't get the zip up properly,' she told him without preamble. 'It needs two hands. Can you do it for me?'

She turned her back to him as she spoke, breathing in sharply as she felt his hands on her back.

After all her struggles it seemed unfair that the zip should slide home easily and immediately under Gray's calm hands, and she let out her breath in a jerky sigh as he closed the small top fastener for her.

The dress was quite low at the back, and cut in such a way at the front that it exposed the soft upper curves of her breasts. Conscious that Gray was looking at her as she turned round, she asked huskily, 'Well, what do you think?'

'I can't decide whether you look more beautiful with it on or off,' he said slowly at last, 'but at least now I know the reason for that amazingly sexy piece of underwear you're wearing.'

He was actually teasing her, Stephanie realised, her spirits lightening as she responded lightly, 'Ah, but you weren't supposed to see that.'

'No, I don't think I should have done,' Gray agreed huskily. 'The memory of seeing you in it is likely to cause me to keep awake at nights, Stephanie.'

He looked at her broodingly, and she held her breath, wondering what he intended to say. The sharp ring of the doorbell shattered the silence and Gray frowned.

'Damn, that will be the taxi.'

The party would have been one of the most enjoyable she had ever attended had it not been for her continuing anxiety over the Fastnet race and the misery of her own incredibly foolish love for Gray.

He danced with her most of the evening, holding her as close as the full skirts of her gown would allow, and at midnight, when balloons were released from the ceiling and everyone toasted the success of the Race he swung her into his arms and kissed her with passion and something almost approaching violence, holding her against his body long after most of the other revellers had drifted apart.

The fierce passion of that kiss stayed with her on the drive home. Was it the frustration, or his need for Carla that had driven him into her arms? She would not be used as a substitute for the other woman, no matter how much she loved him, but even as she made that determined vow, she knew that if he touched her, if he kissed her, she might not be able to resist him.

Nervous tension kept her wide awake and restless on the ride home. Once inside the cottage, habit made her ask Gray if he would like a nightcap.

'Not for me,' he told her abruptly. 'I think I'll go up.'

His retreat from her, after she had half expected him to at least attempt to make love to her, brought her down to earth with shattering speed. It was no use telling herself that Gray was acting honourably in removing temptation from them both; it was no use telling herself that she would not have wanted him to make love to her while craving another woman.

As she prepared for bed, all she could think of was how he had looked at her earlier in the evening; how he had held and kissed her, and how much she ached to have him with her now.

* * *

The morning of the Fastnet dawned bright and clear. Stephanie went with Carla and Alex to see Gray off. She was a mass of nerves, so tense that even her bones seemed to ache with it.

Gray kissed her briefly before going on board, a hard, all-too-short embrace that left her aching and alone.

'Don't worry about him. He'll be fine,' Alex reassured her as they waited for the starting signal. 'You wait and see.'

They watched until Gray's boat was just a distant speck before joining the other onlookers drifting away.

Carla and Alex invited her to go back with them, but she shook her head. There was work to do at the yard; work which would keep her occupied physically if not mentally. As always when she saw Carla, she was confused by her own ambivalent feelings towards the other woman, unable to escape from the knowledge that in other circumstances she would have liked her.

It was all so easy to understand why Gray loved her, and it was equally hard to equate the Carla who appeared to be a devoted and loving wife with the Carla she knew to have cheated on her husband.

All day she barely moved out of range of the radio, like everyone else working in the yard.

So far the weather was ideal, but Stephanie was haunted by memories of the tragic outcome of the Fastnet race only years before.

The news bulletin on television that evening showed that Gray was well to the forefront of the race. He had been interviewed by local television the week before and this interview was now re-run.

Stephanie felt her stomach muscles clench as she fought against a wave of longing to be with him as she looked at his familiar and beloved face.

Time dragged, losing all real meaning. She couldn't sleep, waking almost hourly to check on the radio bulletins.

All day she was lethargic and tense. Luckily, the yard was not too busy, apart from callers coming to enquire about Gray and his boat following the item on TV.

Gray had been right, Stephanie decided as she left the yard that evening; his entry in the race *had* indeed caused an upsurge of interest in the yard.

The week dragged on, her sleepless nights beginning to take their toll.

Carla rang her almost every day, solicitous and concerned for her; more like a good and close friend than the woman who was her rival. She was invited to their house several times, but she refused, knowing that she was hardly likely to be a social asset in her present anxious mood.

Gray was still among the lead yachts, and they were now in the dangerous seas round Ireland.

At last her sleepless nights took their toll, and she woke one morning having slept heavily and dreamlessly to the news that one of the lead yachts in the race had capsized, with the loss of at least one member of the crew.

Gray's yacht was one of the smallest ones in the race—he was its sole crew—and she expelled a taut sigh of relief as she realised the damaged boat could not be his.

Even so, the accident increased her anxiety. The weather was changing, growing more dangerous, and there were reports of heavy seas and other yachts in trouble.

On the last day of the race, Gray and three other yachts were in the lead, but they were encountering heavy seas, and the helicopter carrying the TV crew following the race had reported that conditions were fast becoming dangerous.

Just before lunchtime a bulletin on the radio announced that another boat had capsized, with no sign of any life on board. The announcement was followed by the information that the Air Sea Rescue were searching for the one-man crew of the yacht *Good Hope*, sailed by Gray ...

Stephanie went cold and clung desperately to her desk as she listened with disbelieving ears to what she had dreaded hearing all along.

Gray's boat had overturned and Gray was lost at sea. She knew all too well what that meant, and if the Air Sea Rescue team had not found him already, then there was scant hope for his survival, unless he had been picked up by another contestant.

Almost immediately the phone rang, and although she knew it would probably be Carla she didn't answer it. The pain of what she was feeling was unendurable, intolerable, almost unbelievable, as though somehow it wasn't quite real and that soon she would be able to open her eyes and discover that it was all part of some dreadful nightmare.

There was no one in the yard as she walked through it like someone in a trance, heading almost automatically for the narrow path that followed the coast.

It had started to rain, and the wind was cold, gathering in force as it swept in from the sea, but Stephanie ignored it. She could barely feel the icy sting of rain on her skin for the greater pain in her heart.

Gray was gone . . . lost . . . drowned as Paul had been; and in her overwrought state she felt as though *she* had been the one to cause his death; as though she had brought him bad luck by loving him. She was crying without realising it, hot tears pouring down her cold cheeks, her body shivering convulsively, locked in the grip of intense pain.

How long she walked she didn't know. It began to grow dark, and her body hurt. She had walked almost in a complete circle, along the estuary, over the mouth of the river, then down the other side, and now she was almost back in the village. The walk had exhausted her physically, but mentally . . . Walking had done nothing to ease her inner pain.

As she approached the cottage she saw that the lights were on, and she shuddered, anticipating the ordeal that lay ahead.

When Paul had drowned, Gray had shielded her from all the formalities, protecting and cosseting her from the reality of what had happened, but there was no one to protect her now.

They would all be there, the police, other authorities . . . the Press, somehow they must have found a way into the house. The police, she supposed tiredly, reluctantly approaching the back door and pushing it open.

The kitchen was empty. They would all be in the sitting-room, she thought, numbly crossing the hall.

As she reached for the sitting-room door-handle it turned from the other side. She stepped back, waiting. The door opened and Gray emerged, his black hair tousled, his face drawn in lines of exhaustion.

For a moment she stood rooted to the spot, unable to move, unable to believe the evidence of her own eyes, and then with a sob of relief she flung herself into his arms and felt them close round her.

'Gray . . . Gray . . . I thought you were dead!' She was gabbling wildly, but he seemed to understand because he cradled her reassuringly against his body, ignoring her soaking clothes and bedraggled appearance.

'It was a mistake. They thought the sinking yacht was the *Good Hope* because of its size, but it wasn't. I saw the other yacht capsize and turned back to help him. That's why I'm here now. That delay meant that I'd lose the race, and the guy from the other yacht had been pretty badly knocked about when it capsized.

'Carla tried to ring you to tell you it had been a mistake, but there was no answer. Alex recognised from the TV bulletin that the yacht wasn't the *Good Hope* and that there'd been a mistake, and they knew that you'd be listening to the radio and that you wouldn't realise. She couldn't get through to you. Where have you been?' he added roughly, holding her away from him and cupping her face in his palms. 'God, I've been driven damn near out of my mind worrying about you. I didn't even know where to begin looking.'

'I went for a walk,' Stephanie told him shakily. 'I just wanted to be by myself. Oh, Gray . . . I thought I'd lost you. I thought . . .'

She was crying in earnest now and he took her back in his arms, soothing and comforting her.

'We'll have to get you out of these wet things. I'm the one who should have come home in that state, not you,' he teased her, trying to lighten the situation.

'You didn't win the race. Are you very disappointed?' The relief of finding him safe was making her slightly light-headed. She knew she ought to go upstairs and get changed into something warm and dry, but she was so desperate to be with him that she was practically inventing conversation just to stay.

'Not really. The yacht proved that it could do everything we claimed, sufficiently so to ensure that we get a fair number of orders, and there'll always be next year.'

'No way,' she told him fiercely. 'If you think I'm going to go through this again . . .'

She wasn't even aware of the betraying possessiveness in her voice and face, but Gray was, and as he looked down at her he was gripped with a sudden surge of love and need.

He had been frantic when he rushed back and found her missing. The moment Carla told him they had been unable to get in touch with her he had guessed she would believe he was dead, and he had cut through the red tape of his rescue of a fellow entrant in the race and his own subsequent withdrawal from it with a despatch that had left the authorites at the small port where he had put ashore stunned and rather bewildered.

'I think you'd better get upstairs and out of those wet clothes,' he began, only to break off abruptly.

Was he remembering what had happened last time she had come in wet and cold? Stephanie wondered. She shivered in sudden need and love. Even now she had hardly believed he was real; real and safe and here with her. He started to release her and she ached to cling to him.

'Go on, go upstairs and get into something warm and dry. I'll find us something to eat.'

He was as good as his word, and the appetising smell of pasta and rich sauce that greeted her as she walked into the kitchen, dressed in a soft woolly dress that outlined her curves, made her realise how long it was since she had eaten a proper meal.

They ate off trays in the sitting-room, and this time she refused more than a single glass of wine.

Gray had switched on the television, and they were just in time to catch the news, which included an item on his rescue of the other entrant and to announce the winner of the race.

The warmth and comfort of the rich pasta coming on top of the shock she had sustained earlier in the day made Stephanie feel sleepy and relaxed. Slipping off her shoes, she curled up on the settee feeling warm and comfortable.

Her eyes started to close and, although she tried to resist the wave of tiredness washing over her, within minutes she was deeply asleep.

When she woke later the room was almost in darkness, illuminated only by the flames from the fire.

She was pillowed against something hard and warm, which she only gradually realised was Gray's shoulders.

'That must have been some walk you had today. You've been fast asleep for almost three hours.'

'I haven't been sleeping well,' she admitted, knowing that the darkness would conceal from him the reasons for her inability to sleep. She felt him move slightly, and instinctively she moved with him, not sure how she came to be in his arms, but knowing that she didn't want to leave them.

The reality of how it felt to believe that she had lost him for good swept over her, making her go rigid and shudder. As Gray felt the vibration pass through her body he asked softly, 'What is it?'

'I was just remembering how I felt . . . Gray!'

He heard the agony in her voice, and she felt his quickly indrawn breath.

His hand cupped her face tilting it up towards his own. 'You'll never lose me,' he reassured her huskily. 'Never!'

And then he was kissing her, his mouth soft and gentle, only that tender pressure wasn't what she wanted; she wanted more, and her lips told him so, clinging urgently to his as her fingers dug into the solid muscles of his arms.

'Hold me, Gray. Hold me and never let me go.'

She wasn't conscious of whispering the pleading words against his mouth, only of her need to be with him, to be part of him.

She trembled as she felt the sudden upsurge of desire through his body as his kiss deepened and their mouths clung as though desperate for the taste and texture of one another.

She slid her hands under his sweater, feeling the padded muscles of his body, resenting the presence of his soft woollen shirt; burning up with a need and pain that only his love could assuage.

'Stephanie, don't do this to me. You're making it impossible for me to stop,' Gray moaned against her ear. 'I want you so much.'

When her only response was to scatter frantic kisses over every inch of his face, he cried out hoarsely, 'Stephanie, Stephanie, feel what you're doing to me,' and taking her hand he placed it against his body, shuddering tensely as her fingers touched the hard evidence of his arousal, straining at the fabric of his jeans.

The brief contact thrilled and tormented her. She wanted more, so much more, and she wanted it now, with a frantic urgency that was a legacy from her long afternoon of pain.

Her fingers found the fastening of his jeans and then the zip, overlooking the fact that this was the first time they had ever performed such an intimate exercise.

Gray made no move to stop her, plundering her mouth with achingly demanding kisses that echoed the fierce need she could feel burning in herself. His hand cupped and stroked her breast, feeling the urgent burgeoning of her flesh through the fine silk of her bra and the wool of her dress.

As her hand slipped inside his jeans and caressed the hard flatness of his belly above the edge of his briefs, Gray gasped with pleasure, and in the firelight she saw the vulnerability and need in his face, as he closed his eyes and swallowed hard past rigid throat muscles before giving himself up to the pleasure she was inducing.

'I shouldn't be letting you do this,' was his moaned comment as she dragged her nails tormentingly through the soft, fine line of hair her questing hands had revealed. But when she tugged impotently at his jeans, wanting more of him than they allowed her to enjoy, he helped her to ease them off and then tugged off his sweater and shirt with a ruthless despatch that made her mouth go dry with excitement.

'Is that enough?' he demanded hoarsely, watching her wide-eyed concentration on his body. 'Or do you want me to take off more?'

She swallowed, all too conscious that all he had on was the dark barrier of his briefs, and even they could not prevent her from being aware of the power of his body as he stood silhouetted against the fire.

'I . . .' She didn't know what to say; how to tell him how much she desired and loved him.

'Do you want to see me? To touch me?' he demanded roughly, his body shuddering tautly in response to his words. 'Come here.'

She went to him like a sleep-walker, standing completely still as he undressed her, the stillness of her outer body in direct contrast to the frenzied tumult building within it.

The firelight highlighted the rosy peaks of her breasts, and their sensitivity intensified as Gray took her in his arms with a low groan, crushing her against his body as he kissed her with fierce passion.

Just the sensation of his mouth moving against hers was enough to make her ache with need. She twisted against him, gasping with pleasure when his hands slid over her body to cup the rounded softness of her bottom and lift her against him.

'We should go upstairs.' He mouthed the words against her throat as he caressed it with his lips, but she shook her head, terrified of breaking the spell between them.

The sensation of his mouth against her skin, exploring the shape and texture of her breast made her shake with desire. It seemed a lifetime before his lips eventually possessed the aching heat of her nipple, making her arch wildly against him as she felt the onset of a wild spasm of pleasure.

'Stephanie . . . Stephanie, I want you . . . I need you.'

He released her so abruptly that she staggered

slightly, sinking down on her knees, clasping his thigh for support.

As he bent down to lift her up she touched her lips to his thigh in an instinctive gesture of love.

'Stephanie!' The taut thickness in his voice, the way he shuddered and then tensed told her how much he had enjoyed her tentative caress, and she repeated it, letting her lips linger and taste the unique flavour of him.

'Stephanie. No!' He groaned the protest like a man under torture, as she grew more confident and her tongue stroked tantalisingly along his inner thigh, his body tensing under its need to thrust against the torment of her mouth.

Stephanie heard the thick sound of pleasure and protest stifled in his throat and felt a heady upsurge of her own female power. She could make him weak and fill him with the same need that filled her; she could make him ache for the touch of her hands and mouth in the way she ached for him.

She felt his hands come down and grip her shoulders ready to force her away as her lips continued to drift across his skin, but when she reached higher and her nails dragged teasingly through the fine hair coating his thighs, they fastened instead in the thickness of her hair, urging her against him with hoarse words of praise and need as he gave in to his body's unashamed desire for the delicate caress of her mouth.

That she, who had never before even contemplated sharing such intimacy with anyone, should derive such pleasure from his body's response to her touch was an awesome experience, and when Gray suddenly cried out in hoarse protest, picking her up and fastening his mouth over hers, she yielded herself completely, melting

against him, softly inciting him to fit his body against
hers and fill her with its potent strength.

He released her only to put her down on the rug and
cover her with the heat of his flesh, entering her with a
harsh cry of need that melted her bones and filled her
with dizzying pleasure.

They made love with a wildness that half shocked
her, falling asleep in one another's arms, only to wake
and make love again, more slowly this time, until their
bodies exploded in fierce surges of pleasure that left
them drained and at peace.

CHAPTER TEN

STEPHANIE woke up alone in her own bed, and knew from the angle of the sun shining in through the window that it was late . . . very late.

She got up and dressed quickly, going downstairs, anxious to see Gray, pausing outside the kitchen door as she heard voices.

Her blood turned to ice as she recognised Carla's. To her knowledge Carla had not visited the cottage once since she herself had arrived, and she hated the thought of her being here now. Had Gray *told* her about last night? Had he begged her to leave her husband . . . had he . . .?

She was just about to make her presence known and push open the door when she heard Carla saying unhappily, 'Gray, I like Stephanie, and I hate deceiving her like this.'

As she stepped back from the door in shock, Gray's response was lost to her.

She reached the stairs and stumbled up them to the sanctuary of her own room, Carla's betraying words ringing in her ears. Her mouth was trembling and she tried to keep it still. Carla's words could have only one meaning. Gray had been using her . . . carrying on his affair with Carla, despite what he had told her. Oh, how bitterly ironic it was that *Carla* should be the one to feel remorse, and not Gray.

How could he do this to her? How could he use her

175

Restlessly she got off the bed. Why delude herself any further? He had probably been pretending she was Carla. The pain that racked her body reinforced her decision to leave. If she stayed . . . She *couldn't* stay.

Recklessly she flung clothes into her suitcase without folding them. She had half an hour, that was all. She made it with five minutes to spare, not even turning once to look behind her as she drove out of the village heading for the motorway and London.

She had left Gray a note simply stating that she thought it best to leave. That way at least she could salvage something of her pride.

It didn't sustain her for very long. Before she was even half-way back she would have given anything for Gray to simply materialise beside her and take her back. It was degrading to love someone so intensely, especially when there was not the remotest chance of her feelings being returned.

After such thoughts, it came as something of a shock to look in her driving mirror and discover the flashing lights of the car racing up behind her.

Her ridiculous hope that Gray might actually have pursued her died the moment she recognised the woman behind the wheel of the other car.

Carla!

For one mad moment she was tempted to try to out-speed her, but one look at Carla's sporty, expensive-looking car confirmed that her own VW would have no hope of outrunning it, and so instead she pulled off the road at the first lay-by, and stopped her car, fighting against the fierce tension gripping her as she heard Carla stop behind her.

In her driving mirror she could see the other woman

running towards her VW.

'Stephanie, where are you going? When I saw Gray, he told me . . .'

'That he and I have been lovers.'

Pride made her say the words before Carla could, her chin tilting defiantly. She had no idea why Carla had followed her, nor could she totally understand the concerned note in the older woman's voice, but she was too wrought up to dwell on these anomalies now.

'Stephanie, I don't think you understand.'

Incredibly, Carla sounded sympathetic and was actually reaching out to touch her, her hand resting lightly on her arm as though she was half afraid that Stephanie might dash away.

'You're running away, aren't you? Leaving Gray? Look, come and sit in my car for a moment so that we can talk.'

Much as she wanted to refuse, Stephanie discovered that she wasn't going to be given the opportunity to do so. Taking her arm in a firm grip, Carla all but dragged her over to her car, and somehow or other Stephanie discovered that she was sitting in its passenger seat, while Carla turned to face her in the driver's seat, an earnest and very determined expression on her face.

'I know you probably think this is none of my business . . . but I can't simply stand by and let you ruin Gray's life.'

'*Me* . . . ruin *Gray's* life . . .' Stephanie began indignantly, but Carla wasn't listening.

'I couldn't believe it when I spotted you driving away from the village. When I saw Gray this morning . . .'

'You told him that you weren't prepared to go on deceiving me,' Stephanie told her grimly.

'So you *did* overhear us! I thought I heard someone. Look, Stephanie, I know that you think Gray and I are romantically involved, but you couldn't be more wrong. Please, just let me ask you one thing. Do you love Gray?'

She wanted to deny it; she fully intended to deny it, but instead of doing so she heard herself saying huskily, 'Yes, yes I do.'

'Thank God for that!'

Carla's heartfelt exclamation was the last thing she had expected to hear.

'Look, let's start at the beginning, shall we?'

'You mean the beginning of your affair with Gray?' Stephanie demanded grittily, already regretting the weakness that had lulled her into betraying her feelings.

'No,' Carla denied softly. 'I mean the beginning of his love for you.'

Shock held Stephanie right in her seat. What sort of cruel game was Carla playing?

'Gray doesn't love *me*,' she began bitterly.

But Carla cut across her objections and said firmly, 'Oh yes, he does, and I'm betraying his confidence to tell you this, Stephanie. He's loved you since you were eighteen. He told me so when he begged me for my help. You see, when he realised you thought that he and I were having an affair, he begged me to go along with your misconception. He told me how you had offered to help him to save him from my clutches.'

Carla grinned unrepentantly at Stephanie's shocked expression. 'That was when I began to think that there was hope for Gray, after all. No woman could be so self-sacrificing without caring. I have to confess, though, that it hasn't been easy playing the part you cast for me, and as I told Gray this morning, it's time he told you the truth, and how he feels about you. That was what you overheard,' Carla told her softly. 'Gray loves you, Stephanie.'

'Then why hasn't he told me so?'

'Because he's frightened of driving you away . . . of losing what little he believes he has of you. This morning he told me that he couldn't stand it any longer, and that he had to tell you how he feels. When I saw you driving away from the village I couldn't believe it. I had to stop you to find out what had happened . . .'

It took two hours of emotionally exhausting but steadfast talking on Carla's part before Stephanie came anywhere near believing her, but in the end not even she was proof against the other woman's obvious sincerity and concern.

Now so many of the previous anomalies in Carla's behaviour were explained.

'When I overheard the two of you this morning, I thought he had been deceiving me all the time,' she said shakily at last.

'Shouldn't you be telling Gray this and not me?' Carla asked gently. 'He won't come to you, Stephanie; he's too scared of losing you completely. When he finds out that you've gone, he'll draw the obvious conclusion—that you don't care enough about him to stay. If you want him, I'm afraid you'll have to tell him so.'

If she wanted him? She gave the other woman a shaky smile.

'And just for the record,' Carla added firmly, 'I like and admire Gray as a friend, both of us do, but *Alex* is the man I love, I hope that's understood.'

Stephanie wasn't quite sure what she understood apart from the fact that it was imperative that she get back to Gray just as quickly as possible.

As she got out of Carla's car she turned impulsively to the other woman and asked hesitantly, 'Are you sure . . .?'

'I know a man who's in love when I see one.'

'Wish me luck, then.'

'You won't need it,' Carla assured her. 'Just walk in, open your arms and tell him you love him. That's all you need to do.'

Never had twenty miles taken so long to cover. Even pressing her VW as hard as she dared it seemed to take for ever before she saw the familiar outline of the estuary and the huddle of the village rooftops.

All her old fear had gone, and in its place was a feeling of peace and homecoming. At long last she had buried all her ghosts and she was free to step into the future.

A future that would be no future at all without Gray to share it with her, she reminded herself as she drove down the village street, and parked outside the cottage.

To her intense disappointment there was no sign of Gray anywhere. He had obviously returned to the cottage since her departure, because her note was gone, and she grimaced distastefully over the bowl full of dirty washing up—that was unlike Gray, who was normally such a tidy person.

In the sitting-room she discovered a half-empty bottle of whisky and a tumbler, and then as she moved round the corner of the settee she discovered that Gray wasn't out at all; instead he was lying curled up on the settee, deeply asleep.

Gray drinking! It was practically unheard of. Compassion, guilt and love welled up inside her and she bent to touch his face lightly with her fingertips.

He made a sound in his sleep but didn't wake up. She debated about what to do for several minutes, and then decided to let him have his sleep out. To stop herself from losing her fragile courage while she waited, she set about cleaning up the kitchen, and then collected some logs and lit the fire in the sitting-room.

It was a cold day with a rough breeze coming off the sea, chilly enough to raise goose-bumps on her flesh, and certainly cool enough to merit a fire. Besides, it gave her something to do. She was mortally afraid that if Gray didn't wake up soon she would lose her courage completely and turn tail and run.

She sat back on her heels and watched him after she had lit the fire. The beginnings of a dark stubble covered his jaw; in sleep he looked vulnerable and pale. She sighed and got up to go and wash her hands, and then on impulse made some coffee. He might welcome a cup when he eventually woke up.

She couldn't let him sleep much longer. If she did . . . She sensed that Carla was right when she said that Gray would not tell her voluntarily how he felt. So many mistakes between them . . . so much wasted time.

She kneeled beside him and took his hand in her own, bending over him to feather a light kiss against his lips.

Almost immediately his eyelashes lifted. The look in his eyes when he saw her told its own story. Almost immediately he shielded them, and as she swallowed the lump that had gathered in her throat, she said huskily, 'Wake up, Sleeping Beauty.'

He frowned and struggled to sit up, clutching his

head as he did so. 'My God, have I got a hangover!'

'A well-deserved one, to judge from this,' Stephanie told him wryly, displaying the half-empty bottle.

He frowned and looked at her. 'You left . . .'

'Yes.' It had to be now, before she lost her courage completely. 'And now I'm back. Gray, before either of us says anything else, there's something I must tell you.' She was unconsciously pleating the fabric of his shirt as she avoided looking directly at him.

'I . . . I left this morning because . . . because I love you far too much to stay here with you any longer as your friend . . .'

For a moment she thought Carla had been wrong and that she had just made the most embarrassing admission of her life, and then Gray said weakly, 'Say that again. I don't think I heard it properly.'

'I love you,' she repeated huskily. 'I love you, Gray.'

She held out her arms and was almost lifted off her feet as he got up in one lithe motion and closed his own round her, kissing her with open hunger.

'If you feel like that about me, then why the hell did you leave?' he demanded thickly against her mouth. 'Have you any *idea* of what you've put me through? Of how many empty years I've waited to hear you say that to me?'

Tears burned her eyes and she shook her head.

'We can talk later. Just hold me now, Gray. I still can't believe it's true. I thought you loved Carla . . . I . . .'

'And I was too damned scared of driving you away to tell you how I felt. I told myself it was enough that I could arouse you . . . that through me you'd learned what it meant to be a woman. I told myself that if I was

patient love would come, and then I thought I'd gone
and ruined everything by frightening you half to death
with my need for you, making you run away.'

Stephanie laughed at that, a delicious sound that
smoothed the tension.

'You can frighten me like that any time you like,' she
teased, squirming at his mock growl of annoyance,
loving the way his body immediately hardened against
hers at her provocatively enticing movement.

'When ... when did you first know how you felt
about me?' Gray demanded. 'And why the hell have
you waited so long to tell me?'

'I don't really know ... it just sort of grew on me ... at
first I just thought my jealousy of Carla was because I
resented what she was doing to you—then I realised it
was more than that.'

She swallowed and offered him a small smile.

'That day when I walked into your room and saw
you, I was stunned by how I felt ... I thought I must
have imagined it. Paul never made me feel like that, not
even in the beginning when I first thought I loved him.
Then, later, I remembered you lifting me out of my
father's boat one day when we first came down to the
estuary. I mooned about the yard for weeks after that
just longing for a glimpse of you, but you were never
there. Paul was, though ...'

Both of them fell silent, and then Gray said huskily, 'I
remember that afternoon; the feel of you in my arms,
the knowledge that I wanted you. I kept out of your way
deliberately. You were seventeen, Steph,' he told her
roughly, seeing the pain in her eyes. 'The thoughts I was
having about you were almost criminal. I told myself I'd
have to wait until you'd grown up a little, but Paul ...

After the two of you got married, I told myself I had to forget you, but I couldn't. When Paul died I told myself I was getting a second chance, but you wouldn't let me get near you. I thought it was because you loved him so much.'

Stephanie shook her head. 'I never loved him—not really, but I couldn't bear to tell anyone the truth. It took the fear of losing you to someone else to make me face up to it.'

'If only I'd known, I would have made you jealous years ago,' Gray teased. 'I could hardly believe it when you accused me of having an affair with Carla, but I seized on it as an excuse to get closer to you, to keep you with me. If I couldn't be your lover, then pretending to be was the next best thing.'

'I've been such a fool,' Stephanie groaned. 'Can you forgive me?'

Gray pretended to consider the matter, a teasing smile curling his mouth as he said judiciously, 'I think I just might, providing . . .'

'Providing what?'

'Providing you wear that peach ballgown for me the night we get married.'

Stephanie stared at him. Tiny laughter lines creased round his eyes as he fought to control his grin.

'You liked it that much?' she asked still confused.

'Umm. Well, actually,' he confessed outrageously, drawing her closer to him, 'what I liked was what you were wearing underneath it.'

He laughed softly and dodged out of the way of her soft fists as they landed against his arm, and despite the pink flush of embarrassment mantling her skin, Stephanie couldn't help laughing a little herself.

She and Paul had never shared anything like this, and as though he was aware of how overwhelmed she was feeling by the reality of knowing that he loved her, the laughter faded from his eyes and he said roughly, 'God, Steph, I love you so much.' His fingertips traced the shape of her face. 'Right now there's nothing I want more than to take you to bed and stake my claim on you in the most intimate way there is.'

His words only echoed what she herself was feeling. She had come so close to losing him. She made a small, yielding movement and saw his eyes darken, but he shook his head and pushed her gently away.

'No . . . we're going to do this properly. We're going to ring your folks and give them the good news, then we're going out to dinner to celebrate our engagement, and then you're going to move in with Carla and Alex until we get married.'

He saw her face and groaned huskily. 'It won't be for very long—three weeks, no more. I want to court you the way I would have done if Paul hadn't beaten me to it,' he said softly. 'I want to take you out to show you off.' He shook his head and grimaced. 'Does any of this make any sense?'

'All of it,' she told him softly. 'But something tells me it's going to be a very, very long three weeks.'

She felt him smiling as he kissed her, and when eventually he released her he said teasingly, 'Not for me. Every night I'll be dreaming of you wearing that peach dress.'

She wore it to get married in, with the discreet addition of some pretty net veiling to make it less revealing.

She hadn't told Gray, and as he turned round to

watch her walking down the aisle on her father's arm she saw his eyes widen.

Her own laughed back at him as they shared their private knowledge. They were spending their honeymoon in a private villa on a small island in the Aegean where they could sail, swim and snorkel in perfect clear seas; but tonight after the ceremony, they would be going back to the cottage, and the look in Gray's eyes as they burned over her told her how much he was looking forward to the moment when they would be alone. As she was herself.

She turned to face the vicar and the service began. Her heart swelled with love and gratitude. Gray turned to look at her, the love she felt for him mirrored in his eyes.

As the vicar spoke sonorously she saw Gray mouth silently, 'I love you,' and she was filled with a sense of homecoming and peace.

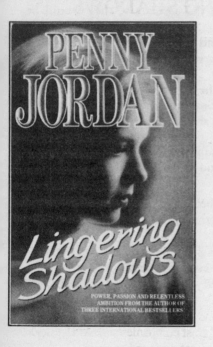

If you enjoyed reading this special collection of earlier novels by Penny Jordan, then you will want to get hold of a copy of her latest blockbuster, LINGERING SHADOWS. As a taste of what's in store, here is a brief introduction to the principal characters, followed by a short extract...

LINGERING SHADOWS

Leo von Hessler—head of his family's business empire. But an empire built at what terrible cost? Leo must discover the truth.

Saul Jardine—corporate raider. He has pursued his career single-mindedly, sacrificing love and family ties. His life is now at a crossroads.

Davina James—beautiful widow. She will fight anyone who tries to take her inheritance away from her.

Giles Redwood—Davina's help and support. While his wife is all fire and sparks, Giles yearns for Davina's calm and serenity.

Lucy Redwood—haunted woman. She's turned from her husband since the loss of their child. But, fiercely jealous of Davina's hold over Giles, she will do anything to win him back.

Christie Jardine—doctor and single parent. She's an outspoken woman who takes a stand against companies such as Hessler's. She will not allow any man to get close to her again.

A mystery from the past, and emotions hidden and long suppressed, inexorably draw all of these lives together. How long will it take to dispel the last, lingering shadows?

Wryly Davina shook her head, dismissing her thoughts of the past. What was the point in dwelling on the past? She had chosen to marry Gregory, no one had forced her, and it was pointless wondering what her life might have been had she married someone like Giles. Gregory was dead now, and his death had brought her far more important things to worry about than the emotional barrenness of her own life.

It had been cowardice, and a too strongly rooted dread of offending against her father's idea of convention, that had kept her in her marriage; it was that which had trapped her just as much as Gregory's manipulation of her. She couldn't blame everything on him.

Not even the failure of the company?

She closed her eyes tiredly. That was a different matter. What on earth had prompted him to get involved in something as volatile and dangerous as the currency market, and with money that should have been used to secure the future of the company and of its employees?

How much real chance did she have of finding a backer . . . an investor? Virtually none, the bank manager had told her grimly. These were difficult times for industry; money was tight, especially the kind of risk-money involved in supporting something like Carey's.

Davina turned into the drive. She was home. Home; she smiled mirthlessly to herself as she stopped the car and got out.

She had lived in this house all her life and she felt very little affinity towards it. It had never truly been hers. During her father's lifetime it had been his, and after his death. . . Well, he might have willed it to her, but she had never truly felt it belonged to her.

It had been Gregory, during one of his many affairs,

who had produced the interior designer responsible for its present décor; she and Gregory had been having a passionate affair at the time, and even though she knew it was quite ridiculous, since she knew Gregory could never have had sex with her here at home, Davina felt somehow as though the very fabrics the woman had chosen were impregnated with the musky odour of sex.

She loathed the brilliant harsh colours the woman had chosen, the dramatic blacks and reds, the—to her—ugly rawness of so much colour and emotion. They made the rooms seem claustrophobic, reminding Davina of that awful honeymoon with its cramped room and lack of air.

* * *

For quite a long time after his conversation with Sir Alex was over Saul sat motionlessly where he was.

Beside him on his desk was the small file containing the basic facts about Carey Chemicals. He picked it up, flipping it open as he started to read.

He read quickly, pausing only a handful of times, once when he read how the company had originally come into being, a second time when he read of Gregory James's heavy losses on the money markets, and a third time when he read that the company was now in the hands of his widow, the founder's granddaughter, Davina James.

She would want to sell. She would have to. There was no other option open to her. The business was on the verge of bankruptcy. Saul suspected he knew the kind of woman she would be. The investigating agents Sir Alex had employed had been thorough. There were no details of Gregory James's many affairs, just a couple of paragraphs stating that his unfaithfulness was a constant and ongoing situation and that it would seem that his wife must have been aware of it.

Saul thought he knew the type. He had met enough of them over the years; elegant, brittle, too thin, too tense and too expensively dressed, they reminded him of fragile ornaments. You always had the feeling that if they were asked to participate in anything real they would crack and fall apart.

Some of them turned to sex as a means of solace for the uninterest of their husbands, some of them turned to drink, some to good works, but none of them, it seemed to Saul, seemed prepared to take the simple step of freeing themselves from the humiliation and destruction of their marriages by divorcing their husbands. Wealth, position, appearances, it seemed, were always more important than pride, self-respect or self-worth.

He had once made the mistake of saying as much to Christie and she had turned on him immediately, challenging him to put himself in their shoes, to be what life and circumstances had forced them to be.

He winced a little as he remembered her anger, her vehemence about the fact that so many members of her sex were taught almost from birth to accept second best, to put others first, to give instead of to take. Many of them were held in those marriages by their children, she had told him fiercely.

But Davina James did not have any children. He frowned as he lifted the last sheet of paper from the file and saw the photographs pinned neatly behind it.

There were several of Carey Chemicals, showing the

like this? How could he have changed so much?

She curled up on her bed, frozen with shock and grief. She heard the back door open and close and a car start up, and knew that Carla had left; but still she didn't move.

She heard Gray come upstairs and knock on her door.

'Stephanie, are you awake?'

If she didn't reply, he would come in and she couldn't face him yet, she thought in panic.

'Yes . . . yes. I'm getting up now,' she called back, hoping the closed door would distort her voice enough for him not to recognise its betraying tremor.

'I've got to go down to the yard for half an hour.'

The yard . . . or to see Carla.

Heartsick, she called out some response which must have satisfied him because she heard him going back downstairs, and then within minutes the back door opened and closed again.

She had to get away, she thought feverishly. She couldn't stay here any longer. She couldn't endure any more pain. She had already inflicted sufficient on herself surely, she thought bitterly. She had known all along that Gray didn't love her . . . but she had also thought he had meant what he said about ending his affair with Carla. Had she secretly hoped that he might eventually turn to her?

Oh, what did it matter now? She *had* to get away. She had to escape before she betrayed herself any further. When she thought about last night, when she remembered how she had adored and worshipped him in the most intimate way there could be . . . She closed her eyes and swallowed.

And he had seemed to share her feelings, to . . .

run-down state of the buildings and how totally ill equipped it was to compete with even the poorest of its competitors. Without that all-important heart-drug patent which had been revised over the years to create a second patent it would have disappeared decades ago.

There was another photograph. He stiffened as he saw the name written on the back: 'Davina James'.

He turned it over.

She was nothing like what he had imagined. The file quoted her date of birth, so he knew she was thirty-seven years old, but in this photograph she looked younger and vulnerable in a way that made his body tense with rejection.

There was none of the glossy sophistication that he had expected about her. She was dressed in jeans and what looked like a man's shirt, one hand lifted to push a strand of soft fair hair out of her eyes. She was wearing gardening gloves and there was a smear of dirt along one cheekbone, a fork in the ground at her feet. Her skin, free of make-up, looked clear and soft, and without even realising what he was doing Saul suddenly discovered that his thumb was touching her face.

~